EVERYMAN'S LIBRARY

ROMANCE

GARGANTUA AND PANTAGRUEL
BY FRANÇOIS RABELAIS · INTRO-
DUCTION BY D. B. WYNDHAM LEWIS
IN 2 VOLS.   VOL. 2

FRANÇOIS RABELAIS, born in Touraine about 1494. Before 1530, when he graduated in medicine, he had been in both Franciscan and Benedictine monasteries. Appointed physician at the Hôtel-Dieu at Lyons. In 1534 went to Italy under patronage of Cardinal Jean du Bellay, and passed his life partly there and partly in Paris until 1550, when he was made Curé of Meudon. Left Meudon in 1552 and died, probably in 1553, in Paris.

GARGANTUA AND PANTAGRUEL

VOLUME TWO

FRANÇOIS RABELAIS

LONDON: J. M. DENT & SONS LTD.
NEW YORK: E. P. DUTTON & CO. INC.

All rights reserved
Printed in Great Britain
by Spottiswoode Ballantyne & Co. Ltd.
The Hythe Colchester
for
J. M. Dent & Sons Ltd.
Aldine House Bedford St. London
First published in this edition 1929
Last reprinted 1950

CONTENTS

BOOK III (*Continued*)

TREATING OF THE HEROIC DEEDS AND SAYINGS OF THE GOOD PANTAGRUEL

BOOK IV

CONTENTS

CONTENTS

BOOK V

BOOK III (*Continued*)

CHAPTER XXIX

How Pantagruel convocated together a Theologian, Physician, Lawyer, and Philosopher, for extricating Panurge out of the perplexity wherein he was

No sooner were they come into the royal palace, but they, to the full, made report unto Pantagruel of the success of their expedition, and showed him the response of Raminagrobis. When Pantagruel had read it over and over again, the oftener he perused it, being the better pleased therewith, he said, in addressing his speech to Panurge, I have not as yet seen any answer framed to your demand, which affordeth me more contentment. For in this his succinct copy of verses, he summarily, and briefly, yet fully enough expresseth, how he would have us to understand, that every one, in the project and enterprise of marriage, ought to be his own carver, sole arbitrator of his proper thoughts, and from himself alone take counsel in the main and peremptory closure of what his determination should be, in either his assent to, or dissent from it. Such always hath been my opinion to you, and when at first you spoke thereof to me, I truly told you this same very thing; but tacitly you scorned my advice, and would not harbour it within your mind. I know for certain, and therefore may I with the greater confidence utter my conception of it, that philauty, or self love, is that which blinds your judgment and deceiveth you.

Let us do otherways, and that is this. Whatever we are, or have, consisteth in three things—the soul, the body, and the goods. Now, for the preservation of these three, there are three sorts of learned men ordained, each respectively to have care of that one which is recommended to his charge. Theologues are appointed for the soul, physicians for the welfare of the body, and lawyers for the safety of our goods. Hence it is, that it is my resolution to have on Sunday next with me at dinner a divine, a physician, and a lawyer, that with those three assembled thus together, we may in every point and particle confer at large of your perplexity. By Saint Picot, answered Panurge, we never shall do any good that way, I see it already. And you see yourself how the world is vilely abused, as when with a fox-tail one claps another's breech, to cajole him. We give our souls to keep to the theologues, who for the greater part are heretics. Our bodies we commit to the physicians, who never themselves take any physic. And then we intrust our goods to the lawyers, who never go to law against one another. You speak like a courtier, quoth Pantagruel. But the first point of your assertion is to be denied; for we daily see how good theologues make it their chief business, their whole and sole employment, by their deeds, their words, and writings, to extirpate errors and heresies out of the hearts of men, and in their stead profoundly plant the true and lively faith. The second point you spoke of I commend; for, in truth the professors of the art of medicine give so good order to the prophylactic, or conservative part of their faculty, in what concerneth their proper healths, that they stand in no need of making use of the other branch, which is the curative, or therapeutic, by medicaments. As for the third, I grant it to be true, for learned advocates and counsellors at law are so much taken up with the affairs of others in their consultations, pleadings, and such-like patrocinations of those who are their clients, that they have no leisure to attend any controversies of their own. Therefore, on the next ensuing Sunday, let the divine be our goodly Father Hippothadeus, the physician our honest Master Rondibilis, and our legist our friend Bridlegoose. Nor will it be (to my thinking) amiss, that we enter into the pythagoric field, and choose for an assistant to the three aforenamed doctors our ancient faithful acquaintance, the philosopher Trouillogan, especially seeing a perfect philosopher, such as is Trouillogan, is able positively to resolve all whatsoever doubts you can propose. Carpalim, have you a care to have them here all four on Sunday next to dinner, without fail.

I believe, quoth Epistemon, that throughout the whole country, in all the corners thereof, you could not have pitched upon such other four. Which I speak not so much in regard of the most excellent qualifications and accomplishments wherewith all of them are endowed for the respective discharge and management of each his own vocation and calling, (wherein without all doubt or controversy, they are the paragons of the land and surpass all others,) as for that Rondibilis, is married now, who before was not,—Hippothadeus was not before, nor is yet,—Bridlegoose was married once, but is not now,—and Trouillogan is married now, who wedded was to another wife before. Sir, if it may stand with your good liking, I will ease Carpalim of some parcel of his labour, and invite Bridlegoose myself, with whom I of a long time have had a very intimate familiarity, and unto whom I am to speak on the behalf of a pretty hopeful youth who now studieth at Tholouse, under the most learned, virtuous Doctor Boissonet. Do what you deem most expedient, quoth Pantagruel, and tell me, if my recommendation can in anything be steadable for the promoval of the good of that youth, or otherwise serve for bettering of the dignity and office of the worthy Boissonet, whom I do so love and respect for one of the ablest and most sufficient in his way, that anywhere are extant. Sir, I will use therein my best endeavours, and heartily bestir myself about it.

CHAPTER XXX

How the theologue, Hippothadeus, giveth counsel to Panurge in the matter and business of his nuptial enterprise

THE dinner on the subsequent Sunday was no sooner made ready, than that the aforenamed invited guests gave thereto their appearance, all of them, Bridlegoose only excepted, who was the deputy-governor of Fonsbeton. At the ushering in of the second service, Panurge, making a low reverence, spake thus. Gentlemen, the question I am to propound unto you shall be uttered in very few words; Should I marry or no? If my doubt herein be not resolved by you, I shall hold it altogether insolvable, as are the *Insolubilia de Aliaco*; for all of you are elected, chosen and culled out from amongst others, every one in his own condition and quality, like so many picked peas on a carpet.

The Father Hippothadeus, in obedience to the bidding of Pantagruel, and with much courtesy to the company, answered exceeding modestly after this manner. My friend, you are pleased to ask counsel of us; but first you must consult with yourself. Do you find any trouble or disquiet in your body by the importunate stings and pricklings of the flesh? That I do, quoth Panurge, in a hugely strong and almost irresistible measure. Be not offended, I beseech you, good father at the freedom of my expression. No truly, friend, not I, quoth

Hippothadeus, there is no reason why I should be displeased therewith. But in this carnal strife and debate of yours, have you obtained from God the gift and special grace of continency? In good faith not, quoth Panurge. My counsel to you in that case, my friend, is that you marry, quoth Hippothadeus; for you should rather choose to marry once, than to burn still in fires of concupiscence. Then Panurge, with a jovial heart and a loud voice, cried out, That is spoke gallantly, without circumbilivaginating about and about, and never hitting it in its central point. Grammercy, my good father! In truth I am resolved now to marry, and without fail I shall do it quickly. I invite you to my wedding. By the body of a hen, we shall make good cheer, and be as merry as crickets. You shall wear the bridegroom's colours, and, if we eat a goose, my wife shall not roast it for me. I will intreat you to lead up the first dance of the bride's maids, if it may please you to do me so much favour and honour. There resteth yet a small difficulty, a little scruple, yea, even less than nothing, whereof I humbly crave your resolution. Shall I be a cuckold, father, yea or no? By no means, answered Hippothadeus, will you be a cuckold, if it please God. O the Lord help us now, quoth Panurge whither are we driven to, good folks? To the conditionals, which, according to the rules and precepts of the dialectic faculty, admit of all contradictions and impossibilities. If my Transalpine mule had wings, my Transalpine mule would fly. If it please God, I shall not be a cuckold, but I shall be a cuckold, if it please him. Good God, if this were a condition which I knew how to prevent, my hopes should be as high as ever, nor would I despair. But you here send me to God's privy council, to the closet of his little pleasures. You, my French country-men, which is the way you take to go thither?

My honest father, I believe it will be your best not to come to my wedding. The clutter and dingle dangle noise of marriage guests will but disturb you, and break the serious fancies of your brain. You love repose with solitude and silence; I really believe you will not come. And then you dance but indifferently, and would be out of countenance at the first entry. I will send you some good things to your chamber, together with the bride's favour, and there you may drink our health, if it may stand with your good liking. My friend, quoth Hippothadeus, take my words in the sense wherein I mean them, and do not misinterpret me. When I tell you,— if it please God,—do I to you any wrong therein? Is it an ill expression? Is it a blaspheming clause, or reserve any way scandalous unto the world? Do not we thereby honour the Lord God Almighty, Creator, Protector, and Conserver of all things? Is not that a mean, whereby we do acknowledge him to be the sole giver of all whatsoever is good? Do not we in that manifest our faith, that we believe all things to depend upon his infinite and incomprehensible bounty? and that without him nothing can be produced, nor after its production be of any value, force, or power, without the concurring aid and favour of his assisting grace? Is it not a canonical and authentic exception, worthy to be premised to all our undertakings? Is it not expedient that what we propose unto ourselves, be still referred to what shall be disposed of by the sacred will of God, unto which all things must acquiesce in the heavens as well as on the earth? Is not that verily a sanctifying of his holy name? My friend, you shall not be a cuckold, if it please God, nor shall we need to despair of the knowledge of his good will and pleasure herein, as if it were such an abstruse and mysteriously hidden secret, that for the clear understanding thereof it were necessary to consult with those of his celestial privy council, or expressly make a voyage unto the empyrean chamber, where order is given for the effectuating of his most holy pleasures. The great God hath done us this good, that he hath declared and revealed them to us openly and plainly, and described them in the Holy Bible. There will you find that you shall never be a cuckold, that is to say, your wife shall never be a strumpet, if you make choice of one of a commendable extraction, descended of honest parents, and instructed in all piety and virtue—such a one as hath not at any time haunted or frequented the company or conversation of those that are of corrupt and depraved manners, one loving and fearing God, who taketh a singular delight in drawing near to him by faith, and the cordial observing of his sacred commandments—and finally, one who, standing in awe of the Divine Majesty of the Most High, will be loth to offend him, and lose the favourable kindness of his grace, through any defect of faith, or transgression against the ordinances of his holy law, wherein adultery is most rigorously forbidden, and a close adherence to her husband alone, most strictly and severely enjoined; yea, in such sort, that she is to cherish, serve, and love him above any thing, next to God, that meriteth to be beloved. In the interim, for the better schooling of her in these instructions, and that the wholesome doctrine of a matrimonial duty may take the deeper root in her mind, you must needs carry yourself so on your part, and your behaviour is to be such that you are to go before her in a good example, by entertaining her unfeignedly with a conjugal amity, by continually approving yourself in all your words and actions a faithful and discreet husband; and by living, not only at home and privately with your own household and family, but in the face also of all men, and open view of the world, devoutly, virtuously, and chastely, as you would have her on her side to deport and to demean herself towards you, as becomes a godly, loyal, and respectful wife, who maketh conscience to keep inviolable the tie of a matrimonial oath. For as that looking-glass is not the best, which is most decked with gold and precious stones, but that which representeth to the eye the liveliest shapes of objects set before it, even so that wife should not be most esteemed who richest is, and of the noblest race, but she who, fearing God, conforms herself nearest unto the humour of her husband.

Consider how the moon doth not borrow her light from Jupiter, Mars, Mercury, or any other of the planets, nor yet from any of those splendid stars which are set in the spangled firmament, but from her husband only, the bright sun, which she receiveth from him more or less, according to the manner of his aspect and variously bestowed eradiations. Just so should you be a pattern to your wife in virtue, goodly zeal, and true devotion, that by your radiance in darting on her the aspect of an exemplary goodness, she, in your imitation, may outshine the luminaries of all other women. To this effect you daily must implore God's grace to the protection of you both. You would have me then, quoth Panurge, twisting the whiskers of his beard on either side with the thumb and forefinger of his left hand, to espouse and take to wife the prudent frugal woman described by Solomon. Without all doubt she is dead, and truly to my best remembrance I never saw her; the Lord forgive me! Nevertheless I thank you, father. Eat this slice of marchpane, it will help your digestion; then shall you be presented with a cup of claret hypocras, which is right healthful and stomachal. Let us proceed.

CHAPTER XXXI

How the physician Rondibilis counselleth Panurge

PANURGE, continuing his discourse, said, The first word which was spoken by him who gelded the lubbardly quaffing monks of Saussiniac, after that he had unstoned Friar Cauldaureil, was this, Now for the rest. In like manner, I say, Now for the rest. Therefore, I beseech you, my good master Rondibilis, should I marry or not? By the raking pace of my mule, quoth Rondibilis, I know not what answer to make to this problem of yours.

You say that you feel in you the pricking stings of sensuality, by which you are stirred up to venery. I find in our faculty of medicine, and we have founded our opinion therein upon the deliberate resolution and final decision of the ancient Platonics, that carnal concupiscence is cooled and quelled five several ways.

First, by the means of wine. I shall easily believe that, quoth Friar John, for when I am well whittled with the juice of the grape, I care for nothing else, so I may sleep. When I say, quoth Rondibilis, that wine abateth lust, my meaning is, wine immoderately taken; for by intemperance proceeding from the excessive drinking of strong liquor, there is brought upon the body of such a swill-down bouser, a chillness in the blood, a slackening in the sinews, a dissipation of the generative seed, a numbness and hebetation of the senses, with a perversive wryness and convulsion of the muscles; all which are great lets and impediments to the act of generation. Hence it is, that Bacchus, the god of bibbers, tipplers, and drunkards, is most commonly painted beardless, and clad in a woman's habit, as a person altogether effeminate, or like a libbed eunuch. Wine, nevertheless, taken moderately, worketh quite contrary effects, as is implied by the old proverb, which saith,—That Venus takes cold, when not accompanied with Ceres and Bacchus. This opinion is of great antiquity, as appeareth by the testimony of Diodorus the Sicilian, and confirmed by Pausanias, and universally held amongst the Lampsacians, that Don Priapus was the son of Bacchus and Venus.

Secondly, The fervency of lust is abated by certain drugs, plants, herbs, and roots, which make the taker cold, male-ficiated, unfit for, and unable to perform the act of generation;

as hath been often experimented in the water-lily, Heraclea, Agnus Castus, willow-twigs, hemp-stalks, woodbine, honey-suckle, tamarisk, chaste-tree, mandrake, bennet, keck-bugloss, the skin of a hippopotamus, and many other such, which, by convenient doses proportioned to the peccant humour and constitution of the patient, being duly and seasonably received within the body,—what by their elementary virtues on the one side, and peculiar properties on the other,—do either be-numb, mortify, and beclumpse with cold the prolific semence, or scatter and disperse the spirits, which ought to have gone along with, and conducted sperm to the places destinated and appointed for its reception,—or lastly, shut up, stop, and obstruct the ways, passages, and conduits through which the seed should have been expelled, evacuated, and ejected. We have never-theless of those ingredients, which, being of a contrary operation, heat the blood, bend the nerves, unite the spirits, quicken the senses, strengthen the muscles, and thereby rouse up, provoke, excite, and enable a man to the vigorous accomplishment of the feat of amorous dalliance. I have no need of those, quoth Panurge, God be thanked, and you, my good master. Howso-ever, I pray you, take no exception or offence at these my words; for what I have said was not out of any ill will I did bear to you, the Lord, he knows.

Thirdly, The ardour of lechery is very much subdued and check'd by frequent labour and continual toiling. For by painful exercises and laborious working, so great a dissolution is brought upon the whole body, that the blood, which runneth alongst the channels of the veins thereof, for the nourishment and alimentation of each of its members, hath neither time, leisure, nor power to afford the seminal resudation, or superfluity of the third concoction, which nature most carefully reserves for the conservation of the individual, whose preservation she more heedfully regardeth than the propagating of the species, and the multiplication of human kind. Whence it is, that Diana is said to be chaste, because she is never idle, but always busied about her hunting. For the same reason was a camp, or leaguer, of old called *Castrum*, as if they would have said *Castum*; because the soldiers, wrestlers, runners, throwers of the bar, and other such like athletic champions, as are usually seen in a military circumvallation, do incessantly travail and turmoil, and are in perpetual stir and agitation. To this pur-pose Hippocrates also writeth in his book, *De Aere, Aqua, et Locis*, That in his time there was a people in Scythia, as impotent as eunuchs in the discharge of a venerean exploit; because that without any cessation, pause, or respite, they were never from off horseback, or otherwise assiduously employed in some troublesome and molesting drudgery.

On the other part, in opposition and repugnancy hereto, the philosophers say, That idleness is the mother of luxury. When it was asked Ovid, Why Ægisthus became an adulterer? he made no other answer but this, Because he was idle. Who were able to rid the world of loitering and laziness, might easily frustrate and disappoint Cupid of all his designs, aims, engines, and devices, and so disable and appal him that his bow, quiver, and darts should from thenceforth be a mere needless load and burthen to him: for that it could not then lie in his power to strike, or wound any of either sex, with all the arms he had. He is not, I believe, so expert an archer, as that he can hit the cranes flying in the air, or yet the young stags skipping through the thickets, as the Parthians knew well how to do: that is to say, people moiling, stirring, and hurrying up and down, restless, and without repose. He must have those hushed, still, quiet, lying at a stay, lither, and full of ease, whom he is able to pierce with all his arrows. In confirmation hereof, Theophrastus being asked on a time, What kind of beast or thing he judged a toyish, wanton love to be? he made answer, That it was a passion of idle and sluggish spirits. From which pretty description of tickling love-tricks, that of Diogenes's hatching was not very discrepant, when he defined lechery, The occupation of folks destitute of all other occupation. For this cause the Sicyonian sculptor Canachus, being desirous to give us to understand that sloth, drowsiness, negligence, and laziness were the prime guardians and governesses of ribaldry, made the statue of Venus, not standing, as other stone-cutters had used to do, but sitting.

Fourthly, The tickling pricks of incontinency, are blunted by an eager study; for from thence proceedeth an incredible resolution of the spirits, that oftentimes there do not remain so many behind as may suffice to push and thrust forwards the generative resudation to the places thereto appropriated, and there withal inflate the cavernous nerve, whose office is to ejaculate the moisture for the propagation of human progeny. Lest you should think it is not so, be pleased but to contemplate a little the form, fashion, and carriage of a man exceeding earnestly set upon some learned meditation, and deeply plunged therein, and you shall see how all the arteries of his brains are

stretched forth, and bent like the string of a cross-bow, the
more promptly, dexterously, and copiously to suppeditate,
furnish, and supply him with store of spirits, sufficient to re-
plenish and fill up the ventricles, seats, tunnels, mansions,
receptacles, and cellules of common sense,—of the imagination,
apprehension, and fancy,—of the ratiocination, arguing, and
resolution, — as likewise of the memory, recordation, and
remembrance; and with great alacrity, nimbleness, and agility
to run, pass, and course from the one to the other, through those
pipes, windings, and conduits, which to skilful anatomists are
perceivable at the end of the wonderful net, where all the arteries
close in a terminating point: which arteries, taking their rise
and origin from the left capsule of the heart, bring through several
circuits, ambages, and anfractuosities, the vital spirits, to sub-
tilize and refine them to the ætherial purity of animal spirits.
Nay, in such a studiously musing person, you may espy so
extravagant raptures of one, as it were, out of himself, that
all his natural faculties for that time will seem to be suspended
from each their proper charge and office, and his exterior senses
to be at a stand. In a word, you cannot otherwise choose than
think, that he is by an extraordinary ecstacy quite transported
of what he was, or should be; and that Socrates did not speak
improperly, when he said, That philosophy was nothing else
but a meditation upon death. This possibly is the reason why
Democritus, deprived himself of the sense of seeing, prizing at
a much lower rate the loss of his sight, than the diminution of
his contemplations, which he frequently had found disturbed
by the vagrant, flying-out strayings of his unsettled and roving
eyes. Therefore is it, that Pallas, the goddess of wisdom,
tutoress and guardianess of such as are diligently studious, and
painfully industrious, is, and hath been still, accounted a virgin.
The muses upon the same consideration are esteemed perpetual
maids: and the graces for the like reason, have been held to
continue in a sempiternal pudicity.

I remember to have read, that Cupid on a time being asked
of his mother Venus, why he did not assault and set upon the
Muses, his answer was, That he found them so fair, so sweet,
so fine, so neat, so wise, so learned, so modest, so discreet, so
courteous, so virtuous, and so continually busied and employed,
—one in the speculation of the stars,—another in the supputa-
tion of numbers,—the third in the dimension of geometrical
quantities,—the fourth in the composition of heroic poems,—
the fifth in the jovial interludes of a comic strain,—the sixth

in the stately gravity of a tragic vein,—the seventh in the melodious disposition of musical airs,—the eighth in the completest manner of writing histories, and books on all sorts of subjects,—and the ninth in the mysteries, secrets, and curiosities of all sciences, faculties, disciplines, and arts whatsoever, whether liberal or mechanic, that approaching near unto them he unbent his bow, shut his quiver, and extinguished his torch, through mere shame, and fear that by mischance he might do them some hurt or prejudice. Which done, he thereafter put off the fillet wherewith his eyes were bound, to look them in the face, and to hear their melody and poetic odes. There took he the greatest pleasure in the world, that many times he was transported with their beauty and pretty behaviour, and charmed asleep by the harmony; so far was he from assaulting them, or interrupting their studies. Under this article may be comprised what Hippocrates wrote in the afore-cited treatise concerning the Scythians; as also that in a book of his, entitled, Of Breeding and Production, where he hath affirmed all such men to be unfit for generation, as have their parotid arteries cut—whose situation is beside the ears—for the reason given already, when I was speaking of the resolution of the spirits, and of that spiritual blood whereof the arteries are the sole and proper receptacles; and that likewise he doth maintain a large portion of the parastatic liquor to issue and descend from the brains and backbone.

Fifthly, by the too frequent reiteration of the act of venery. There did I wait for you quoth Panurge, and shall willingly apply it to myself, whilst any one that pleaseth may, for me, make use of any of the four preceding. That is the very same thing, quoth Friar John, which Father Scyllino, Prior of Saint Victor at Marseilles, calleth by the name of maceration, and taming of the flesh. I am of the same opinion,—and so was the hermit of Saint Radegonde, a little above Chinon: for, quoth he, the hermits of Thebaide can no way more aptly or expediently macerate and bring down the pride of their bodies, daunt and mortify their lecherous sensuality, or depress and overcome the stubbornness and rebellion of the flesh, than by duffling and fanfreluching it five and twenty or thirty times a day. I see Panurge, quoth Rondibilis, neatly featured, and proportioned in all the members of his body, of a good temperament in his humours, well complexioned in his spirits, of a competent age, in an opportune time, and of a reasonably forward mind to be married. Truly, if he encounter with a wife

of the like nature, temperament, and constitution, he may
beget upon her children worthy of some transpontine monarchy;
and the sooner he marry, it will be the better for him, and the
more conducible for his profit, if he would see and have his
children in his own time well provided for.   Sir, my worthy
master, quoth Panurge, I will do it, do not you doubt thereof;
and that quickly enough, I warrant you.   Nevertheless, whilst
you were busied in the uttering of your learned discourse, this
flea which I have in mine ear hath tickled me more than ever.
I retain you in the number of my festival guests, and promise
you, that we shall not want for mirth, and good cheer enough,
yea, over and above the ordinary rate.   And, if it may please
you, desire your wife to come along with you, together with her
she-friends and neighbours—that is to be understood—and there
shall be fair play.

CHAPTER XXXII

*How Rondibilis declareth cuckoldry to be naturally one of the
appendances of marriage*

THERE remaineth, as yet, quoth Panurge, going on in his discourse, one small scruple to be cleared.   You have seen heretofore, I doubt not, in the Roman standards, S.P.Q.R. Si, Peu,
Que, Rien.   Shall not I be a cuckold?   By the haven of safety,
cried out Rondibilis, what is this you ask of me?   If you shall
be a cuckold?   My noble friend, I am married, and you are like
to be so very speedily; therefore be pleased, from my experiment in the matter, to write in your brain with a steel-pen this
subsequent ditton, 'there is no married man who doth not run
the hazard of being made a cuckold.'   Cuckoldry naturally
attendeth marriage.   The shadow doth not more naturally
follow the body, than cuckoldry ensueth after marriage, to
place fair horns upon the husbands' heads.

And when you shall happen to hear any man pronounce these
words—he is married—if you then say he is, hath been, shall
be, or may be a cuckold, you will not be accounted an unskilful
artist in framing of true consequences.   Tripes and bowels of
all the devils, cries Panurge, what do you tell me?   My dear
friend, answered Rondibilis, as Hippocrates on a time was in
the very nick of setting forwards from Lango to Polistillo, to
visit the philosopher Democritus, he wrote a familiar letter to

his friend Dionysius, wherein he desired him, that he would, during the interval of his absence, carry his wife to the house of her father and mother, who were an honourable couple, and of good repute; because I would not have her at my home, said he, to make abode in solitude. Yet, notwithstanding this her residence beside her parents, do not fail, quoth he, with a most heedful care and circumspection, to pry into her ways, and to espy what places she shall go to with her mother, and who those be that shall repair unto her. Not, quoth he, that I do mistrust her virtue, or that I seem to have any diffidence of her pudicity, and chaste behaviour,—for of that I have frequently had good and real proofs,—but I must freely tell you, she is a woman. There lies the suspicion.

My worthy friend, the nature of women is set forth before our eyes, and represented to us by the moon in divers other things as well as in this, that they squat, skulk, constrain their own inclinations, and, with all the cunning they can, dissemble and play the hypocrite in the sight and presence of their husbands; who come no sooner to be out of the way, but that forthwith they take their advantage, pass the time merrily, desist from all labour, frolic it, gad abroad, lay aside their counterfeit garb, and openly declare and manifest the interior of their dispositions, even as the moon, when she is in conjunction with the sun, is neither seen in the heavens, nor on the earth, but in her opposition, when remotest from him, shineth in her greatest fulness, and wholly appeareth in her brightest splendour whilst it is night. Thus women are but women.

When I say womankind, I speak of a sex so frail, so variable, so changeable, so fickle, inconstant, and imperfect, that, in my opinion, Nature, under favour nevertheless, of the prime honour and reverence which is due unto her, did in a manner mistake the road which she had traced formerly, and stray exceedingly from that excellence of providential judgment, by the which she had created and formed all other things, when she built, framed, and made up the woman. And having thought upon it a hundred and five times, I know not what else to determine therein, save only that in the devising, hammering, forging, and composing of the woman, she hath had a much tenderer regard, and by a great deal more respectful, heed to the delightful consortship, and sociable delectation of the man, than to the perfection and accomplishment of the individual womanishness or muliebrity. The divine philosopher Plato was doubtful in what rank of living creatures to place and collocate them, whether amongst the rational animals, by elevating them to an upper seat in the specifical classes of humanity; or with the irrational, by degrading them to a lower bench on the opposite side, of a brutal kind, and mere bestiality. For nature hath posited in a privy, secret and intestine place of their bodies, a sort of member, by some not impertinently termed an animal, which is not to be found in men. Therein sometimes are engendered certain humours, so saltish, brackish, clammy, sharp, nipping, tearing, prickling, and most eagerly tickling, that by their stinging acrimony, rending nitrosity, figging itch, wriggling mordacity, and smarting salsitude, (for the said member is altogether sinewy, and of a most quick and lively feeling,) their whole body is shaken and ebrangled. their senses totally ravished and transported, the operations of their judgment and understanding utterly confounded, and all disordinate passions and perturbations of the mind throughly and absolutely allowed, admitted, and approved of; yea, in such sort, that if nature had not been so favourable unto them as to have sprinkled their forehead with a little tincture of bashfulness and modesty, you should see them in a so frantic mood run mad after lechery, and hie apace up and down with haste and lust, in quest of, and to fix some chamber-standard in their Paphian ground, that never did the Proëtides, Mimallonides, nor Lyæan Thyads deport themselves in the time of their Bacchanalian festivals more shamelessly, or with a so effronted and brazen-faced impudency; because this terrible animal is knit unto, and hath an union with all the chief and most principal parts of the body, as to anatomists is evident. Let it not here be thought strange that I should call it an animal, seeing therein I do no otherwise than follow and adhere to the doctrine of the academic and peripatetic philosophers. For if a proper motion be a certain mark and infallible token of the life and animation of the mover, as Aristotle writeth, and that any such thing as moveth of itself ought to be held animated, and of a living nature, then assuredly Plato with very good reason did give it the denomination of an animal, for that he perceived and observed in it the proper and self-stirring motions of suffocation, precipitation, corrugation, and of indignation, so extremely violent, that oftentimes by them is taken and removed from the woman all other sense and moving whatsoever, as if she were in a swounding lipothymy, benumbing syncope, epileptic, apoplectic palsy, and true resemblance of a pale-faced death.

Furthermore, in the said member there is a manifest discerning faculty of scents and odours very perceptible to women, who feel it fly from what is rank and unsavoury, and follow fragrant and aromatic smells. It is not unknown to me how Cl. Galen striveth with might and main to prove that these are not proper and particular notions proceeding intrinsically from the thing itself, but accidentally, and by chance. Nor hath it escaped my notice, how others of that sect have laboured hardly, yea, to the utmost of their abilities, to demonstrate that it is not a sensitive discerning or perception in it of the difference of wafts and smells, but merely a various manner of virtue and efficacy, passing forth and flowing from the diversity of odoriferous substances applied near unto it. Nevertheless, if you will studiously examine, and seriously ponder and weigh in Critolaus's balance the strength of their reasons and arguments, you shall find that they, not only in this, but in several other matters also of the like nature, have spoken at random, and rather out of an ambitious envy to check and reprehend their betters, than for any design to make inquiry into the solid truth.

I will not launch my little skiff any further into the wide ocean of this dispute, only will I tell you that the praise and commendation is not mean and slender which is due to those honest and good women, who living chastely and without blame, have had the power and virtue to curb, range, and subdue that unbridled, heady, and wild animal to an obedient, submissive, and obsequious yielding unto reason. Therefore here will I make an end of my discourse thereon, when I shall have told you, that the said animal being once satiated—if it be possible that it can be contented or satisfied—by that aliment which nature hath provided for it out of the epididymal storehouse of man, all its former and irregular and disordered motions are at an end, laid and assuaged,—all its vehement and unruly longings lulled, pacified, and quieted,—and all the furious and raging lusts, appetites, and desires thereof appeased, calmed, and extinguished. For this cause let it seem nothing strange unto you, if we be in a perpetual danger of being cuckolds, that is to say, such of us as have not wherewithal fully to satisfy the appetite and expectation of that voracious animal. Ods fish! quoth Panurge, have you no preventive cure in all your medicinal art for hindering one's head to be horny-graffed at home, whilst his feet are plodding abroad? Yes, that I have, my gallant friend, answered Rondibilis, and that which is a sovereign remedy, whereof I frequently make use myself; and,

that you may the better relish, it is set down and written in
the book of a most famous author, whose renown is of a standing of two thousand years. Hearken and take good heed.
You are, quoth Panurge, by cocks-hobby, a right honest man,
and I love you with all my heart. Eat a little of this quince-
pie; it is very proper and convenient for the shutting up of the
orifice of the ventricle of the stomach, because of a kind of
astringent stypticity, which is in that sort of fruit, and is helpful
to the first concoction. But what? I think I speak Latin
before clerks. Stay till I give you somewhat to drink out of
this Nestorian goblet. Will you have another draught of
white hippocras? Be not afraid of the squinzy, no. There is
neither squinanthus, ginger, nor grains in it; only a little choice
cinnamon, and some of the best refined sugar, with the delicious
white wine of the growth of that vine, which was set in the
slips of the great sorb-apple, above the walnut tree.

CHAPTER XXXIII

Rondibilis the Physician's cure of cuckoldry

At what time, quoth Rondibilis, when Jupiter took a view of
the state of his olympic house and family, and that he had
made the calendar of all the gods and goddesses, appointing
unto the festival of every one of them its proper day and season,
establishing certain fixed places and stations for the pronouncing
of oracles, and relief of travelling pilgrims, and ordaining victims,
immolations, and sacrifices suitable and correspondent to the
dignity and nature of the worshipped and adored deity. Did
not he do, asked Panurge, therein, as Tinteville the bishop of
Auxerre is said once to have done? This noble prelate loved
entirely the pure liquor of the grape, as every honest and
judicious man doth; therefore was it that he had an especial
care and regard to the bud of the vine tree, as to the great
grandfather of Bacchus. But so it is, that for sundry years
together, he saw a most pitiful havoc, desolation, and destruction
made amongst the sprouts, shootings, buds, blossoms, and
scions of the vines, by hoary frost, dank fogs, hot mists, un-
seasonable colds, chill blasts, thick hail, and other calamitous
chances of foul weather, happening, as he thought, by the
dismal inauspiciousness of the Holy Days of St. George, St.
Mary, St. Paul, St. Eutropius, Holy Rood, the Ascension, and

other festivals, in that time when the sun passeth under the sign of Taurus; and thereupon harboured in his mind this opinion, that the aforenamed saints were Saint Hail-flingers, Saint Frost-senders, Saint Fog-mongers, and Saint Spoilers of the vine-buds. For which cause he went about to have transmitted their feasts from the spring to the winter, to be celebrated between Christmas and Epiphany, so the mother of the three kings called it, allowing them with all honour and reverence the liberty then to freeze, hail, and rain as much as they would; for that he knew that at such a time frost was rather profitable than hurtful to the vine-buds, and in their steads to have placed the festivals of St. Christopher, St. John the Baptist, St. Magdalene, St. Ann, St. Domingo, and St. Lawrence; yea, and to have gone so far as to collocate and transpose the middle of August in and to the beginning of May, because during the whole space of their solemnity there was so little danger of hoary frosts and cold mists, that no artificers are then held in greater request, than the afforders of refrigerating inventions, makers of junkets, fit disposers of cooling shades, composers of green arbours, and refreshers of wine.

Jupiter, said Rondibilis, forgot the poor devil Cuckoldry, who was then in the court at Paris, very eagerly soliciting a piddling suit at law for one of his vassals and tenants. Within some few days thereafter, I have forgot how many, when he got full notice of the trick, which in his absence was done unto him, he instantly desisted from prosecuting legal processes in the behalf of others, full of solicitude to pursue after his own business, lest he should be fore-closed, and thereupon he appeared personally at the tribunal of the great Jupiter, displayed before him the importance of his preceding merits, together with the acceptable services, which in obedience to his commandments he had formerly performed; and therefore, in all humility, begged of him that he would be pleased not to leave him alone amongst all the sacred potentates, destitute and void of honour, reverence, sacrifices, and festival ceremonies. To this petition Jupiter's answer was excusatory, That all the places and offices of his house were bestowed. Nevertheless, so importuned was he by the continual supplications of Monsieur Cuckoldry, that he, in fine, placed him in the rank, list, toll, rubric, and catalogue, and appointed honours, sacrifices, and festival rites to be observed on earth in great devotion, and tendered to him with solemnity. The feast, because there was no void, empty, nor vacant place in all the calendar, was to be celebrated jointly with and on the same day that had been consecrated to the goddess Jealousy. His power and dominion should be over married folks, especially such as had handsome wives. His sacrifices were to be suspicion, diffidence, mistrust, a lowering pouting sullenness, watchings, wardings, researchings, plyings, explorations, together with the waylayings, ambushes, narrow observations, and malicious doggings of the husbands' scouts and espials of the most privy actions of their wives. Herewithal every married man was expressly and rigorously commanded to reverence, honour, and worship him, to celebrate and solemnize his festival with twice more respect than that of any other saint or deity, and to immolate unto him, with all sincerity and alacrity of heart, the above-mentioned sacrifices and oblations, under pain of severe censures, threatenings, and comminations of these subsequent fines, mulcts, amercements, penalties, and punishments to be inflicted on the delinquents; that Monsieur Cuckoldry should never be favourable nor propitious to them,—that he should never help, aid, supply, succour, nor grant them any subventitious furtherance, auxiliary, suffrage, or adminiculary assistance,—that he should never hold them in any reckoning, account, or estimation,—that he should never deign to enter within their houses, neither at the doors, windows, nor any other place thereof,—that he should never haunt nor frequent their companies or conversations, how frequently soever they should invocate him, and call upon his name,—and that not only he should leave and abandon them to rot alone with their wives in a sempiternal solitariness, without the benefit of the diversion of any copesmate or corrival at all, but should withal shun and eschew them, fly from them, and eternally forsake and reject them as impious heretics and sacrilegious persons, according to the accustomed manner of other gods, towards such as are too slack in offering up the duties and reverences which ought to be performed respectively to their divinities; as is evidently apparent in Bacchus towards negligent vine-dressers; in Ceres, against idle ploughmen and tillers of the ground; in Pomona, to unworthy fruiterers and costard-mongers; in Neptune, towards dissolute mariners and seafaring men; in Vulcan towards loitering smiths and forgemen; and so throughout the rest. Now, on the contrary, this infallible promise was added, that unto all those who should make a Holy Day of the above-recited festival, and cease from all manner of worldly work and negotiation, lay aside all their own most important occasions, and be so retchless, heedless, and careless of what might concern the management of their proper affairs, as to mind nothing else but a suspicious espying and prying into the secret deportments of their wives, and how to coop, shut up, hold at under, and deal cruelly and austerely with them, by all the harshness and hardships that an implacable and every way inexorable jealousy can devise and suggest, conform to the sacred ordinances of the afore-mentioned sacrifices and oblations, he should be continually favourable to them, should love them, sociably converse with them, should be day and night in their houses, and never leave them destitute of his presence. Now I have said, and you have heard my cure.

Ha, ha, ha, quoth Carpalim, laughing, this is a remedy yet more apt and proper than Hans Carvel's ring. The devil take me if I do not believe it! The humour, inclination, and nature of women is like the thunder, whose force in its bolt, or otherwise, burneth, bruiseth, and breaketh only hard, massive and resisting objects, without staying or stopping at soft, empty, and yielding matters. For it dasheth into pieces the steel sword, without doing any hurt to the velvet scabbard which insheatheth it. It crusheth also, and consumeth the bones, without wounding or endamaging the flesh, wherewith they are veiled and covered. Just so it is, that women for the greater part never bend the contention, subtlety, and contradictory disposition of their spirits, unless it be to do what is prohibited and forbidden. Verily, quoth Hippothadeus, some of our doctors aver for a truth, that the first woman of the world, whom the Hebrews call Eve, had hardly been induced or allured into the temptation of eating of the fruit of the tree of life, if it had not been forbidden her so to do. And that you may give the more credit to the validity of this opinion, consider how the cautelous and wily tempter did commemorate unto her, for an antecedent to his enthymeme, the prohibition which was made to taste it; as being desirous to infer from thence, It is forbidden thee; therefore thou shouldest eat of it, else thou canst not be a woman.

CHAPTER XXXIV

How women ordinarily have the greatest longing after things prohibited

WHEN I was, quoth Carpalim, a whore-master at Orleans, the whole art of rhetoric, in all its tropes and figures, was not able to afford unto me a colour or flourish of greater force and value; nor could I by any other form or manner of elocution pitch upon a more persuasive argument for bringing young beautiful married ladies into the snares of adultery, through alluring and enticing them to taste with me of amorous delights, than with a lively sprightfulness to tell them in downright terms, and to remonstrate to them, (with a great show of detestation of a crime so horrid,) how their husbands were jealous. This was none of my invention. It is written, and we have laws, examples, reasons, and daily experiences confirmative of the same. If this belief once enter into their noddles, their husbands will infallibly be cuckolds; yea, by God, will they, without swearing, although they should do like Semiramis, Pasiphaë, Egesta, the women of the Isle Mandez in Egypt, and other such like queanish flirting harlots, mentioned in the writings of Herodotus, Strabo, and such like puppies.

Truly, quoth Ponocrates, I have heard it related, and it hath been told me for a verity, that Pope John XXII, passing on a day through the abbey of Toucherome, was in all humility required and besought by the abbess, and other discreet mothers of the said convent, to grant them an indulgence, by means whereof they might confess themselves to one another, alleging, That religious women were subject to some petty secret slips and imperfections, which would be a foul and burning shame for them to discover and to reveal to men, how sacerdotal soever their function were: but that they would freelier, more familiarly, and with greater cheerfulness, open to each other their offences, faults, and escapes, under the seal of confession. There is not anything, answered the pope, fitting for you to impetrate of me, which I would not most willingly condescend unto: but I find one inconvenience. You know, confession should be kept secret, and women are not able to do so. Exceeding well, quoth they, most holy father, and much more closely than the best of men.

The said pope on the very same day gave them in keeping

a pretty box, wherein he purposely caused a little linnet to be put, willing them very gently and courteously to lock it up in some sure and hidden place, and promising them, by the faith of a pope, that he should yield to their request, if they would keep secret what was enclosed within that deposited box: enjoining them withal, not to presume one way nor other, directly or indirectly, to go about the opening thereof, under pain of the highest ecclesiastical censure, eternal excommunication. The prohibition was no sooner made, but that they did all of them boil with a most ardent desire to know and see what kind of thing it was that was within it. They thought it long already, that the pope was not gone, to the end they might jointly, with the more leisure and ease, apply themselves to the box-opening curiosity.

The holy father, after he had given them his benediction, retired and withdrew himself to the pontifical lodgings of his own palace. But he was hardly gone three steps from without the gates of their cloister, when the good ladies throngingly, and as in a huddled crowd, pressing hard on the backs of one another, ran thrusting and shoving who should be first at the setting open of the forbidden box, and descrying of the *Quod latitat* within.

On the very next day thereafter, the pope made them another visit, of a full design, purpose, and intention, as they imagined, to dispatch the grant of their sought and wished for indulgence. But before he would enter into any chat or communing with them, he commanded the casket to be brought unto him. It was done so accordingly; but, by your leave, the bird was no more there. Then was it, that the pope did represent to their maternities, how hard a matter and difficult it was for them to keep secrets revealed to them in confession, unmanifested to the ears of others, seeing for the space of four-and-twenty hours they were not able to lay up in secret a box, which he had highly recommended to their discretion, charge, and custody.

Welcome, in good faith, my dear master, welcome! If did me good to hear you talk, the Lord be praised for all. I do not remember to have seen you before now, since the last time that you acted at Montpellier with our ancient friends, Anthony Saporta, Guy Bourguyer, Balthasar, Noyer, Tolet, John Quentin, Francis Robinet, John Perdrier, and Francis Rabelais, the moral comedy of him who had espoused and married a dumb wife. I was there, quoth Epistemon. The good honest man, her husband, was very earnestly urgent to have the fillet of her

tongue untied, and would needs have her speak by any means.
At his desire, some pains were taken on her, and partly by the
industry of the physician, other part by the expertness of the
surgeon, the encyliglotte which she had under her tongue being
cut, she spoke, and spoke again; yea, within a few hours she
spoke so loud, so much, so fiercely, and so long, that her poor
husband returned to the same physician for a receipt to make
her hold her peace. There are, quoth the physician, many
proper remedies in our art to make dumb women speak, but
there are none that ever I could learn therein to make them
silent. The only cure which I have found out is their husband's
deafness. The wretch became within few weeks thereafter, by
virtue of some drugs, charms, or enchantments, which the
physician had prescribed unto him, so deaf, that he could not
have heard the thundering of nineteen hundred cannons at a
salvo. His wife perceiving that indeed he was as deaf as a
door-nail, and that her scolding was but in vain, sith that he
heard her not, she grew stark mad.

Some time after, the doctor asked for his fee of the husband;
who answered, That truly he was deaf, and so was not able
to understand what the tenour of his demand might be. Whereupon the leech bedusted him with a little, I know not what,
sort of powder; which rendered him a fool immediately, so great
was the stultificating virtue of that strange kind of pulverised
dose. Then did this fool of a husband, and his mad wife, join
together, and falling on the doctor and the surgeon, did so scratch,
bethwack, and bang them, that they were left half dead upon
the place, so furious were the blows which they received. I
never in my lifetime laughed so much, as at the acting of that
buffoonery.

Let us come to where we left off, quoth Panurge. Your
words, being translated from the clapper-dudgeons to plain
English, do signify, that it is not very inexpedient that I marry,
and that I should not care for being a cuckold. You have
there hit the nail on the head. I believe, master doctor, that
on the day of my marriage you will be so much taken up with
your patients, or otherwise so seriously employed, that we shall
not enjoy your company. Sir, I will heartily excuse your absence.

Stercus et urina medici sunt prandia prima.
Ex aliis paleas, ex istis collige grana.

You are mistaken, quoth Rondibilis, in the second verse of
our distich; for it ought to run thus—

Nobis sunt signa, vobis sunt prandia digna.

If my wife at any time prove to be unwell, and ill at ease, I will look upon the water which she shall have made in an urinal glass, quoth Rondibilis, grope her pulse, and see the disposition of her hypogaster, together with her umbilicary parts,—according to the prescript rule of Hippocrates, 2. Aph. 35,—before I proceed any further in the cure of her distemper. No, no, quoth Panurge, that will be but to little purpose. Such a feat is for the practice of us that are lawyers, who have the rubric, *De ventre inspiciendo.* Do not therefore trouble yourself about it master doctor: I will provide for her a plaster of warm guts. Do not neglect your more urgent occasions otherwhere, for coming to my wedding. I will send you some supply of victuals to your own house, without putting you to the trouble of coming abroad, and you shall always be my special friend. With this, approaching somewhat nearer to him, he clapped into his hand, without the speaking of so much as one word, four rose nobles. Rondibilis did shut his fist upon them right kindly; yet, as if it had displeased him to make acceptance of such golden presents, he in a start, as if he had been wroth, said, He, he, he, he, he, there was no need of anything, I thank you nevertheless. From wicked folks I never get enough, and from honest people I refuse nothing. I shall be always, sir, at your command. Provided that I pay you well, quoth Panurge. That, quoth Rondibilis, is understood.

CHAPTER XXXV

How the philosopher Trouillogan handleth the difficulty of marriage

As this discourse was ended, Pantagruel said to the philosopher Trouillogan, Our loyal, honest, true, and trusty friend, the lamp from hand to hand is come to you. It falleth to your turn to give an answer, should Panurge, pray you, marry, yea, or no? He should do both, quoth Trouillogan. What say you, asked Panurge? That which you have heard, answered Trouillogan. What have I heard? replied Panurge. That which I have said, replied Trouillogan. Ha, ha, ha, are we come to that pass? quoth Panurge. Let it go nevertheless, I do not value it at a rush, seeing we can make no better of the game. But howsoever tell me, should I marry or no? Neither the one nor the other, answered Trouillogan. The devil take me, quoth Panurge, if these odd answers do not make me dote,

and may he snatch me presently away, if I do understand you.
Stay awhile, until I fasten these spectacles of mine on this
left ear, that I may hear you better. With this Pantagruel
perceived at the door of the great hall, which was that day
their dining room, Gargantua's little dog, whose name was
Kyne; for so was Toby's dog called, as is recorded. Then did
he say to these who were there present, Our king is not far
off,—let us all rise.

That word was scarcely sooner uttered, than that Gargantua
with his royal presence graced that banqueting and stately
hall. Each of the guests arose to do their king that reverence
and duty which became them. After that Gargantua had most
affably saluted all the gentlemen there present, he said, Good
friends, I beg this favour of you, and therein you will very
much oblige me, that you leave not the places where you sate,
nor quit the discourse you were upon. Let a chair be brought
hither unto this end of the table, and reach me a cup full of
the strongest and best wine you have, that I may drink to all
the company. You are, in faith, all welcome, gentlemen.
Now let me know, what talk you were about. To this Pantagruel answered, that at the beginning of the second service
Panurge had proposed a problematic theme, to wit, Whether
he should marry, or not marry? that Father Hippothadeus and
Doctor Rondibilis had already dispatched their resolutions
thereupon; and that, just as his majesty was coming in, the
faithful Trouillogan in the delivery of his opinion hath thus
far proceeded, that when Panurge asked,—whether he ought
to marry, yea, or no?—at first he made this answer, Both
together. When this same question was again propounded,
his second answer was, Neither the one, nor the other. Panurge
exclaimeth, that those answers are full of repugnancies and
contradictions, protesting that he understands them not, nor
what it is that can be meant by them. If I be not mistaken,
quoth Gargantua, I understand it very well. The answer is
not unlike to that which was once made by a philosopher in
ancient time, who being interrogated, if he had a woman, whom
they named him, to his wife? I have her, quoth he, but she
hath not me,—possessing her, by her I am not possest. Such
another answer, quoth Pantagruel, was once made by a certain
bouncing wench of Sparta who being asked, if at any time she
had had to do with a man? No, quoth she, but sometimes men
have had to do with me. Well then, quoth Rondibilis, let it
be a neuter in physic,—as when we say a body is neuter, when

it is neither sick nor healthful,—and a mean in philosophy; that, by an abnegation of both extremes, and this, by the participation of the one and of the other. Even as when lukewarm water is said to be both hot and cold; or rather, as when time makes the partition, and equally divides betwixt the two, a while in the one, another while as long in the other opposite extremity. The holy apostle, quoth Hippothadeus, seemeth, as I conceive, to have more clearly explained this point, when he said, Those that are married, let them be as if they were not married; and those that have wives let them be as if they had no wives at all. I thus interpret, quoth Pantagruel, the having and not having of a wife. To have a wife, is to have the use of her in such a way as nature hath ordained, which is for the aid, society, and solace of man, and propagating of his race. To have no wife is not to be uxorious, play the coward, and be lazy about her, and not for her sake to distain the lustre of that affection which man owes to God; or yet for her to leave those offices and duties which he owes unto his country, unto his friends and kindred; or for her to abandon and forsake his precious studies, and other businesses of account, to wait still on her will, her beck, and her buttocks. If we be pleased in this sense to take having and not having of a wife, we shall indeed find no repugnancy nor contradiction in the terms at all.

CHAPTER XXXVI

A continuation of the answers of the Ephectic and Pyrrhonian philosopher Trouillogan

You speak wisely, quoth Panurge, if the moon were green cheese. Such a tale once pissed my goose. I do not think but that I am let down into that dark pit, in the lowermost bottom where the truth was hid, according to the saying of Heraclitus. I see no whit at all, I hear nothing, understand as little, my senses are altogether dulled and blunted; truly I do very shrewdly suspect that I am enchanted. I will now alter the former style of my discourse, and talk to him in another strain. Our trusty friend, stir not, nor imburse any; but let us vary the chance, and speak without disjunctives. I see already, that these loose and ill-joined members of an enunciation do vex, trouble and perplex you.

Now go on, in the name of God! Should I marry?

Trouillogan. There is some likelihood therein.

Panurge. But if I do not marry?

Trouil. I see in that no inconvenience.

Pan. You do not?

Trouil. None, truly, if my eyes deceive me not.

Pan. Yea, but I find more than five hundred.

Trouil. Reckon them.

Pan. This is an impropriety of speech, I confess; for I do no more thereby, but take a certain for an uncertain number, and posit the determinate term for what is indeterminate. When I say therefore five hundred, my meaning is, many.

Trouill. I hear you.

Pan. Is it possible for me to live without a wife, in the name of all the subterranean devils?

Trouil. Away with these filthy beasts.

Pan. Let it be then in the name of God; for my Salmigondinish people used to say, To lie alone, without a wife, is certainly a brutish life. And such a life also was it assevered to be by Dido, in her lamentations.

Trouil. At your command.

Pan. By the pody cody, I have fished fair; where are we now? But will you tell me? Shall I marry?

Trouil. Perhaps.

Pan. Shall I thrive or speed well withal?

Trouil. According to the encounter.

Pan. But if in my adventure I encounter aright, as I hope I will, shall be I fortunate?

Trouil. Enough.

Pan. Let us turn the clean contrary way, and brush our former words against the wool: what if I encounter ill?

Trouil. Then blame not me.

Pan. But, of courtesy, be pleased to give me some advice. I heartily beseech you, what must I do?

Trouil. Even what thou wilt.

Pan. Wishy washy; trolly, lolly.

Trouil. Do not invocate the name of any thing, I pray you.

Pan. In the name of God, let it be so! My actions shall be regulated by the rule and square of your counsel. What is it that you advise and counsel me to do?

Trouil. Nothing.

Pan. Shall I marry?

Trouil. I have no hand in it.

Pan. Then shall I not marry?

Trouil. I cannot help it.

Pan. If I never marry, I shall never be a cuckold.

Trouil. I thought so.

Pan. But put the case that I be married.

Trouil. Where shall we put it?

Pan. Admit it be so then, and take my meaning, in that sense.

Trouil. I am otherwise employed.

Pan. By the death of a hog, and mother of a toad, O Lord, if I durst hazard upon a little fling at the swearing game, though privily and under thumb, it would lighten the burden of my heart, and ease my lights and reins exceedingly. A little patience, nevertheless, is requisite. Well then, if I marry, I shall be a cuckold.

Trouil. One would say so.

Pan. Yet if my wife prove a virtuous, wise, discreet, and chaste woman, I shall never be cuckolded.

Trouil. I think you speak congruously.

Pan. Hearken.

Trouil. As much as you will.

Pan. Will she be discreet and chaste? This is the only point I would be resolved in.

Trouil. I question it.

Pan. You never saw her?

Trouil. Not that I know of.

Pan. Why do you then doubt of that which you know not?

Trouil. For a cause.

Pan. And if you should know her?

Trouil. Yet more.

Pan. Page, my little pretty darling, take here my cap,—I give it to thee. Have a care you do not break the spectacles that are in it. Go down to the lower court. Swear there half an hour for me, and I shall in compensation of that favour swear hereafter for thee as much as thou wilt. But who shall cuckold me?

Trouil. Somebody.

Pan. By the belly of the wooden horse at Troy, Master Somebody, I shall bang, belam thee, and claw thee well for thy labour.

Trouil. You say so.

Pan. Nay, nay, that Nick in the dark cellar, who hath no white in his eye, carry me quite away with him, if, in that case, whensoever I go abroad from the palace of my domestic residence, I do not, with as much circumspection as they use to ring mares in our country to keep them from being sallied by stoned horses, clap a Bergamasco lock upon my wife.

Trouil. Talk better.

Pan. It is *bien chien, chié chanté*, well cacked, and cackled, shitten, and sung in matter of talk. Let us resolve on somewhat.

Trouil. I do not gainsay it.

Pan. Have a little patience. Seeing I cannot on this side draw any blood of you, I will try, if with the lancet of my judgment I be able to bleed you in another vein. Are you married, or are you not?

Trouil. Neither the one nor the other, and both together.

Pan. O the good God help us! By the death of a buffle-ox, I sweat with the toil and travail that I am put to, and find my digestion broke off, disturbed, and interrupted; for all my phrenes, metaphrenes, and diaphragms, back, belly, midrib, muscles, veins, and sinews, are held in a suspense, and for a while discharged from their proper offices, to stretch forth their several powers and abilities, for incornifistibulating, and laying up into the hamper of my understanding your various sayings and answers.

Trouil. I shall be no hinderer thereof.

Pan. Tush, for shame! Our faithful friend, speak, are you married?

Trouil. I think so.

Pan. You were also married before you had this wife.

Trouil. It is possible.

Pan. Had you good luck in your first marriage?

Trouil. It is not impossible.

Pan. How thrive you with this second wife of yours?

Trouil. Even as it pleaseth my fatal destiny.

Pan. But what in good earnest? Tell me—do you prosper well with her?

Trouil. It is likely.

Pan. Come on, in the name of God. I vow, by the burden of Saint Christopher, that I had rather undertake the fetching of a fart forth of the belly of a dead ass, than to draw out of you a positive and determinate resolution. Yet shall I be sure at this time to have a snatch at you, and get my claws over you. Our trusty friend, let us shame the devil of hell, and confess the verity. Were you ever a cuckold? I say you who are here, and not that other you, who playeth below in the tennis-court?

Trouil. No, if it was not predestinated.

Pan. By the flesh, blood, and body, I swear, reswear, forswear, abjure, and renounce: he evades and avoids, shifts and escapes me, and quite slips and winds himself out of my gripes and clutches.

At these words Gargantua arose, and said, Praised be the good God in all things, but especially for bringing the world into the height of refinedness beyond what it was when I first became acquainted therewith, that now the most learned and most prudent philosophers are not ashamed to be seen entering in at the porches and frontispieces of the schools of the Pyrrhonian, Aporrhetic, Sceptic, and Ephetic sects. Blessed be the holy name of God! Veritably, it is like henceforth to be found an enterprise of much more easy undertaking, to catch lions by the neck, horses by the mane, oxen by the horns, bulls by the muzzle, wolves by the tail, goats by the beard, and flying birds by the feet, than to entrap such philosophers in their words. Farewell, my worthy, dear, and honest friends.

When he had done thus speaking, he withdrew himself from the company. Pantagruel, and others with him would have followed and accompanied him, but he would not permit them so to do. No sooner was Gargantua departed out of the banqueting-hall, than that Pantagruel said to the invited guests; Plato's Timæus, at the beginning always of a solemn festival convention, was wont to count those that were called thereto. We, on the contrary, shall at the closure and end of this treatment, reckon up our number. One, two, three; where is the fourth? I miss my friend Bridlegoose. Was not he sent for? Epistemon answered,—That he had been at his house to bid and invite him, but could not meet with him; for that a messenger from the parliament of Myrelingois, in Myrelingues, was come to him, with a writ of summons, to cite and warn him personally to appear before the reverend senators of the High Court there, to vindicate and justify himself at the bar, of the crime of prevarication laid to his charge, and to be peremptorily instanced against him, in a certain decree, judgment, or sentence lately awarded, given, and pronounced by him: and that, therefore, he had taken horse, and departed in great haste from his own house, to the end, that without peril or danger of falling into a default, or contumacy, he might be the better able to keep the prefixed and appointed time.

I will, quoth Pantagruel, understand how that matter goeth. It is now above forty years, that he hath been constantly the judge of Fonsbeton, during which space of time he hath given four thousand definitive sentences. Of two thousand three hundred and nine whereof, although appeal was made by the parties whom he had judicially condemned, from his inferior judicatory to the supreme court of the parliament of Myrelingois, in Myrelingues, they were all of them nevertheless confirmed, ratified, and approved of by an order, decree, and final sentence of the said sovereign court, to the casting of the appellants, and utter overthrow of the suits wherein they had been foiled at law, for ever and a day. That now, in his old age, he should be personally summoned, who in all the foregoing time of his life hath demeaned himself so unblameably in the discharge of the office and vocation he had been called unto, it cannot assuredly be, that such a change hath happened without some notorious misfortune and disaster. I am resolved to help and assist him in equity and justice to the uttermost extent of my power and ability. I know the malice, despite and wickedness of the world to be so much more now-a-days exasperated, increased, and aggravated by what it was not long since, that the best cause that is, how just and equitable soever it be, standeth in great need to be succoured, aided, and supported. Therefore presently, from this very instant forth, do I purpose, till I see the event and closure thereof, most heedfully to attend and wait upon it, for fear of some under-hand tricky surprisal, cavilling pettifoggery, or fallacious quirks in law, to his detriment, hurt, or disadvantage.

Then dinner being done, and the tables drawn and removed, when Pantagruel had very cordially and affectionately thanked his invited guests for the favour which he had enjoyed of their company, he presented them with several rich and costly gifts, such as jewels, rings set with precious stones, gold and silver vessels, with a great deal of other sort of plate besides, and lastly, taking of them all his leave, retired himself into an inner chamber.

CHAPTER XXXVII

How Pantagruel persuaded Panurge to take counsel of a fool

WHEN Pantagruel had withdrawn himself, he, by a little sloping window in one of the galleries, perceived Panurge in a lobby not far from thence, walking alone, with the gesture, carriage, and garb of a fond dotard, raving, wagging, and shaking his hands, dandling, lolling, and nodding with his head, like a cow bellowing for her calf; and, having then called him nearer, spoke unto him thus. You are at this present, as I think, not unlike to a mouse entangled in a snare, who the more that she goeth about to rid and unwind herself out of the gin wherein she is caught, by endeavouring to clear and deliver her feet from the pitch whereto they stick, the fouler she is bewrayed with it, and the more strongly pestered therein. Even so is it with you. For the more that you labour, strive, and inforce yourself to disencumber, and extricate your thoughts out of the implicating involutions and fetterings of the grievous and lamentable gins and springs of anguish and perplexity, the greater difficulty there is in the relieving of you, and you remain faster bound than ever. Nor do I know for the removal of this inconveniency any remedy but one.

Take heed, I have often heard it said in a vulgar proverb, The wise may be instructed by a fool. Seeing the answers and responses of sage and in judicious men have no manner of way satisfied you, take advice of some fool, and possibly by so doing you may come to get that counsel which will be agreeable to your own heart's-desire and contentment. You know how by the advice and counsel and prediction of fools, many kings, princes, states, and commonwealths have been preserved, several battles gained, and divers doubts of a most perplexed intricacy resolved. I am not so diffident of your memory, as to hold it needful to refresh it with a quotation of examples; nor do I so far undervalue your judgment, but that I think it will acquiesce in the reason of this my subsequent discourse. As he who narrowly takes heed to what concerns the dexterous management of his private affairs, domestic businesses, and those adoes which are confined within the strait-laced compass of one family,—who is attentive, vigilant, and active in the economic rule of his own house,—whose frugal spirit never strays from home,—who loseth no occasion whereby

he may purchase to himself more riches, and build up new heaps
of treasure on his former wealth,—and who knows warily how
to prevent the inconveniences of poverty, is called a worldly
wise man, though perhaps in the second judgment of the intelligences which are above, he be esteemed a fool,—so, on the
contrary is he most like, even in the thoughts of celestial spirits,
to be not only sage, but to presage events to come by divine
inspiration, who laying quite aside those cares which are conducible to his body, or his fortunes, and, as it were departing
from himself, rids all his senses of terrene affections, and clears
his fancies of those plodding studies which harbour in the minds
of thriving men.   All which neglects of sublunary things are
vulgarly imputed folly.   After this manner, the son of Picus,
King of the Latins, the great soothsayer Faunus, was called
Fatuus by the witless rabble of the common people.   The
like we daily see practised amongst the comic players, whose
dramatic rolls, in distribution of the personages, appoint the
acting of the fool to him who is the wisest of the troop.   In
approbation also of this fashion the mathematicians allow the
very same horoscope to princes and to sots.   Whereof a right
pregnant instance by them is given in the nativities of Æneas
and Chorœbus; the latter of which two is by Euphorion said to
have been a fool; and yet had with the former the same aspects,
and heavenly genethliac influences.

I shall not, I suppose, swerve much from the purpose in hand,
if I relate unto you, what John Andrew said upon the return
of a papal writ, which was directed to the mayor and burgesses
of Rochelle, and after him by Panorme, upon the same Pontifical
canon; Barbatias on the Pandects, and recently by Jason, in
his councils, concerning Seyny John, the noted fool of Paris,
and Caillette's fore great grandfather.   The case is this.

At Paris, in the roast-meat cookery of the Petit-Chastelet,
before the cook-shop of one of the roast-meat sellers of that
lane, a certain hungry porter was eating his bread, after he
had by parcels kept it a while above the reek and steam of a
fat goose on the spit, turning at a great fire, and found it so
besmoked with the vapour, to be savoury; which the cook
observing, took no notice, till after having ravined his penny
loaf, whereof no morsel had been unsmokified, he was about
decamping and going away.   But, by your leave, as the fellow
thought to have departed thence shot-free, the master-cook
laid hold upon him by the gorget, and demanded payment
for the smoke of his roast-meat.   The porter answered, That

he had sustained no loss at all,—that by what he had done there was no diminution made of the flesh,—that he had taken nothing of his, and that therefore he was not indebted to him in anything. As for the smoke in question, that, although he had not been there, it would howsoever have been evaporated: besides, that before that time it had never been seen nor heard, that roast-meat smoke was sold upon the streets of Paris. The cook hereto replied, That he was not obliged nor any way bound to feed and nourish for nought a porter whom he had never seen before, with the smoke of his roast-meat, and thereupon swore, that if he would not forthwith content and satisfy him with present payment for the repast which he had thereby got, that he would take his crooked staves from off his back; which, instead of having loads thereafter laid upon them, should serve for fuel to his kitchen fires. Whilst he was going about so to do, and to have pulled them to him by one of the bottom rungs, which he had caught in his hand, the sturdy porter got out of his gripe, drew forth the knotty cudgel, and stood to his own defence. The altercation waxed hot in words, which moved the gaping hoydens of the sottish Parisians to run from all parts thereabouts, to see what the issue would be of that babbling strife and contention. In the interim of this dispute, to very good purpose Seyny John, the fool and citizen of Paris, happened to be there, whom the cook perceiving, said to the porter, Wilt thou refer and submit unto the noble Seyny John, the decision of the difference and controversy which is betwixt us? Yes, by the blood of a goose, answered the porter, I am content. Seyny John the fool, finding that the cook and porter had compromised the determination of their variance and debate to the discretion of his award and arbitrement, after that the reasons on either side, whereupon was grounded the mutual fierceness of their brawling jar, had been to the full displayed and laid open before him, commanded the porter to draw out of the fob of his belt a piece of money, if he had it. Whereupon the porter immediately without delay, in reverence to the authority of such a judicious umpire, put the tenth part of a silver Philip into his hand. This little Philip Seyny John took, then set it on his left shoulder, to try by feeling if it was of a sufficient weight. After that, laying it on the palm of his hand, he made it ring and tingle, to understand by the ear if it was of a good alloy in the metal whereof it was composed. Thereafter he put it to the ball or apple of his left eye, to explore by the sight, if it was well stamped and marked; all which being done, in a profound silence of the whole doltish people, who were the spectators of this pageantry, to the great hope of the cook's, and despair of the porter's prevalency in the suit that was in agitation, he finally caused the porter to make it sound several times upon the stall of the cook's shop. Then with a presidential majesty holding his bauble, sceptre-like, in his hand, muffling his head with a hood of marten skins, each side whereof had the resemblance of an ape's face, sprucified up with ears of pasted paper, and having about his neck a bucked ruff, raised, furrowed, and ridged, with pointing sticks of the shape and fashion of small organ pipes, he first with all the force of his lungs coughed two or three times, and then with an audible voice pronounced this following sentence. The Court declareth, that the porter, who ate his bread at the smoke of the roast, hath civilly paid the cook with the sound of his money. And the said Court ordaineth, that every one return to his own home, and attend his proper business, without costs and charges, and for a cause. This verdict, award, and arbitrement of the Parisian fool did appear so equitable, yea, so admirable to the aforesaid doctors, that they very much doubted, if the matter had been brought before the sessions for justice of the said place; or that the judges of the Rota at Rome had been umpires therein; or yet that the Areopagites themselves had been the deciders thereof; if by any one part, or all of them together, it had been so judicially sententiated and awarded. Therefore advise, if you will be counselled by a fool.

CHAPTER XXXVIII

How Triboulet is set forth and blazoned by Pantagruel and Panurge

By my soul, quoth Panurge, that overture pleaseth me exceedingly well. I will therefore lay hold thereon, and embrace it. At the very motioning thereof, my right entrail seemeth to be widened and enlarged, which was but just now hard-bound, contracted, and costive. But as we have hitherto made choice of the purest and most refined cream of wisdom and sapience for our counsel, so would I now have to preside and bear the prime sway in our consultation as very a fool in the supreme degree. Triboulet, quoth Pantagreul, is completely foolish, as I conceive. Yes, truly, answered Panurge, he is properly and totally a fool, a

Pantagruel.	*Panurge.*
Fatal f.	Jovial f.
Natural f.	Mercurial f.
Celestial f.	Lunatic f.
Erratic f.	Ducal f.
Eccentric f.	Common f.
Ætherial and Junonian f.	Lordly f.
Arctic f.	Palatin f.
Heroic f.	Principal f.
Genial f.	Pretorian f.
Inconstant f.	Elected f.
Earthly f.	Courtly f.
Salacious and Sporting f.	Primipilary f.
Jocund and wanton f.	Triumphant f.
Pimpled f.	Vulgar f.
Freckled f.	Domestic f.
Bell-tinging f.	Exemplary f.
Laughing and lecherous f.	Rare outlandish f.
Nimming and filching f.	Satrapal f.
Unpressed f.	Civil f.
First broached f.	Popular f.
Augustal f.	Familiar f.
Cæsarine f.	Notable f.
Imperial f.	Favourized f.
Royal f.	Latinized f.
Patriarchal f.	Ordinary f.
Original f.	Transcendent f.
Loyal f.	Rising f.
Episcopal f.	Papal f.
Doctoral f.	Consistorian f.
Monachal f.	Conclavist f.
Fiscal f.	Bullist f.
Extravagant f.	Synodal f.
Writhed f.	Doting and raving f.
Canonical f.	Singular and surpassing f.
Such another f.	Special and excelling f.
Graduated f.	Metaphysical f.
Commensal f.	Ecstatical f.
Primolicentiated f.	Predicamental and categoric f.
Trainbearing f.	
Supererogating f.	Predicable and enunciatory f.
Collateral f.	
Haunch and side f.	Decumane and superlative f.
Nestling, ninny, and young-ling f.	Dutiful and officious f.
Flitting, giddy, and unsteady f.	Optical and perspective f.
	Algoristic f.
Brancher, novice, and cockney f.	Algebraical f.
Haggard, cross, and forward f.	Cabalistical and Massoretical f.
Gentle, mild, and tractable f.	Talmudical f.
Mail-coated f.	Algamalized f.
Pilfering and purloining f.	Compendious f.
Tail-grown f.	Abbreviated f.
Grey peckled f.	Hyperbolical f.
Pleonasmical f.	Anatomastical f.
Capital f.	Allegorical f.
Hair-brained f.	Tropological f.
Cordial f.	Micher pincrust f.
Intimate f.	Heteroclit f.

Pantagruel.

Hepatic f.
Cupshotten and swilling f.
Splenetic f.
Windy f.
Legitimate f.
Azymathal f.
Almicantarized f.
Proportioned f.
Chinnified f.
Swollen and puffed-up f.
Overcockrilifedled and fied f.
Corollary f.
Eastern f.
Sublime f.
Crimson f.
Ingrained f.
City f.
Basely-accoutred f.
Mast-headed f.
Model f.
Second notial f.
Cheerful and buxom f.
Solemn f.
Annual f.
Festival f.
Recreative f.
Boorish and counterfeit f.
Pleasant f.
Privileged f.
Rustical f.
Proper and peculiar f.
Ever ready f.
Diapasonal f.
Resolute f.
Hieroglyphical f.
Authentic f.
Worthy f.
Precious f.
Fanatic f.
Fantastical f.
Symphatic f.
Panic f.
Limbecked and distilled f.
Comportable f.
Wretched and heartless f.
Fooded f.
Thick and threefold f.
Damasked f.
Ferny f.
Unleavened f.
Barytonant f.
Pink and spot-powdered f.
Musket-proof f.
Pedantic f.
Strouting f.
Wood f.
Greedy f.
Senseless f.
Godderlich f.

Panurge.

Summist f.
Abridging f.
Morish f.
Leaden-sealed f.
Mandatory f.
Compassionate f.
Titulary f.
Crooching, showking, ducking f.
Grim, stern, harsh, and wayward f.
Well-hung and timbered f.
Ill-clawed, pounced, and pawed f.
Well-stoned f.
Crabbed and unpleasing f.
Winded and untainted f.
Kitchen-haunting f.
Lofty and stately f.
Spitrack f.
Architrave f.
Pedestal f.
Tetragonal f.
Renowned f.
Rheumatic f.
Flaunting and braggadochio f.
Egregious f.
Humorous and capricious f.
Rude, gross, and absurd f.
Large-measured f.
Babble f.
Down-right f.
Broad-listed f.
Downsical-bearing f.
Stale and over-worn f.
Saucy and swaggering f.
Full-bulked f.
Gallant and vainglorious f.
Gorgeous and gaudy f.
Continual and intermitting f.
Rebasing and roundling f.
Prototypal and precedenting f.
Prating f.
Catechetic f.
Cacodoxical f.
Meridional f.
Nocturnal f.
Occidental f.
Trifling f.
Astrological and figure-flinging f.
Genethliac and horoscopal f.
Knavish f.
Idiot f.
Blockish f.
Beetle-headed f.
Grotesque f.

Pantagruel.	*Panurge.*
Obstinate f.	Impertinent f.
Contradictory **f.**	Quarrelsome f.
Pedagogical f.	Unmannerly f.
Daft f.	Captious and sophistical **f.**
Drunken f.	Soritic f.
Peevish f.	Catholoproton f.
Prodigal f.	Hoti and Dioti f.
Rash f.	Alphos and Catati **f**
Plodding **f.**	

Pantagruel. If there was any reason why at Rome the Quirinal holiday of old was called the Feast of Fools; I know not, why we may not for the like cause institute in France the Tribouletic Festivals, to be celebrated and solemnized over all the land.

Panurge. If all fools carried cruppers.

Pant. If he were the god Fatuus, of whom we have already made mention, the husband of the goddess Fatua, his father would be Good Day, and his grand-mother Good Even.

Pan. If all fools paced, albeit he be somewhat wry-legged, he would overlay at least a fathom at every rake. Let us go toward him without any further lingering or delay;—we shall have, no doubt, some fine resolution of him. I am ready to go, and long for the issue of our progress impatiently. I must needs, quoth Panutgruel, according to my former resolution therein, be present at Bridlegoose's trial. Nevertheless, whilst I shall be upon my journey towards Myrelingues, which is on the other side of the river of Loire, I will dispatch Carpalim to bring along with him from Blois the fool Triboulet. Then was Carpalim instantly sent away, and Pantagruel at the same time, attended by his domestics, Panurge, Epistemon, Ponocrates, Friar John, Gymnast, Ryzotomus, and others, marched forward on the high road to Myrelingues.

CHAPTER XXXIX

How Pantagruel was present at the trial of Judge Bridlegoose, who decided causes and controversies in law by the chance and fortune of the dice

On the day following, precisely at the hour appointed, Pantagruel came to Myrelingues. At his arrival the presidents, senators, and counsellors prayed him to do them the honour to enter in with them, to hear the decision of all the causes

arguments, and reasons, which Bridlegoose in his own defence
would produce, why he had pronounced a certain sentence,
against the subsidy assessor, Toucheronde, which did not seem
very equitable to that centumviral court. Pantagruel very
willingly condescended to their desire, and accordingly entering
in, found Bridlegoose sitting within the middle of the inclosure
of the said court of justice; who immediately upon the coming
of Pantagruel, accompanied with the senatorian members of
that worshipful judicatory, arose, went to the bar, had his
indictment read, and for all his reasons, defences, and excuses,
answered nothing else, but that he was become old, and that
his sight of late was very much failed, and become dimmer
than it was wont to be; instancing therewithal many miseries
and calamities, which old age bringeth along with it, and are
concomitant to wrinkled elders; which *not. per Archid. d. l.*
lxxxvi. c. tanta. By reason of which infirmity he was not able
so distinctly and clearly to discern the points and blots of the
dice, as formerly he had been accustomed to do: whence it
might very well have happened, said he, as old dim-sighted
Isaac took Jacob for Esau, that I, after the same manner, at
the decision of causes and controversies in law, should have been
mistaken in taking a quatre for a cinque, or trois for a deuce.
This, I beseech your worships, quoth he, to take into your
serious consideration and to have the more favourable opinion
of my uprightness, (notwithstanding the prevarication whereof
I am accused, in the matter of Toucheronde's sentence,) for
that at the time of that decree's pronouncing I only had made
use of my small dice; and your worships, said he, knew very
well, how by the most authentic rules of the law it is provided,
That the imperfections of nature should never be imputed unto
any for crimes and transgressions; as appeareth, *ff. de re milit.*
l. qui cum uno. ff. de reg. Jur. l. fere. ff. de ædil. edict. per totum.
ff. de term. mod. l. Divus Adrianus, resolved by *Lud. Rom. in*
l. si vero. ff. Sol. Matr. And who would offer to do otherwise,
should not thereby accuse the man, but nature, and the all-
seeing providence of God, as is evident in *l. maximum vitium,*
c. de lib. prætor.

What kind of dice, quoth Trinquamelle, grand president of
the said court, do you mean, my friend Bridlegoose? The
dice, quoth Bridlegoose, of sentences at law, decrees, and
peremptory judgments, *Alea Judiciorum,* whereof is written
Per Doct. 26. qu. 2. cap. sort. l. nec emptio ff. de contrahend.
empt. l. quod debetur. ff. de pecul. et ibi Bartol., and which your

worships do, as well as I, use, in this glorious sovereign court of yours. So do all other righteous judges in their decision of processes, and final determination of legal differences, observing that which hath been said thereof by D. Henri. Ferrandat, *et not. gl. in c. fin. de sortil. et l. sed cum ambo. ff. de jud. Ubi Docto*. Mark, that chance and fortune are good, honest, profitable, and necessary for ending of, and putting a final closure to dissensions and debates in suits at law. The same hath more clearly been declared by Bald. Bartol. et Alex. c. *communia de leg. l. si duo*. But how is it that you do these things? asked Trinquamelle. I very briefly, quoth Bridlegoose, shall answer you, according to the doctrine and instructions of *Leg. ampliorem in refutatoriis par. c. de appel.*; which is conformable to what is said in *Gloss. l.* 1. *ff. quod. met. causa Gaudent brevitate moderni*. My practice is therein the same with that of your other worships, and as the custom of the judicatory requires, unto which our law commandeth us to have regard, and by the rule thereof still to direct and regulate our actions and procedures; *ut not. extra. de consuet. c. ex literis et ibi innoc.* For having well and exactly seen, surveyed, overlooked, reviewed, recognized, read, and read over again, turned and tossed over, seriously perused and examined the bills of complaint, accusations, impeachments, indictments, warnings, citations, summonings, comparitions, appearances, mandates, commissions, delegations, instructions, informations, inquests, preparatories, productions, evidences, proofs, allegations, depositions, cross speeches, contradictions, supplications, requests, petitions, inquiries, instruments of the deposition of witnesses, rejoinders, replies, confirmations of former assertions, duplies, triplies, answers to rejoinders, writings, deeds, reproaches, disabling of exceptions taken, grievances, salvation-bills, re-examination of witnesses, confronting of them together, declarations, denunciations, libels, certificates, royal missives, letters of appeal, letters of attorney, instruments of compulsion, declinatories, anticipatories, evocations, messages, dimissions, issues, exceptions, dilatory pleas, demurs, compositions, injunctions, reliefs, reports, returns, confessions, acknowledgements, exploits, executions, and other such like confects, and spiceries, both at the one and the other side, as a good judge ought to do, conform to what hath been noted thereupon. *Spec. de ordination. paragr.* 3. *et Tit. de Offi. omn. jud. paragr. fin. et de rescriptis præsentat. parag.* 1.—I posit on the end of a table in my closet, all the pokes and bags of the defendant, and then allow unto him the first hazard of the dice, according

to the usual manner of your other worships.   And it is mentioned, *l. favorabiliores ff. de reg. jur. et in cap. cum sunt eod. tit.
lib.* 6. which saith, *Quum sunt partium jura obscura, reo potius
tavendum est quam actori.*   That being done, I thereafter
lay down upon the other end of the same table the bags and
sachels of the plaintiff, as your other worships are accustomed
to do, *visum visu,* just over against one another: for, *Opposita
juxta se posita clarius elucescunt: ut not. in lib.*1. *parag. Videamus.
ff. de his qui sunt sui vel alieni juris, et in l. munerum* § *mixta ff.
de mun. et hon.*   Then do I likeways and semblably throw the
dice for him, and forthwith liver him his chance.   But, quoth
Trinquamelle, my friend, how come you to know, understand,
and resolve, the obscurity of these various and seeming contrary passages, in law, which are laid claim to by the suitors
and pleading parties?   Even just, quoth Bridlegoose, after the
fashion of your other worships: to wit, when there are many
bags on the one side, and on the other, I then use my little small
dice, after the customary manner of your other worships, in
obedience to the law, *Semper in stipulationibus ff. de reg. jur.*
and the law *versale* verifieth that *Eod. tit. semper in obscuris
quod minimum est sequimur*: canonized in *c. in obscuris, eod.
tit. lib.* 6.   I have other large great dice, fair, and goodly ones,
which I employ in the fashion that your other worships use to
do, when the matter is more plain, clear, and liquid, that is to
say, when there are fewer bags.   But when you have done all
these fine things, quoth Trinquamelle, how do you, my friend,
award your decrees, and pronounce judgment?   Even as your
other worships, answered Bridlegoose; for I give out sentence
in his favour unto whom hath befallen the best chance by dice,
judiciary, tribunian, pretorial, what comes first.   So our laws
command, *ff. qui pot. in pign. l. creditor. c. de consul.* 1. *Et de
regul. jur. in* 6. *Qui prior est tempore potior est jure.*

CHAPTER XL

*How Bridlegoose giveth reasons, why he looked over those law-
papers which he decided by the chance of the dice*

YEA, but, quoth Trinquamelle, my friend, seeing it is by the
lot, chance, and throw of the dice that you award your judgments and sentences, why do not you deliver up these fair
throws and chances, the very same day and hour, without

any further procrastination or delay, that the controverting party-pleaders appear before you? To what use can those writings serve you, those papers, and other procedures contained in the bags and pokes of the law-suitors? To the very same use, quoth Bridlegoose, that they serve your other worships. They are behoveful unto me, and serve my turn in three things very exquisite, requisite, and authentic. First, For formality-sake; the omission whereof, that it maketh all, whatever is done, to be of no force nor value, is excellently well proved, by *Spec. 1. tit. de instr. edit. et tit. de rescript. present.* Besides that, it is not unknown to you, who have had many more experiments thereof than I, how oftentimes, in judicial proceedings, the formalities utterly destroy the materialities and substances of the causes and matters agitated; for *forma mutata, mutatur substantia. ff. ad exhib. l. Julianus ff. ad leg. fals. l. si is qui quadraginta. Et extra, de decim. c. ad audientiam, et de celebrat. miss. c. in quadam.*

Secondly, They are useful and steadable to me, even as unto your other worships, in lieu of some other honest and healthful exercise. The late Master Othoman Vadat, [Vadere,] a prime physician, as you would say, *Cod. de commit. et archi. lib.* 12, hath frequently told me, That the lack and default of bodily exercise is the chief, if not the sole and only, cause of the little health and short lives of all officers of justice, such as your worships and I am. Which observation was singularly well, before him, noted and remarked by Bartholus in *lib. 1. c. de sent. quæ pro eo quod.* Therefore is it that the practice of suchlike exercitations is appointed to be laid hold on by your other worships, and consequently not to be denied unto me, who am of the same profession; *Quia accessorium naturam sequitur principalis. de reg. jur. l. 7 et l. cum principalis, et l. nihil dolo ff. eod. tit. ff. de fide-jus. l. fide-jus. et extra de officio de leg. cap. 1.* Let certain honest and recreative sports and plays of corporeal exercises be allowed and approved of; and so far *ff. de al. lus. et aleat. l. solent. et authent. ut omnes obed. in princ. col. 7. et ff. de præscript. verb. l. si gratuitam; et l. 1. cod. de spect. l.* 11. Such also is the opinion of D. Thomæ, *in secunda, secundæ, Q.* 1. 168. Quoted to very good purpose, by D. Albert de Rosa, who *fuit magnus practicus,* and a solemn doctor, as Barbaria attesteth in *principiis consil.* Wherefore the reason is evidently and clearly deduced and set down before us in *gloss. in proæmio ff. par. ne autem tertii.*

Interpone tuis interdum gaudia curis.

In very deed, once, in the year a thousand four hundred fourscore and nine, having a business concerning the portion and inheritance of a younger brother depending in the court and chamber of the four High Treasurers of France, whereinto as soon as ever I got leave to enter, by a pecuniary permission of the usher thereof,—as your other worships know very well, that *pecuniæ obediunt omnia*, and there, says Baldus, in *l. singularia ff. si cert. pet. et Salic. in l. receptitia. Cod. de constit. pecuni. et Card. in Clem. 1. de baptism.*—I found them all recreating and diverting themselves at the play called muss, either before or after dinner: to me, truly, it is a thing altogether indifferent, whether of the two it was, provided that *hic not.*, that the game of the muss is honest, healthful, ancient, and lawful, *a Muscho inventore, de quo cod. de petit. hæred. l. si post motam, et Muscarii.* Such as play and sport at the muss are excusable in and by law, *lib. 1. c. de excus. artific. lib. 10.* And at the very same time was Master Tielman Piquet one of the players of that game of muss. There is nothing that I do better remember, for he laughed heartily, when his fellow-members of the aforesaid judicial chamber spoiled their caps in swingeing of his shoulders. He, nevertheless, did even then say unto them, that the banging and flapping of him to the waste and havoc of their caps, should not, at their return from the palace to their own houses, excuse them from their wives, *Per c. extra. de præsumpt. et ibi gloss.* Now, *resolutorie loquendo* I should say, according to the style and phrase of your other worships, that there is no exercise, sport, game, play, nor recreation in all this palatine, palacial, or parliamentary world, more aromatizing and fragrant, than to empty and void bags and purses—turn over papers and writings—quote margins and backs of scrolls and rolls, fill panniers, and take inspection of causes *Ex Bart. et Joan. de Pra. in l. falsa de condit. et demonst. ff.*

Thirdly, I consider, as your own worships used to do, that time ripeneth and bringeth all things to maturity,—that by time everything cometh to be made manifest and patent,—and that time is the father of truth and virtue. *Gloss. in l. 1. cod. de servit. authent. de restit. et ea quæ pa. et spec. tit. de requisit. cons.* Therefore is it, that after the manner and fashion of your other worships, I defer, protract, delay, prolong, intermit, surcease, pause, linger, suspend, prorogate, drive out, wire-draw, and shift off the time of giving a definitive sentence, to the end that the suit or process, being well fanned and winnowed, tossed and canvassed to and fro, narrowly, precisely, and nearly garbelled, sifted, searched, and examined, and on all hands exactly argued, disputed, and debated, may, by succession of time, come at last to its full ripeness and maturity. By means whereof, when the fatal hazard of the dice ensueth thereupon, the parties cast or condemned by the said aleatory chance will with much greater patience, and more mildly and gently, endure and bear up the disastrous load of their misfortune, than if they had been sentenced at their first arrival unto the court, as *not. gl. ff. de excus. tut. l. tria onera.*

> Portatur leviter quod portat quisque libenter.

On the other part, to pass a decree or sentence, when the action is raw, crude, green, unripe, and unprepared as at the beginning, a danger would ensue of a no less inconveniency than that which the physicians have been wont to say befalleth to him in whom an imposthume is pierced before it be ripe, or unto any other, whose body is purged of a strong predominating humour before its digestion. For as it is written, *in authent. hæc constit. in Innoc. de consist. princip.*—so is the same repeated *in gloss. in c. cæterum extra de jura. calumn. Quod medicamenta morbis exhibent, hoc jura negotiis.* Nature furthermore admonisheth and teacheth us to gather and reap, eat and feed on fruits when they are ripe, and not before. *Instit. de rer. div. paragr. is ad quem. et ff. de action. empt. l. Julianus.* To marry likewise our daughters when they are ripe, and no sooner, *ff. de donation. inter vir. et uxor. l. cum. hic status. paragr. si quis sponsam et 27 qu. 1. c. sicut dicit gloss.*

> Jam matura thoro plenis adoleverat annis
> Virginitas.

And, in a word, she instructeth us to do nothing of any considerable importance, but in a full maturity and ripeness, *23 q. 2. § ult. et 23. de c. ultimo.*

CHAPTER XLI

How Bridlegoose relateth the history of the reconcilers of parties at variance in matters of law

I REMEMBER to the same purpose, quoth Bridlegoose, in continuing his discourse, that in the time when at Poictiers I was a student of law under Brocadium Juris, there was at Semerve one Peter Dendin, a very honest man, careful labourer of the ground, fine singer in a church desk, of good repute and credit.

and older than the most aged of all your worships, who was
wont to say, that he had seen the great and goodly good man,
the Council of Lateran, with his wide and broad-brimmed red
hat. As also, that he had beheld and looked upon the fair and
beautiful pragmatical sanction, his wife, with her huge rosary
or patenotrian chapelet of jet beads, hanging at a large sky-
coloured riband. This honest man compounded, attoned, and
agreed more differences, controversies, and variances at law,
than had been determined, voided, and finished during his time
in the whole palace of Poictiers, in the auditory of Montmorillon,
and in the town-house of the old Partenay. This amicable
disposition of his rendered him venerable, and of great estimation, sway, power, and authority throughout all the neighbouring places of Chauvigny, Nouaillé, Legugé, Vivonne,
Mezeaux, Estables, and other bordering and circumjacent towns,
villages, and hamlets. All their debates were pacified by him;
he put an end to their brabling suits at law, and wrangling
differences. By his advice and counsels were accords and
reconcilements no less firmly made, than if the verdict of a
sovereign judge had been interposed therein, although, in very
deed, he was no judge at all, but a right honest man, as you may
well conceive,—*arg. in l. sed si unius ff. de jurejur. et de verbis
obligatoriis l. continuus.* There was not a hog killed within
three parishes of him, whereof he had not some part of the
haslet and puddings. He was almost every day invited either
to a marriage-banquet, christening-feast, an uprising or women-
churching treatment, a birthday's anniversary, solemnity, a
merry frolic gossiping, or otherwise to some delicious entertainment in a tavern, to make some accord and agreement
between persons at odds, and in debate with one another.
Remark what I say; for he never yet settled and compounded
a difference betwixt any two at variance, but he straight made
the parties agreed and pacified to drink together, as a sure and
infallible token and symbol of a perfect and completely well-
cemented reconciliation, a sign of a sound and sincere amity,
and proper mark of a new joy and gladness to follow thereupon,—*Ut not. per doct. ff. de peric. et com. rei vend. l. 1.* He had
a son, whose name was Tenot Dendin, a lusty, young, sturdy,
frisking roister, so help me God, who likewise, in imitation of
his peace-making father, would have undertaken and meddled
with the making up of variances and deciding of controversies
between disagreeing and contentious party-pleaders: as you
know,

Sæpe solet similis filius esse patri,
Et sequitur leviter filia matris iter.

*Ut ait gloss. 6, quæst. 1. c. Si quis, gloss. de cons. dist. 5. c. 2.
fin. et est not. per Doct. cod. de impub. et aliis substit. l. ult. et l.
legitime. ff. de stat. hom. gloss. in l. quod. si nolit. ff. de ædil. edict.
l. quisquis c. ad leg. Jul. majest. Excipio filios à moniali susceptos
ex monacho. per gloss. in c. impudicas. 27. quæstione 1.* And
such was his confidence to have no worse success than his father,
that he assumed unto himself the title of Lawstrife-settler.
He was likewise in these pacificatory negotiations so active and
vigilant,—for, *Vigilantibus jura subveniunt. ex l. pupillus. ff.
quæ in fraud. cred. et ibid. l. non enim, et instit. in proæm.*—that
when he had smelt, heard, and fully understood,—*ut ff. si
quando paup. fec. l. Agaso. gloss. in verb. olfecit, id est, nasum
ad culum posuit*—and found that there was anywhere in the
country a debateable matter at law, he would incontinently
thrust in his advice, and so forwardly intrude his opinion in the
business, that he made no bones of making offer, and taking
upon him to decide it, how difficult soever it might happen to
be, to the full contentment and satisfaction of both parties. It
is written, *Qui non laborat non manige ducat*; and the said *gl. ff.
de damn. infect. l. quamvis* and *Currere* plus que le pas *vetulam
compellit egestas. gloss. ff. de lib. agnosc. l. si quis pro qua facit.
l. si plures. c. de condit. incert.* But so hugely great was his misfortune in this his undertaking, that he never composed any
difference, how little soever you may imagine it might have
been, but that, instead of reconciling the parties at odds, he did
incense, irritate, and exasperate them to a higher point of
dissension and enmity than ever they were at before. Your
worships know, I doubt not that,

Sermo datur cunctis, animi sapientia paucis.

Gl. ff. de alien. jud. mut. caus. fa. lib. 2. This administered
unto the tavern-keepers, wine-drawers and vintners of Semerve
an occasion to say, that under him they had not in the space
of a whole year so much reconciliation-wine, for so were they
pleased to called the good wine of Legugé, as under his father
they had done in one half hour's time. It happened a little
while thereafter, that he made a most heavy regret thereof to
his father, attributing the causes of his bad success in pacificatory
enterprizes to the perversity, stubbornness, froward, cross, and
backward inclinations of the people of his time; roundly, boldly,
and irreverently upbraiding, that if, but a score of years before

the world had been so wayward, obstinate, pervicacious, implacable, and out of all square, frame, and order, as it was then, his father had never attained to and acquired the honour and title of Strife-appeaser, so irrefragably, inviolably, and irrevocably as he had done. In doing whereof Tenot did heinously transgress against the law which prohibiteth children to the actions of their parents; *per gl. et Bart. l. 3. paragr. si quis. ff. de cond. ob caus. et authent. de nupt. par. sed quod sancitum. col. 4.* To this the honest old father answered thus. My son Dendin, when Don Oportet taketh place, this is the course which we must trace. *gl. c. de appell. l. eos etiam.* For the road that you went upon was not the way to the fuller's mill, nor in any part thereof was the form to be found wherein the hare did sit. Thou hast not the skill and dexterity of settling and composing differences. Why? Because thou takest them at the beginning, in the very infancy and bud as it were, when they are green, raw, and indigestible. Yet I know, handsomely and featly, how to compose and settle them all. Why? Because I take them at their decadence, in their weaning, and when they are pretty well digested. So saith *gloss*.

Dulcior est fructus post multa pericula ductus.

L. non moriturus. c. de contrahend. et committ. stip. Didst thou ever hear the vulgar proverb, "Happy is the physician, whose coming is desired at the declension of a disease"? For the sickness being come to a crisis is then upon the decreasing hand, and drawing towards an end, although the physician should not repair thither for the cure thereof; whereby, though nature wholly do the work, he bears away the palm and praise thereof. My pleaders, after the same manner, before I did interpose my judgment in the reconciling of them, were waxing faint in their contestations. Their altercation heat was much abated, and, in declining from their former strife, they of themselves inclined to a firm accommodation of their differences; because there wanted fuel to that fire of burning rancour and despightful wrangling, whereof the lower sort of lawyers were the kindlers. That is to say, their purses were emptied of coin, they had not a win in their fob, nor penny in their bag, wherewith to solicit and present their actions.

Deficiente pecu, deficit omne, nia.

There wanted then nothing but some brother to supply the place of a paranymph, braw-broker, proxenete, or mediator, who acting his part dexterously, should be the first broacher of the motion of an agreement, for saving both the one and the other party from that hurtful and pernicious shame, whereof he could not have avoided the imputation, when it should have been said, that he was the first who yielded and spoke of a reconcilement; and that, therefore, his cause not being good, and being sensible where his shoe did pinch him, he was willing to break the ice, and make the greater haste to prepare the way for a condescendment to an amicable and friendly treaty. Then was it that I came in pudding time, Dendin, my son, nor is the fat of bacon more relishing to boiled peas, than was my verdict then agreeable to them. This was my luck, my profit, and good fortune. I tell thee, my jolly son Dendin, that by this rule and method I could settle a firm peace, or at least clap up a cessation of arms, and truce for many years to come betwixt the Great King and the Venetian State,—the Emperor and the Cantons of Switzerland,—the English and the Scots, and betwixt the pope and the Ferrarians. Shall I go yet further? Yea, as I would have God to help me, betwixt the Turk and the Sophy, the Tartars and the Muscoviters. Remark well, what I am to say unto thee. I would take them at that very instant nick of time, when both those of the one and the other side should be weary and tired of making war, when they had voided and emptied their own cashes and coffers of all treasure and coin, drained and exhausted the purses and bags of their subjects, sold and mortgaged their domains and proper inheritances, and totally wasted, spent, and consumed the munition, furniture, provision, and victuals, that were necessary for the continuance of a military expedition. There I am sure, by God, or by his mother, that, would they, would they not, in spite of all teeth, they should be forced to take a little respite and breathing time to moderate the fury and cruel rage of their ambitious aims. This is the doctrine in *Gl. 37. d. c. si quando.*

Odero, si potero; si non, invitus amabo.

CHAPTER XLII

How suits at law are bred at first, and how they come afterwards to their perfect growth

For this cause, quoth Bridlegoose, going on in his discourse, I temporize and apply myself to the times, as your other worships use to do, waiting patiently for the maturity of the process, the full growth and perfection thereof in all its members, to wit, the writings and the bags. *Arg. in l. si major. c. commun. divid. et de cons. di. 1. c. solemnitates, et ibi gl.* A suit in law at its production, birth, and first beginning, seemeth to me, as unto your other worships, shapeless, without form or fashion, incomplete, ugly, and imperfect even as a bear, at his first coming into the world, hath neither hands, skin, hair, nor head, but is merely an inform, rude, and ill-favoured piece and lump of flesh, and would remain still so, if his dam, out of the abundance of her affection to her hopeful cub, did not with much licking put his members into that figure and shape which nature had provided for those of an arctic and ursinal kind; *ut not. Doct. ad. l. Aquil. l. 2. in fin.* Just so do I see, as your other worships do, processes and suits of law, at their first bringing forth to be numberless, without shape, deformed, and disfigured, for that then they consist only of one or two writings, or copies of instruments, through which defect they appear unto me, as to your other worships, foul, loathsome, filthy, and mis-shapen beasts. But when there are heaps of these legiformal papers packed, piled, laid up together, impoked, insacheled, and put up in bags, then is it that with a good reason we may term that suit, to which, as pieces, parcels, parts, portions, and members thereof, they do pertain, and belong, well-formed and fashioned, big-limbed, strong set, and in all and each of its dimensions most completely membered. Because *forma dat esse rei. l. si is qui. ff. ad leg. Falcid. in c. cum dilecta de rescript. Barbat. concil. 12. lib. 2.* and before him Baldus, *in c. ult. extra de consuet. et l. Julianus ff. ad exhib. et. l. quæsitum ff. de leg. 3.* The manner is such as is set down in *gl. p. quæst. 1. c. Paulus.*

Debile principium melior fortuna sequetur.

Like your other worships also, the sergeants, catchpoles, pursuivants, messengers, summoners, apparitors, ushers, door-keepers, pettifoggers, attornies, proctors, commissioners, justices of the peace, judge delegates, arbitrators, overseers, sequestrators, advocates, inquisitors, jurors, searchers, examiners, notaries, tabellions, scribes, scriveners, clerks, prenotaries, secondaries, and expedanean judges, *de quibus tit. est. l. 3. c.,* by sucking very much, and that exceeding forcibly, and licking at the purses of the pleading parties, they, to the suits already begot and engendered, form, fashion, and frame head, feet, claws, talons, beaks, bills, teeth, hands, veins, sinews, arteries, muscles, humours, and so forth, through all the similary and dissimilary parts of the whole; which parts, particles, pendicles, and appurtenances, are the law pokes and bags, *gl. de cons. d.* 4. *accepisti.*

Qualis vestis erit, talia corda gerit.

Hic notandum est, that in this respect the pleaders, litigants, and law-suiters are happier than the officers, ministers, and administrators of justice, For *beatius est dare quam accipere, ff. commun. l. 3. extra. de celebr. Miss. c. cum Marthæ. et 24. quæst. 1. cap. Od. gl.*

Affectum dantis pensat censura tonantis,

Thus becometh the action or process, by their care and industry to be of a complete and goodly bulk, well-shaped, framed, formed, and fashioned, according to the canonical gloss.

Accipe, sume, cape, sunt verba placentia Papæ.

Which speech hath been more clearly explained by Albert de Ros, *in verbo Roma.*

Roma manus rodit, quas rodere non valet, odit.
Dantes custodit, non dantes spernit, et odit.

The reason whereof is thought to be this:

Ad præsens ova, cras pullis sunt meliora.

ut est gl. in l. quum hi. ff. de transact. Nor is this all; for the inconvenience of the contrary is set down in *gloss. c. de aliu. fin.*

Quum labor in damno est, crescit mortalis egestas.

In confirmation whereof we find, that the true etymology and exposition of the word *process* is *purchase*; viz. of good store of money to the lawyers, and of many pokes,—*id est Prou Sacks,*—to the pleaders: upon which subject we have most celestial quips, gibes, and girds.

Litigando jura crescunt, litigando jus acquiritur.

Item gl. in cap. illud extrem. de præsympt. et c. de prob. l. instrum. l. non epistolis. l. non nudis.

Et si non prosunt singula, multa juvant.

Yea, but, asked Trinquamelle, how do you proceed, my friend, in criminal causes, the culpable and guilty party being taken and seized upon, *flagrante crimine?* Even as your other worships use to do, answered Bridlegoose. First, I permit the plaintiff to depart from the court, enjoining him not to presume to return thither, till he preallably should have taken a good sound and profound sleep, which is to serve for the prime entry and introduction to the legal carrying on of the business. In the next place, a formal report is to be made to me of his having

slept.   Thirdly, I issue forth a warrant to convene him before
me.   Fourthly, He is to produce a sufficient and authentic
attestation of his having thoroughly and entirely slept, conform
to the *Gloss. 32. Quest. 7. c. Si quis cum.*

Quandoque bonus dormitat Homerus.

Being thus far advanced in the formality of the process, I
find that this consopiating act engendereth another act, whence
ariseth the articulating of a member.   That again produceth a
third act, fashionative of another member; which third bringeth
forth a fourth, procreative of another act.   New members in
a no fewer number are shapen and framed, one still breeding
and begetting another—as link after link, the coat of mail at
length is made—till thus piece after piece, by little and little,
by information upon information, the process be completely
well-formed and perfect in all his members.   Finally, having
proceeded this length, I have recourse to my dice, nor is it to
be thought, that this interruption, respite, or interpellation is
by me occasioned without very good reason inducing me thereunto, and a notable experience of a most convincing and irrefragable force.

I remember, on a time, that in the camp at Stockholm, there
was a certain Gascon named Gratianauld, native of the town
of Saint Sever, who having lost all his money at play, and con-
secutively being very angry thereat—as you know, *Pecunia est
alter sanguis, ut ait Anto. de Burtio, in c. accedens. 2. extra ut
lit. non contest. et Bald. in l. sis tuis. c. de opt. leg. per tot. in l.
advocati. c. de advoc. div. jud. pecunia est vita hominis fide-
iussor in necessitatibus*,—did, at his coming forth of the gaming-
house in the presence of the whole company that was there,
with a very loud voice, speak in his own language these following
words: "Pao cap de bious, hillots, que mau de pippe bous
tresbire: ares que de pergudes sont les mies bingt, et quouatre
baquettes, ta pla donnerien picz, trucz, et patactz; Sei degun
de bous aulx, qui boille truquar ambe iou a bels embis."   Finding
that none would make him any answer, he passed from thence
to that part of the leaguer where the huff-snuff, honder-sponder,
swash-buckling High Germans were, to whom he renewed these
very terms, provoking them to fight with him; but all the return
he had from them to his stout challenge was only, "Der Gas-
congner thut sich ausz mit eim ieden zu schlagen, aber er ist
geneigter zu stehlen; darum, liebe frauwen, habt sorg zu euerm
hauszrath."   Finding also, that none of that band of Teutonic

soldiers offered himself to the combat, he passed to that quarter of the leaguer where the French free-booting adventurers were encamped, and, reiterating unto them what he had before repeated to the Dutch warriors, challenged them likewise to fight with him, and therewithal made some pretty little Gasconado frisking gambols, to oblige them the more cheerfully and gallantly to cope with him in the lists of a duellizing engagement; but no answer at all was made unto him. Whereupon the Gascon, despairing of meeting with any antagonists, departed from thence, and laying himself down, not far from the pavilions of the grand Christian cavalier Crissé, fell fast asleep. When he had thoroughly slept an hour or two, another adventurous and all-hazarding blade of the forlorn hope of the lavishingly-wasting gamesters, having also lost all his monies, sallied forth with a sword in his hand, in a firm resolution to fight with the aforesaid Gascon, seeing he had lost as well as he.

Ploratur lachrymis amissa pecunia veris,

saith the *Gl. de pœnitent. distinct. 3. c. sunt plures.* To this effect having made inquiry and search for him throughout the whole camp, and in sequel thereof found him asleep, he said unto him, Up, ho, good fellow, in the name of all the devils of hell rise up, rise up, get up! I have lost my money as well as thou hast done, let us therefore go fight lustily together, grapple and scuffle it to some purpose. Thou mayest look and see that my tuck is no longer than thy rapier. The Gascon, altogether astonished at his unexpected provocation, without altering his former dialect, spoke thus: "Cap de Sanct Arnaud, quau seys tu, qui me rebeilles? Que mau de taoverne te gire. Ho San Siobé, cap de Gasciogne, ta pla dormie iou, quand aquoest taquain me bingut estée." The venturous roister inviteth him again to the duel, but the Gascon, without condescending to his desire, said only this. "Hé pauvret, iou te esquinerio ares que son pla reposat. Vayne un pauque qui te posar comme iou, puesse truqueren." Thus, in forgetting his loss, he forgot the eagerness which he had to fight. In conclusion, after that the other had likewise slept a little, they, instead of fighting, and possibly killing one another, went jointly to a sutler's tent, where they drank together very amicably, each upon the pawn of his sword. Thus by a little sleep was pacified the ardent fury of two warlike champions. There, gossip, comes the golden word of John Andr. *in cap. ult. de sent. et re judic. l. sexto.*

Sedendo et quiescendo fit anima prudens.

CHAPTER XLIII

*How Pantagruel excuseth Bridlegoose in the matter of sentencing
actions at law by the chance of the dice*

WITH this Bridlegoose held his peace. Whereupon Trinquamelle bid him withdraw from the court,—which accordingly
was done,—and then directed his discourse to Pantagruel after
this manner. It is fitting, most illustrious prince, not only by
reason of the deep obligations wherein this present parliament,
together with the whole Marquisate of Myrelingues, stand bound
to your Royal Highness, for the innumerable benefits, which,
as effects of mere grace, they have received from your incomparable bounty; but for that excellent wit also, prime judgment,
and admirable learning wherewith Almighty God, the giver of
all good things, hath most richly qualified and endowed you;
that we tender and present unto you the decision of this new,
strange, and paradoxical case of Bridlegoose; who, in your
presence, to your both hearing and seeing, hath plainly confessed his final judging and determinating of suits of law, by
the mere chance and fortune of the dice. Therefore do we beseech you, that you may be pleased to give sentence therein, as
unto you shall seem most just and equitable. To this Pantagruel answered, Gentlemen, It is not unknown to you, how
my condition is somewhat remote from the profession of deciding law controversies; yet, seeing you are pleased to do me
the honour to put that task upon me, instead of undergoing the
office of a judge, I will become your humble supplicant. I
observe, gentlemen, in this Bridlegoose several things, which
induce me to represent before you, that it is my opinion he should
be pardoned. In the first place, his old age; secondly, his
simplicity; to both which qualities our statute and common
laws, civil and municipal together, allow many excuses for any
slips or escapes, which, through the invincible imperfection of
either, have been inconsiderably stumbled upon by a person so
qualified. Thirdly, gentlemen, I must need display before you
another case, which in equity and justice maketh much for the
advantage of Bridlegoose, to wit, that this one, sole, and single
fault of his ought to be quite forgotten, abolished, and swallowed
up by that immense and vast ocean of just dooms and sentences,
which heretofore he hath given and pronounced; his demeanours,
for these forty years and upwards that he hath been a judge,

having been so evenly balanced in the scales of uprightness, that envy itself, till now, could not have been so impudent as to accuse and twit him with any act worthy of a check or reprehension: as, if a drop of the sea were thrown into the Loire, none could perceive, or say, that by this single drop the whole river should be salt and brackish.

Truly, it seemeth unto me, that in the whole series of Bridlegoose's juridical decrees there hath been I know not what of extraordinary savouring of the unspeakable benignity of God, that all these his preceding sentences, awards, and judgments, have been confirmed and approved of by yourselves, in this your own venerable and sovereign court. For it is usual, (as you know well,) with him whose ways are inscrutable, to manifest his own ineffable glory in blunting the perspicacity of the eyes of the wise, in weakening the strength of potent oppressors, in depressing the pride of rich extortioners, and in erecting, comforting, protecting, supporting, upholding, and shoring up the poor, feeble, humble, silly, and foolish ones of the earth. But, waving all these matters, I shall only beseech you, not by the obligations which you pretend to owe to my family, for which I thank you, but for that constant and unfeigned love and affection which you have always found in me, both on this and on the other side of the Loire, for the maintenance and establishment of your places, offices, and dignities, that for this one time you would pardon and forgive him upon these two conditions. First, That he satisfy, or posit sufficient surety for the satisfaction of the party wronged by the injustice of the sentence in question. For the fulfilment of this article, I will provide sufficiently. And, secondly, That for his subsidiary aid in the weighty charge of administrating justice, you would be pleased to appoint and assign unto him some virtuous counsellor, younger, learneder, and wiser than he, by the square and rule of whose advice he may regulate, guide, temper, and moderate in times coming all his judiciary procedures; or otherwise, if you intend totally to depose him from his office, and to deprive him altogether of the state and dignity of a judge, I shall cordially entreat you to make a present and free gift of him to me, who shall find in my kingdoms charges and employments enough wherewith to imbusy him, for the bettering of his own fortunes, and furtherance of my service. In the meantime, I implore the Creator, Saviour, and Sanctifier of all good things, in his grace, mercy, and kindness, to preserve you all, now and evermore, world without end.

These words thus spoken, Pantagruel, veiling his cap and
making a leg with such a majestic grace as became a person of
his paramount degree and eminency, farewelled Trinquamelle,
the president and master speaker of that Myrelinguesian parliament, took his leave of the whole court, and went out of the
chamber: at the door whereof finding Panurge, Epistemon,
Friar John, and others, he forthwith, attended by them, walked
to the outer gate, where all of them immediately took horse to
return towards Gargantua. Pantagruel by the way related to
them from point to point the manner of Bridlegoose's senten-
tiating differences at law. Friar John said, that he had seen
Peter Dendin, and was acquainted with him at that time when
he sojourned in the monastery of Fontaine le Comte, under the
noble Abbot Ardillon. Gymnast likewise affirmed, that he was
in the tent of the grand Christian cavalier de Crissé, when the
Gascon, after his sleep, made an answer to the adventurer.
Panurge was somewhat incredulous in the matter of believing
that it was morally possible Bridlegoose should have been
for such a long space of time so continually fortunate in that
aleatory way of deciding law debates. Epistemon said to
Pantagruel, Such another story, not much unlike to that in
all the circumstances thereof, is vulgarly reported of the provost
of Montlehery. In good sooth, such a perpetuity of good luck
is to be wondered at. To have hit right twice or thrice in a
judgment so given by hap-hazard might have fallen out well
enough, especially in controversies that were ambiguous,
intricate, abstruse, perplexed, and obscure.

CHAPTER XLIV

*How Pantagruel relateth a strange history of the perplexity of
human judgment*

SEEING you talk, quoth Pantagruel, of dark, difficult, hard,
and knotty debates, I will tell you of one controverted before
Cneius Dolabella, Proconsul in Asia. The case was this.

A wife in Smyrna had of her first husband a child named
Abecé. He dying, she, after the expiring of a year and a day,
married again, and to her second husband bore a boy called
Effegé. A pretty long time thereafter it happened, as you know
the affection of step-fathers and step-dames is very rare towards
the children of the first fathers and mothers deceased, that this

husband, with the help of his son Effegé, secretly, wittingly, willingly, and treacherously murdered Abecé. The woman came no sooner to get information of the fact, but, that it might not go unpunished, she caused kill them both, to revenge the death of her first son. She was apprehended and carried before Cneius Dolabella, in whose presence, she, without dissembling anything, confessed all that was laid to her charge; yet alleged, that she had both right and reason on her side for the killing of them. Thus was the state of the question. He found the business so dubious and intricate, that he knew not what to determine therein, nor which of the parties to incline to. On the one hand, it was an execrable crime to cut off at once both her second husband and her son. On the other hand, the cause of the murder seemed to be so natural, as to be grounded upon the law of nations, and the rational instinct of all the people of the world, seeing they two together had feloniously and murderously destroyed her first son;—not that they had been in any mannner of way wronged, outraged, or injured by him, but out of an avaricious intent to possess his inheritance. In this doubtful quandary and uncertainty what to pitch upon, he sent to the Areopagites, then sitting at Athens, to learn and obtain their advice and judgment. That judicious senate, very sagely perpending the reasons of his perplexity, sent him word to summon her personally to compeer before him a precise hundred years thereafter, to answer to some interrogatories touching certain points, which were not contained in the verbal defence. Which resolution of theirs did import, that it was in their opinion so difficult and inextricable a matter, that they knew not what to say or judge therein. Who had decided that plea by the chance and fortune of the dice, could not have erred nor awarded amiss, on which side soever he had past his casting and condemnatory sentence. If against the woman, she deserved punishment for usurping sovereign authority, by taking that vengeance at her own hand, the inflicting whereof was only competent to the supreme power to administer justice in criminal cases. If for her, the just resentment of a so atrocious injury done unto her, in murdering her innocent son, did fully excuse and vindicate her of any trespass or offence about that particular committed by her. But this continuation of Bridlegoose for so many years, still hitting the nail on the head, never missing the mark, and always judging aright, by the mere throwing of the dice, and the chance thereof, is that which most astonisheth and amazeth me.

To answer, quoth Pantagruel, categorically to that which you wonder at, I must ingeniously confess and avow that I cannot; yet, conjecturally to guess at the reason of it, I would refer the cause of that marvellously long-continued happy success in the judiciary results of his definitive sentences, to the favourable aspect of the heavens, and benignity of the intelligences; who out of their love to goodness, after having contemplated the pure simplicity and sincere unfeignedness of Judge Bridlegoose in the acknowledgment of his inabilities, did regulate that for him by chance, which by the profoundest act of his maturest deliberation he was not able to reach unto. That, likewise, which possibly made him to diffide in his own skill and capacity, notwithstanding his being an expert and understanding lawyer, for anything that I know to the contrary, was the knowledge and experience which he had of the antinomies, contrarieties, antilogies, contradictions, traversings, and thwartings of laws, customs, edicts, statutes, orders, and ordinances, in which dangerous opposition, equity and justice being structured and founded on either of the opposite terms, and a gap being thereby opened for the ushering in of injustice and iniquity through the various interpretations of self-ended lawyers; being assuredly persuaded that the infernal calumniator, who frequently transformeth himself into the likeness of a messenger or angel of light, maketh use of these cross glosses and expositions in the mouths and pens of his ministers and servants, the perverse advocates, bribing judges, law-monging attorneys, prevaricating counsellors, and such other like law-wresting members of a court of justice, to turn by those means black to white, green to grey, and what is straight to a crooked ply. For the more expedient doing whereof, these diabolical ministers make both the pleading parties believe that their cause is just and righteous; for it is well known that there is no cause, how bad soever, which doth not find an advocate to patrocinate and defend it, —else would there be no process in the world, no suits at law, nor pleadings at the bar. He did in these extremities, as I conceive, most humbly recommend the direction of his judicial proceedings to the upright judge of judges, God Almighty,— did submit himself to the conduct and guideship of the blessed Spirit, in the hazard and perplexity of the definitive sentence, —and, by this aleatory lot, did as it were implore and explore the divine decree of his good will and pleasure, instead of that which we call the Final Judgment of a Court. To this effect, to the better attaining to his purpose, which was to judge righteously, he did, in my opinion, throw and turn the dice, to the end that by the providence aforesaid, the best chance might fall to him those action was uprightest, and backed with greatest reason. In doing whereof he did not stray from the sense of the Talmudists, who say that there is so little harm in that manner of searching the truth, that in the anxiety and perplexedness of human wits, God oftentimes manifesteth the secret pleasure of his Divine Will.

Furthermore, I will neither think nor say, nor can I believe, that the unstraightness is so irregular, or the corruption so evident, of those of the Parliament of Myrelingois in Myrelingues, before whom Bridlegoose was arraigned for prevarication, that they will maintain it to be a worse practice to have the decision of a suit at law referred to the chance and hazard of a throw of the dice, hab nab, or luck as it will, than to have it remitted to, and past, by the determination of those whose hands are full of blood, and hearts of wry affections. Besides that, their principal direction in all law matters comes to their hands from one Tribonian, a wicked, miscreant, barbarous, faithless, and perfidious knave, so pernicious, unjust, avaricious, and perverse in his ways, that it was his ordinary custom to sell laws, edicts, declarations, constitutions, and ordinances, as at an outroop or putsale, to him who offered most for them. Thus did he shape measures for the pleaders, and cut their morsels to them by and out of these little parcels, fragments, bits, scantlings, and shreds of the law now in use, altogether concealing, suppressing, disannulling, and abolishing the remainder, which did make for the total law; fearing that, if the whole law were made manifest and laid open to the knowledge of such as are interested in it, and the learned books of the ancient doctors of the law upon the exposition of the Twelve Tables and Prætorian Edicts, his villanous pranks, naughtiness, and vile impiety should come to the public notice of the world. Therefore were it better, in my conceit, that is to say less inconvenient, that parties at variance in any juridical case should in the dark, march upon caltrops, than submit the determination of what is their right to such unhallowed sentences and horrible decrees: as Cato in his time wished and advised, that every judiciary court should be paved with caltrops.

CHAPTER XLV

How Panurge taketh advice of Triboulet

ON the sixth day thereafter, Pantagruel was returned home at
the very same hour that Triboulet was by water come from
Blois. Panurge, at his arrival, gave him a hog's bladder, puffed
up with wind, and resounding, because of the hard peas that
were within it. Moreover he did present him with a gilt wooden
sword, a hollow budget made of a tortoise-shell, an osier-wattled
wicker bottle full of Breton wine, and five and twenty apples
of the orchard of Blandureau.

If he be such a fool, quoth Carpalim, as to be won with apples,
there is no more wit in his pate than in the head of an ordinary
cabbage. Triboulet girded the sword and scrip to his side,
took the bladder in his hand, ate some few of the apples, and
drunk up all the wine. Panurge very wistly and heedfully
looking upon him said, I never yet saw a fool, and I have seen
ten thousand franks worth of that kind of cattle, who did not
love to drink heartily, and by good long draughts. When
Triboulet had done with his drinking, Panurge laid out before
him, and exposed the sum of the business wherein he was to
require his advice, in eloquent and choicely-sorted terms,
adorned with flourishes of rhetoric. But, before he had
altogether done, Triboulet with his fist gave him a bouncing
whirret between the shoulders, rendered back into his hand
again the empty bottle, filipped and flirted him on the nose
with the hog's bladder, and lastly, for a final resolution, shaking
and wagging his head strongly and disorderly, he answered
nothing else but this, By God, God, mad fool, beware the monk,
Buzançay hornpipe! These words thus finished, he slipped
himself out of the company, went aside, and, rattling the bladder,
took a huge delight in the melody of the rickling, crackling,
noise of the peas. After which time it lay not in the power of
them all to draw out of his chaps the articulate sound of one
syllable, insomuch that, when Panurge went about to interro-
gate him further, Triboulet drew out his wooden sword, and would
have stuck him therewith. I have fished fair now, quoth
Panurge, and brought my pigs to a fine market. Have I not
got a brave determination of all my doubts, and a response in
all things agreeable to the oracle that gave it? He is a great
fool, that is not to be denied, yet he is a greater fool, who brought

him hither to me,—but of the three I am the greatest fool, who
did impart the secret of my thoughts to such an idiot ass and
native ninny,—That bolt, quoth Carpalim, levels point blank
at me.

Without putting ourselves to any stir or trouble in the least,
quoth Pantagruel, let us maturely and seriously consider and
perpend the gestures and speech which he hath made and
uttered.   In them, veritably, quoth he, have I remarked and
observed some excellent and notable mysteries, yea, of such
important worth and weight, that I shall never henceforth be
astonished, nor think strange, why the Turks, with a great
deal of worship and reverence, honour and respect natural
fools equally with their primest doctors, mufties, divines, and
prophets.   Did not you take heed, quoth he, a little before
he opened his mouth to speak, what a shogging, shaking, and
wagging, his head did keep?   By the approved doctrine of
the ancient philosophers, the customary ceremonies of the
most expert magicians, and the received opinions of the most
learned lawyers, such a brangling agitation and moving should
by us all be judged to proceed from, and be quickened and
suscitated by, the coming and inspiration of the prophetizing
and fatidical spirit, which, entering briskly and on a sudden
into a shallow receptacle of a debil substance, (for, as you know,
and as the proverb shows it, a little head containeth not much
brains,) was the cause of that commotion.   This is conform to
what is avouched by the most skilful physicians, when they
affirm, that shakings and tremblings fall upon the members of
a human body, partly because of the heaviness and violent
impetuosity of the burden and load that is carried, and other
part, by reason of the weakness and imbecility that is in the
virtue of the bearing organ.   A manifest example whereof
appeareth in those who, fasting, are not able to carry to their
head a great goblet full of wine without a trembling and a
shaking in the hand that holds it.   This of old was accounted
a prefiguration and mystical pointing out of the Pythian diviner-
ess, who used always, before the uttering of a response from the
oracle, to shake a branch of her domestic laurel.   Lampridius
also testifieth, that the Emperor Heliogabalus, to acquire unto
himself the reputation of a soothsayer, did, on several holy days,
of prime solemnity, in the presence of the fanatic rabble, make
the head of his idol by some slight within the body thereof,
publicly to shake.   Plautus, in his Asinaria, declareth likewise,
that Saurias, whithersoever he walked, like one quite distracted

of his wits, kept such a furious lolling and mad-like shaking of
his head, that he commonly affrighted those who casually met
with him in their way. The said author in another place,
showing a reason why Charmides shook and brangled his head,
assevered that he was transported, and in an ecstasy. Catullus
after the same manner maketh mention, in his Berecynthia
and Atys, of the place wherein the Menades, Bacchical women,
she priests of the Lyæan god, and demented prophetesses,
carrying ivy boughs in their hands, did shake their heads. As
in the like case, amongst the Galli, the gelded priests of Cybele
were wont to do in the celebrating of their festivals. Whence,
too, according to the sense of the ancient theologues, she herself has her denomination; for κυβιστᾶν signifieth, to turn
round, whirl about, shake the head, and play the part of one
that is wry-necked.

Semblably Titus Livius writeth, that, in the solemnization
time of the Bacchanalian holidays at Rome, both men and
women seemed to prophetize and vaticinate, because of an
affected kind of wagging of the head, shrugging of the shoulders,
and jectigation of the whole body, which they used then most
punctually. For the common voice of the philosophers, together with the opinion of the people, asserteth for an irrefragable truth, that vaticination is seldom by the heavens
bestowed on any, without the concomitancy of a little frenzy,
and a head-shaking, not only when the said presaging virtue
is infused, but when the person also therewith inspired, declareth
and manifesteth it unto others. The learned lawyer Julian,
being asked on a time, if that slave might be truly esteemed to
be healthful and in a good plight, who had not only conversed
with some furious, maniac, and enraged people, but in their
company had also prophesied, yet without a noddle-shaking
concussion, answered, That seeing there was no head-wagging
at the time of his predictions, he might be held for sound and
competent enough. Is it not daily seen, how schoolmasters,
teachers, tutors, and instructors of children, shake the heads
of their disciples, as one would do a pot in holding it by the lugs,
that by this erection, vellication, stretching and pulling their
ears, which, according to the doctrine of the sage Egyptians, is
a member consecrated to the memory, they may stir them up
to recollect their scattered thoughts, bring home those fancies
of theirs, which perhaps have been extravagantly roaming abroad
upon strange and uncouth objects, and totally range their
judgments, which possibly by disordinate affections have been

made wild, to the rule and pattern of a wise, discreet, virtuous, and philosophical discipline. All which Virgil acknowledgeth to be true, in the branglement of Apollo Cynthius.

CHAPTER XLVI

How Pantagruel and Panurge diversely interpret the words of Triboulet

HE says you are a fool. And what kind of fool? A mad fool, who in your old age would enslave yourself to the bondage of matrimony, and shut your pleasures up within a wedlock, whose key some ruffian carries in his codpiece. He says furthermore, Beware of the monk. Upon mine honour, it gives me in my mind, that you will be cuckolded by a monk. Nay, I will engage mine honour, which is the most precious pawn I could have in my possession, although I were sole and peaceable dominator over all Europe, Asia, and Africa, that if you marry, you will surely be one of the horned brotherhood of Vulcan. Hereby may you perceive, how much I do attribute to the wise foolery of our morosoph Triboulet. The other oracles and responses did in the general prognosticate you a cuckold, without descending so near to the point of a particular determination, as to pitch upon what vocation amongst the several sorts of men, he should profess, who is to be the copesmate of your wife and hornifier of your proper self. Thus noble Triboulet tells it us plainly, from whose words we may gather with all ease imaginable, that your cuckoldry is to be infamous, and so much the more scandalous, that your conjugal bed will be incestuously contaminated with the filthiness of a monkery lecher. Moreover he says, that you will be the hornpipe of Buzançay,—that is to say, well horned, hornified, and cornuted. And, as Triboulet's uncle asked from Louis the Twelfth, for a younger brother of his own, who lived at Blois, the hornpipes of Buzançay, for the organ pipes, through the mistake of one word for another, even so, whilst you think to marry a wise, humble, calm, discreet, and honest wife, you shall unhappily stumble upon one, witless, proud, loud, obstreperous, bawling, clamorous, and more unpleasant than any Buzançay hornpipe. Consider withal, how he flirted you on the nose with the bladder, and gave you a sound thumping blow with his fist upon the ridge of the back. This denotes and presageth, that you shall be banged, beaten, and filipped by her, and that also she will steal of your goods from you, as you stole the hog's bladder from the little boys of Vaubreton.

Flat contrary, quoth Panurge;—not that I would impudently exempt myself from being a vassal in the territory of folly. I hold of that jurisdiction, and am subject thereto, I confess it. And why should I not? For the whole world is foolish. In the old Lorrain language, *fou* for *oou*; all and fool were the same thing. Besides, it is avouched by Solomon, that infinite is the number of fools. From an infinity nothing can be deducted or abated, nor yet, by the testimony of Aristotle, can anything thereto be added or subjoined. Therefore were I a mad fool, if, being a fool, I should not hold myself a fool. After the same manner of speaking, we may aver the number of the mad and enraged folks to be infinite. Avicenna maketh no bones to assert, that the several kinds of madness are infinite. Though this much of Triboulet's words tend little to my advantage, howbeit the prejudice which I sustain thereby be common with me to all other men, yet the rest of his talk and gesture maketh altogether for me. He said to my wife, Be weary of the monkey; that is as much as if she should be cheery, and take as much delight in a monkey, as ever did the Lesbia of Catullus in her sparrow; who will, for his recreation pass his time no less joyfully at the exercise of snatching flies, than heretofore did the merciless fly-catcher Domitian. Withal he meant by another part of his discourse, that she should be of a jovial country-like humour, as gay and pleasing as a harmonious hornpipe of Saulieu or Buzançay. The veridical Triboulet did therein hint at what I liked well, as perfectly knowing the inclinations and propensities of my mind, my natural disposition, and the bias of my interior passions and affections. For you may be assured, that my humour is much better satisfied and contented with the pretty, frolic, rural, dishevelled shepherdesses, whose bums through their coarse canvass smocks, smell of the clover-grass of the field, than with those great ladies in magnificent courts, with their flaunting top-knots and sultanas, their polvil, pastillos, and cosmetics. The homely sound, likewise, of a rustic hornpipe is more agreeable to my ears, than the curious warbling and musical quivering of lutes, theorbos, viols, rebecs, and violins. He gave me a lusty rapping thwack on my back,—what then? Let it pass, in the name and for the love of God, as an abatement of, and deduction from so much of my future pains in purgatory. He did it not out of any

evil intent. He thought, belike, to have hit some of the pages.
He is an honest fool, and an innocent changeling. It is a sin
to harbour in the heart any bad conceit of him. As for myself,
I heartily pardon him. He flirted me on the nose. In that
there is no harm; for it importeth nothing else, but that betwixt
my wife and me there will occur some toyish wanton tricks,
which usually happen to all new married folks.

CHAPTER XLVII

*How Pantagruel and Panurge resolved to make a visit to the
oracle of the holy bottle*

THERE is as yet another point, quoth Panurge, which you have
not at all considered on, although it be the chief and principal
head of the matter. He put the bottle in my hand and restored
it me again. How interpret you that passage? What is the
meaning of that? He possibly, quoth Pantagruel, signifieth
thereby, that your wife will be such a drunkard as shall daily
take in her liquor kindly, and ply the pots and bottles apace.
Quite otherwise, quoth Panurge; for the bottle was empty. I
swear to you, by the prickling brambly thorn of St. Fiacre in
Brie, that our unique Morosoph, whom I formerly termed the
lunatic Triboulet, referreth me, for attaining to the final resolution of my scruple, to the response-giving bottle. Therefore do
I renew afresh the first vow which I made, and here in your
presence protest and make oath by Styx and Acheron, to carry
still spectacles in my cap, and never to wear a codpiece in my
breeches, until upon the enterprise in hand of my nuptial undertaking, I shall have obtained an answer from the holy bottle.
I am acquainted with a prudent, understanding, and discreet
gentleman, and besides, a very good friend of mine, who knoweth
the land, country, and place where its temple and oracle is
built and posited. He will guide and conduct us thither sure
and safely. Let us go thither, I beseech you. Deny me not,
and say not, nay; reject not the suit I make unto you, I entreat
you. I will be to you an Achates, a Damis, and heartily accom-
pany you all along in the whole voyage, both in your going forth
and coming back. I have of a long time known you to be a
great lover of peregrination, desirous still to learn new things,
and still to see what you had never seen before.

Very willingly, quoth Pantagruel, I condescend to your

request. But before we enter in upon our progress towards the accomplishment of so far a journey, replenished and fraught with imminent perils, full of innumerable hazards, and every way stored with evident and manifest dangers—What dangers? quoth Panurge, interrupting him. Dangers fly back, run from, and shun me whithersoever I go, seven leagues around,—as in the presence of the sovereign a subordinate magistracy is eclipsed; or as clouds and darkness quite vanish at the bright coming of a radiant sun; or as all sores and sicknesses did suddenly depart, at the approach of the body of St. Martin à Quande. Nevertheless, quoth Pantagruel, before we adventure to set forward on the road of our projected and intended voyage, some few points are to be discussed, expedited, and dispatched. First, let us send back Triboulet to Blois. Which was instantly done, after that Pantagruel had given him a frieze coat. Secondly, our design must be backed with advice and counsel of the king my father. And lastly, it is most needful and expedient for us, that we search for and find out some sibyl, to serve us for a guide, truchman, and interpreter. To this Panurge made answer, That his friend Xenomanes would abundantly suffice for the plenary discharge and performance of the sibyl's office; and that, furthermore, in passing through the Lanternatory revelling country, they should take along with them a learned and profitable Lanternesse, who would be no less useful to them in their voyage, than was the sibyl to Æneas, in his descent to the Elysian fields. Carpalim, in the interim, as he was upon the conducting away of Triboulet, in his passing by, hearkened a little to the discourse they were upon, then spoke out, saying, Ho, Panurge, master freeman, take my Lord Debitis at Calais, along with you, for he is goudfallot, a good fellow. He will not forget those who have been debtors; these are Lanternes. Thus shall you not lack for both fallot and lanterne. I may safely with the little skill I have, quoth Pantagruel, prognosticate, that by the way we shall engender no melancholy. I clearly perceive it already. The only thing that vexeth me is, that I cannot speak the Lanternatory language. I shall, answered Panurge, speak for you all. I understand it every whit as well as I do mine own maternal tongue; I have been no less used to it than to the vulgar French.

> Br sz marg dalgotbric nubstzne zos,
> Isquebsz prusq albork crinqs zacbac.
> Misbe dilbarkz morp nipp stancz bos,
> Strombtz, Panurge, walmap quost gruszbac.

Now guess, friend Epistemon, what is this? They are,

quoth Epistemon, names of errant devils, passant devils, and rampant devils. These words of thine, dear friend of mine, are true, quoth Panurge, yet are they terms used in the language of the court of the Lanternish people. By the way, as we go upon our journey, I will make to thee a pretty little dictionary, which, notwithstanding, shall not last you much longer than a pair of new shoes. Thou shalt have learned it sooner than thou canst perceive the dawning of the next subsequent morning. What I have said in the foregoing tetrastic is thus translated out of the Lanternish tongue into our vulgar dialect.

> All miseries attended me, whilst I
> A lover was, and had no good thereby.
> Of better luck the married people tell;
> Panurge is one of those, and knows it well.

There is little more, then, quoth Pantagruel, to be done, but that we understand what the will of the king my father will be therein, and purchase his consent.

CHAPTER XLVIII

How Gargantua sheweth, that the children ought not to marry without the special knowledge and advice of their fathers and mothers

No sooner had Pantagruel entered in at the door of the great hall of the castle, than that he encountered full butt with the good honest Gargantua coming forth from the council board, unto whom he made a succinct and summary narrative of what had passed and occurred, worthy of his observation, in his travels abroad, since their last interview; then, acquainting him with the design he had in hand, besought him that it might stand with his good will and pleasure, to grant him leave to prosecute and go thorough-stitch with the enterprise which he had undertaken. The good man Gargantua, having in one hand two great bundles of petitions, indorsed and answered, and in the other some remembrancing notes and bills, to put him in mind of such other requests of suppliants, which, albeit presented, had nevertheless been neither read nor heard, he gave both to Ulrich Gallet, his ancient and faithful Master of Requests; then drew aside Pantagruel, and, with a countenance more serene and jovial than customary, spoke to him thus, I praise God, and have great reason so to do, my most dear son,

that he hath been pleased to entertain in you a constant inclination to virtuous actions. I am well content that the
voyage which you have motioned to me be by you accomplished,
but withal I could wish you would have a mind and desire to
marry, for that I see you are of competent years. [Panurge,
in the meanwhile, was in a readiness of preparing and providing
for remedies, salves, and cures against all such lets, obstacles,
and impediments, as he could in the height of his fancy conceive
might by Gargantua be cast in the way of their itinerary design.]
Is it your pleasure, most dear father, that you speak? answered
Pantagruel. For my part, I have not yet thought upon it.
In all this affair I wholly submit and rest in your good liking
and paternal authority. For I shall rather pray unto God that
he would throw me down stark dead at your feet, in your
pleasure, than that against your pleasure I should be found
married alive. I never heard that by any law, whether sacred
or profane, yea, amongst the rudest and most barbarous nations
in the world, it was allowed and appoved of, that children may
be suffered and tolerated to marry at their own good will and
pleasure, without the knowledge, advice, or consent asked and
had thereto, of their fathers, mothers, and nearest kindred.
All legislators, every where upon the face of the whole earth
have taken away and removed this licentious liberty from
children, and totally reserved it to the discretion of the parents.

My dearly beloved son, quoth Gargantua, I believe you, and
from my heart thank God for having endowed you with the
grace of having both a perfect notice of, and entire liking to,
laudable and praiseworthy things; and that through the windows
of your exterior senses he hath vouchsafed to transmit unto the
interior faculties of your mind, nothing but what is good and
virtuous. For in my time there hath been found on the continent
a certain country, wherein are I know not what kind of Pastophorian mole-catching priests, who, albeit averse from engaging
their proper persons into a matrimonial duty, like the pontifical
flamens of Cybele in Phrygia; as if they were capons, and not
cocks; full of lasciviousness, salacity, and wantonness, who yet
have, nevertheless, in the matter of conjugal affairs, taken upon
them to prescribe laws and ordinances to married folks. I
cannot goodly determine what I should most abhor, detest,
loathe, and abominate,—whether the tyrannical presumption
of those dreaded sacerdotal mole-catchers, who not being willing
to contain and coop up themselves within the grates and trellises
of their own mysterious temples, do deal in, meddle with,

obtrude upon, and thrust their sickles into harvests of secular businesses, quite contrary and diametrically opposite to the quality, state, and condition of their callings, professions, and vocations; or the superstitious stupidity and senseless scrupulousness of married folks, who have yielded obedience, and submitted their bodies, fortunes, and estates to the discretion and authority of such odious, perverse, barbarous, and unreasonable laws. Nor do they see that, which is clearer than the light and splendour of the morning star,—how all these nuptial and connubial sanctions, statutes, and ordinances have been decreed, made, and instituted, for the sole benefit, profit, and advantage of the flaminal mysts and mysterious flamens, and nothing at all for the good, utility, or emolument of the silly hood-winked married people. Which administereth unto others a sufficient cause for rendering these churchmen suspicious of iniquity, and of an unjust and fraudulent manner of dealing, no more to be connived at nor countenanced, after that it be well weighed in the scales of reason, than if with a reciprocal temerity the laics, by way of compensation, would impose laws to be followed and observed by those mysts and flamens, how they should behave themselves in the making and performance of their rites and ceremonies, after what manner they ought to proceed in the offering up and immolating of their various oblations, victims, and sacrifices; seeing that, besides the edecimation and tithe-haling of their goods, they cut off and take parings, shreddings, and clippings of the gain proceeding from the labour of their hands, and sweat of their brows, therewith to entertain themselves the better. Upon which consideration, in my opinion, their injunctions and commands would not prove so pernicious and impertinent, as those of the ecclesiastic power, unto which they had tendered their blind obedience. For, as you have very well said, there is no place in the world, where, legally, a licence is granted to the children to marry without the advice and consent of their parents and kindred. Nevertheless, by those wicked laws, and mole-catching customs whereat there is a little hinted in what I have already spoken to you, there is no scurvy, measly, leprous, or pocky ruffian, pander, knave, rogue, scellum, robber, or thief, pilloried, whipped, and burn-marked in his own country for his crimes and felonies, who may not violently snatch away and ravish what maid soever he had a mind to pitch upon, how noble, how fair, how rich, honest, and chaste soever she be, and that out of the house of her own father, in his own presence, from the bosom of her mother, and in the sight and despite of her friends and kindred looking on a so woful spectacle, provided that the rascal villain be so cunning as to associate unto himself some mystical flamen, who, according to the covenant made betwixt them two, shall be in hope some day to participate of the prey.

Could the Goths, the Scythians, or Massagetæ do a worse or more cruel act to any of the inhabitants of a hostile city, when, after the loss of many of their most considerable commanders, the expense of a great deal of money, and a long siege, that they shall have stormed and taken it by a violent and impetuous assault? May not these fathers and mothers, think you, be sorrowful and heavy-hearted, when they see an unknown fellow, a vagabond stranger, a barbarous lout, a rude cur, rotten, fleshless, putrified, scraggy, boily, botchy, poor, a forlorn caitiff, and miserable sneak, by an open rapt, snatch away before their own eyes their so fair, delicate, neat, well-behavioured, richly provided for and healthful daughters, on whose breeding and education they had spared no cost nor charges, by bringing them up in an honest discipline to all the honourable and virtuous employments becoming one of their sex, descended of a noble parentage, hoping by those commendable and industrious means in an opportune and convenient time to bestow them on the worthy sons of their well-deserving neighbours and ancient friends, who had nourished, entertained, taught, instructed, and schooled their children with the same care and solicitude, to make them matches fit to attain to the felicity of a so happy marriage, that from them might issue an offspring and progeny no less heirs to the laudable endowments and exquisite qualifications of their parents, whom they every way resemble, than to their personal and real estates, moveables and inheritances? How doleful, trist, and plangorous would such a sight and pageantry prove unto them? You shall not need to think, that the collachrymation of the Romans and their confederates at the decease of Germanicus Drusus was comparable to this lamentation of theirs? Neither would I have you to believe that the discomfort and anxiety of the Lacedæmonians, when the Greek Helen, by the perfidiousness of the adulterous Trojan, Paris, was privily stolen away out of their country, was greater or more pitiful than this ruthful and deplorable collugency of theirs? You may very well imagine, that Ceres at the ravishment of her daughter Proserpine, was not more attristed, sad, nor mournful than they. Trust me, and your own reason, that the loss of Osiris was not so regrettable to Isis,—nor did

Venus so deplore the death of Adonis,—nor yet did Hercules so bewail the straying of Hylas,—nor was the rapt of Polyxena more throbbingly resented and condoled by Priamus and Hecuba, than this aforesaid accident would be sympathetically bemoaned, grievous, ruthful, and anxious, to the wofully desolate and disconsolate parents.

Notwithstanding all this, the greater part of so vilely abused parents are so timorous and afraid of the devils and hobgoblins, and so deeply plunged in superstition, that they dare not gainsay nor contradict, much less oppose and resist, those unnatural and impious actions, when the mole-catcher hath been present at the perpetrating of the fact, and a party contractor and covenanter in that detestable bargain. What do they do then? They wretchedly stay at their own miserable homes, destitute of their well-beloved daughters,—the fathers cursing the days and the hours wherein they were married,—and the mothers howling and crying, that it was not their fortune to have brought forth abortive issues, when they happened to be delivered of such unfortunate girls; and in this pitiful plight spend at best the remainder of their time, with tears and weeping for those their children, of and from whom they expected, (and, with good reason, should have obtained and reaped,) in these latter days of theirs, joy and comfort. Other parents there have been, so impatient of that affront and indignity put upon them, and their families, that, transported with the extremity of passion, in a mad and frantic mood, through the vehemency of a grievous fury and raging sorrow, they have drowned, hanged, killed, and otherwise put violent hands on themselves. Others, again, of that parental relation, have, upon the reception of the like injury, been of a more magnanimous and heroic spirit, who, in imitation and at the example of the children of Jacob, revenging upon the Sichemites the rapt of their sister Dina, having found the rascally ruffian in the association of his mystical mole-catcher, closely and in hugger-mugger conferring, and parleying, with their daughters, for the suborning, corrupting, depraving, perverting, and enticing these innocent unexperienced maids unto filthy lewdnesses, have without any further advisement on the matter, cut them instantly to pieces, and thereupon forthwith thrown out upon the fields their so dismembered bodies, to serve for food unto the wolves and ravens. Upon the chivalrous, bold, and courageous achievement of a so valiant, stout, and man-like act, the other mole-catching symmists have been so highly incensed, and have

so chafed, fretted, and fumed thereat, that bills of complaint
and accusations having been in a most odious and detestable
manner put in before the competent judges, the arm of secular
authority hath with much importunity and impetuosity been
by them implored and required; they proudly contending,
That the servants of God would become contemptible, if exemplary punishment were not speedily taken upon the persons
of the perpetrators of such an enormous, horrid, sacrilegious,
crying, heinous, and execrable crime.

Yet neither by natural equity, by the law of nations, nor by
any imperial law whatsoever, hath there been found so much
as one rubic, paragraph, point, or tittle, by the which any kind
of chastisement or correction hath been adjudged due to be
inflicted upon any for their delinquency in that kind. Reason
opposeth, and nature is repugnant. For there is no virtuous
man in the world, who both naturally and with good reason
will not be more hugely troubled in mind, hearing of the news
of the rapt, disgrace, ignominy, and dishonour of his daughter,
than of her death. Now any man, finding in hot blood one,
who with a fore-thought felony hath murdered his daughter,
may, without tying himself to the formalities and circumstances
of a legal proceeding, kill him on a sudden, and out of hand,
without incurring any hazard of being attainted and apprehended
by the officers of justice for so doing. It is no wonder then if
a lechering rogue, together with his mole-catching abettor, be
entrapped in the flagrant act of suborning his daughter, and,
stealing her out of his house, though herself consent thereto,
that the father in such a case of stain and infamy by them
brought upon his family, should put them both to a shameful
death, and cast their carcasses upon dunghills to be devoured
and eaten up by dogs and swine, or otherwise fling them a little
further off to the direption, tearing and rending asunder of
their joints and members by the wild beasts of the field, as
being unworthy to receive the gentle, the desired, the last
kind embraces of their great Alma Mater, the earth, commonly
called burial.

Dearly beloved son, have an especial care, that after my
decease none of these laws be received in any of your kingdoms;
for whilst I breathe, by the grace and assistance of God, I shall
give good order. Seeing, therefore, you have totally referred
unto my discretion the disposure of you in marriage, I am fully
of an opinion, that I shall provide sufficiently well for you in
that point. Make ready and prepare yourself for Panurge's

voyage. Take along with you Epistemon, Friar John, and such others as you will choose. Do with my treasures what unto yourself shall seem most expedient. None of your actions, I promise you, can in any manner of way displease me. Take out of my arsenal Thalasse whatsoever equipage, furniture, or provision you please, together with such pilots, mariners, and truchmen, as you have a mind to, and with the first fair and favourable wind set sail and make out to sea, in the name of God our Saviour. In the meanwhile, during your absence, I shall not be neglective of providing a wife for you, nor of those preparations, which are requisite to be made for the more sumptuous solemnizing of your nuptials with a most splendid feast, if ever there was any in the world.

CHAPTER XLIX

How Pantagruel did put himself in a readiness to go to sea; and of the herb named Pantagruelion

WITHIN very few days after that Pantagruel had taken his leave of the good Gargantua, who devoutly prayed for his son's happy voyage, he arrived at the sea-port, near to Sammalo, accompanied with Panurge, Epistemon, Friar John of the Funnels, Abbot of Theleme, and others of the royal house, especially with Xenomanes the great traveller, and thwarter of dangerous ways, who was to come at the bidding and appointment of Panurge, of whose Castlewick of Salmigondin he did hold some petty inheritance by the tenure of a mesne fee. Pantagruel, being come thither, prepared and made ready for launching a fleet of ships, to the number of those which Ajax of Salamine had of old equipped in convoy of the Grecian soldiery against the Trojan state. He likewise picked out for his use so many mariners, pilots, sailors, interpreters, artificers, officers, and soldiers, as he thought fitting, and therewithal made provision of so much victuals of all sorts, artillery, munition of divers kinds, clothes, monies, and other such luggage, stuff, baggage, chaffer, and furniture, as he deemed needful for carrying on the design of a so tedious, long, and perilous voyage, Amongst other things it was observed, how he caused some of his vessels to be fraught and loaded with a great quantity of an herb of his called Pantagruelion, not only of the green and raw sort of it, but of the confected also, and of that which was

notably well befitted for present use, after the fashion of con-
serves. The herb Pantagruelion hath a little root, somewhat
hard and rough, roundish, terminating in an obtuse and very
blunt point, and having some of its veins, strings, or filaments
coloured with some spots of white, never fixeth itself into the
ground above the profoundness almost of a cubit, or foot and
a half. From the root thereof proceedeth the only stalk,
orbicular, cane-like, green without, whitish within, and hollow
like the stem of smyrnium, *olus atrum*, beans, and gentian,
full of long threads, straight, easy to be broken, jagged, snipped,
nicked and notched a little after the manner of pillars and
columns, slightly furrowed, chamfered, guttered and channelled
and full of fibres, or hairs like strings, in which consisteth the
chief value and dignity of the herb, especially in that part thereof
which is termed *mesa*, as one would say the mean; and in that
other, which had got the denomination of *milasea*. Its height
is commonly five or six feet. Yet sometimes it is of such a tall
growth, as doth surpass the length of a lance, but that is only
when it meeteth with a sweet, easy, warm, wet, and well-soaked
soil,—as is the ground of the territory of Olone, and that of
Rasea, near to Preneste in Sabinia,—and that it want not for
rain enough about the season of the fishers' holidays, and the
æstival solstice. There are many trees whose height is by it
very far exceeded, and you might call it *dendromalache* by the
authority of Theophrastus. The plant every year perisheth,
—the tree neither in the trunk, root, bark, or boughs, being
durable.

From the stalk of this Pantagruelion plant there issue forth
several large and great branches, whose leaves have thrice as
much length as breadth, always green, roughish, and rugged
like the orcanet, or Spanish bugloss, hardish, slit round about
like unto a suckle, or as the saxifragum, as betony, and finally
ending as it were in the points of a Macedonian spear, or of
such a lancet as surgeons commonly make use of in their phle-
botomizing tiltings. The figure and shape of the leaves thereof
is not much different from that of those of the ash tree, or of
agrimony; the herb itself being so like the Eupatorian plant,
that many skilful herbalists have called it the Domestic Eupator,
and the Eupator the Wild Pantagruelion. These leaves are
in equal and parallel distances spread around the stalk, by the
number in every rank either of five or seven, nature having so
highly favoured and cherished this plant, that she hath richly
adorned it with these two odd, divine, and mysterious numbers.

The smell thereof is somewhat strong, and not very pleasing to nice, tender, and delicate noses. The seed inclosed therein mounteth up to the very top of its stalk, and a little above it.

This is a numerous herb: for there is no less abundance of it than of any other whatsoever. Some of these plants are spherical, some rhomboid, and some of an oblong shape, and all of these either black, bright-coloured, or tawny, rude to the touch, and mantled with a quickly-blasted-away coat, yet such a one as is of a delicious taste and savour to all shrill and sweetly singing birds, such as linnets, goldfinches, larks, canary birds, yellow hammers, and others of that airy chirping quire; but it would quite extinguish the natural heat and procreative virtue of the semence of any man, who would eat much, and often of it. And although that of old amongst the Greeks there was certain kind of fritters and pancakes, buns and tarts, made thereof, which commonly for a liquorish daintiness were presented on the table after supper, to delight the palate and make the wine relish the better; yet is it of a difficult concoction, and offensive to the stomach. For it engendereth bad and unwholesome blood, and with its exorbitant heat woundeth them with grievous, hurtful, smart, and noisome vapours. And, as in divers plants and trees there are two sexes, male and female, which is perceptible in laurels, palms, cypresses, oaks, holmes, the daffodil, mandrake, fern, the agaric, mushroom, birthwort, turpentine, pennyroyal, peony, rose of the mount, and many other such like, even so in this herb there is a male which beareth no flower at all, yet it is very copious of and abundant in seed. There is likewise in it a female, which hath great store and plenty of whitish flowers, serviceable to little or no purpose, nor doth it carry in it seed of any worth at all, at least comparable to that of the male. It hath also a larger leaf, and much softer than that of the male, nor doth it altogether grow to so great a height. This Pantagruelion is to be sown at the first coming of the swallows, and is to be plucked out of the ground when the grasshoppers begin to be a little hoarse.

CHAPTER L

How the famous Pantagruelion ought to be prepared and wrought

THE herb Pantagruelion in September, under the autumnal equinox, is dressed and prepared several ways, according to the various fancies of the people, and diversity of the climates wherein it groweth. The first instruction which Pantagruel gave concerning it was, to divest and despoil the stalk and stem thereof of all its flowers and seeds, to macerate and mortify it in stagnant, not running water, for five days together, if the season be dry, and the water hot; or for full nine or twelve days, if the weather be cloudish, and the water cold. Then must it be dried in the sun, till it be drained of its moisture. After this it is in the shadow where the sun shines not, to be peeled, and its rind pulled off. Then are the fibres and strings thereof to be parted, wherein, as we have already said, consisteth its prime virtue, price, and efficacy, and severed from the woody part thereof, which is unprofitable, and serveth hardly to any other use than to make a clear and glistering blaze, to kindle the fire, and for the play, pastime, and disport of little children, to blow up hogs' bladders, and make them rattle. Many times some use is made thereof by tippling sweet-lipped bibbers, who out of it frame quills and pipes, through which they with their liquor-attractive breath suck up the new dainty wine from the bung of the barrel. Some modern Pantagruelists, to shun and avoid that manual labour, which such a separating and partitional work would of necessity require, employ certain cataractic instruments, composed and formed after the same manner that the froward, pettish, and angry Juno, did hold the fingers of both her hands interwovenly clenched together, when she would have hindered the childbirth delivery of Alcmena, at the nativity of Hercules; and athwart those cataracts they break and bruise to very trash the woody parcels, thereby to preserve the better the fibres, which are the precious and excellent parts. In and with this sole operation do these acquiesce and are contented, who, contrary to the received opinion of the whole earth, and in a manner paradoxical to all philosophers, gain their livelihoods backwards, and by recoiling. But those that love to hold it at a higher rate, and prize it according to its value, for their own greater profit, do the very same which is told us of the recreation of the three fatal Sister-Parcæ, or of the nocturnal exercise of the noble Circe, or yet of the excuse which Penelope made to her fond wooing youngsters and effeminate courtiers, during the long absence of her husband Ulysses.

By these means is this herb put into a way to display its inestimable virtues, whereof I will discover a part;—for to relate all is a thing impossible to do. I have already interpreted and exposed before you the denomination thereof. I find that plants have their names given and bestowed upon them after several ways. Some got the name of him who first found them out, knew them, sowed them, improved them by culture, qualified them to a tractability, and appropriated them to the uses and subserviences they were fit for. As the Mercurialis from Mercury; Panacea from Panace, the daughter of Esculapius; Armois from Artemis, who is Diana; Eupatoria from the king Eupator; Telephion from Telephus; Euphorbium from Euphorbus, King Juba's physician; Clymenos from Clymenus; Alcibiadium from Alcibiades; Gentian from Gentius, King of Sclavonia, and so forth, through a great many other herbs or plants. Truly, in ancient times, this prerogative of imposing the inventor's name upon an herb found out by him was held in a so great account and estimation, that, as a controversy arose betwixt Neptune and Pallas, from which of them two that land should receive its denomination, which had been equally found out by them both together; though thereafter it was called and had the appellation of Athens, from Athene, which is Minerva, —just so would Lynceus, King of Scythia, have treacherously slain the young Triptolemus whom Ceres had sent to show unto mankind the invention of corn, which until then had been utterly unknown; to the end that, after the murder of the messenger, whose death he made account to have kept secret, he might, by imposing, with the less suspicion of false dealing, his own name upon the said found out seed, acquire unto himself an immortal honour and glory for having been the inventor of a grain so profitable and necessary to and for the use of human life. For the wickedness of which treasonable attempt he was by Ceres transformed into that wild beast, which by some is called a lynx, and by others an ounce. Such also was the ambition of others upon the like occasion, as appeareth, by that very sharp wars, and of a long continuance have been made of old betwixt some residentiary kings in Cappadocia upon this only debate, of whose name a certain herb should have the appellation; by reason of which difference, so trouble-

some and expensive to them all, it was by them called Pole-
monion, and by us for the same cause termed Make-bate.

Other herbs and plants there are, which retain the names of
the countries from whence they were transported; as the Median
apples from Media, where they first grew; Punic apples from
Punicia, that is to say, Carthage; Ligusticum, which we call
Lovage, from Liguria, the coast of Genoa; Rhubarb from a
flood in Barbary, as Ammianus attesteth, called Ru; Santonica
from a region of that name; Fenugreek from Greece; Castanes
from a country so called; Persicaria from Persia; Sabine from
a territory of that appellation; Stœchas from the Stœchad
Islands; Spica Celtica from the land of the Celtic Gauls, and so
throughout a great many other, which were tedious to enumerate.
Some others, again, have obtained their denominations by way
of antiphrasis, or contrariety; as Absinth, because it is contrary
to Ψίντος, for it is bitter to the taste in drinking,—Holosteon,
as if it were all bones, whilst on the contrary, there is no frailer,
tenderer, nor brittler herb in the whole production of nature
than it.

There are some other sorts of herbs, which have got their
names from their virtues and operations; as Aristolochia, because it helpeth women in child-birth; Lichen, for that it cureth
the disease of that name; Mallow, because it mollifieth; Calli-
thricum, because it maketh the hair of a bright colour; Alyssum,
Ephemerum, Bechium, Nasturtium, Henbane, and so forth
through many more.

Other some there are, which have obtained their names from
the admirable qualities that are found to be in them; as Helio-
tropium, which is the marigold, because it followeth the sun,
so that at the sun rising it displayeth and spreads itself out,
at his ascending it mounteth, at his declining it waneth, and
when he is set, it is close shut; Adianton, because, although it
grow near unto watery places, and albeit you should let it lie
in water a long time, it will nevertheless retain no moisture nor
humidity; Hierachia, Eringium, and so throughout a great
many more. There are also a great many herbs and plants,
which have retained the very same names of the men and women
who have been metamorphosed and transformed in them; as
from Daphne, the laurel is called also Daphne; Myrrh from
Myrrha, the daughter of Cinarus; Pythis from Pythis; Cinara,
which is the artichoke, from one of that name; Narcissus, with
Saffron, Smilax, and divers others.

Many herbs, likewise, have got their names of those things

which they seem to have some resemblance to; as Hippuris, because it hath the likeness of a horse's tail; Alopecuris, because it representeth in similitude the tail of a fox; Psyllion, from a flea which it resembleth; Delphinium, for that it is like the dolphin fish; Bugloss is so called, because it is an herb like an ox's tongue; Iris, so called, because in its flowers it hath some resemblance of the rainbow; Myosota, because it is like the ear of a mouse; Coronopus, for that it is of the likeness of a crow's foot. A great many other such there are, which here to recite were needless. Furthermore, as there are herbs and plants which have had their names from those of men, so by a reciprocal denomination have the surnames of many families taken their origin from them; as the Fabii, *à fabis*, beans; the Pisons, *à pisis*, peas; the Lentuli, from lentils; the Cicerons, *à ciceribus vel ciceris*, a sort of pulse called chickpeas, and so forth. In some plants and herbs, the resemblance or likeness hath been taken from a higher mark or object, as when we say Venus' navel, Venus' hair, Venus' tub, Jupiter's beard, Jupiter's eye, Mars' blood, the Hermodactyl or Mercury's fingers, which are all of them names of herbs, as there are a great many more of the like appellation. Others, again, have received their denomination from their forms; such as the trefoil, because it is three-leaved; Pentaphylon, for having five leaves; Serpolet, because it creepeth along the ground; Helxine, Petast, Myrobalon, which the Arabians called Been, as if you would say an acorn, for it hath a kind of resemblance thereto, and withal is very oily.

CHAPTER LI

Why it is called Pantagruelion, and of the admirable virtues thereof

By such like means of attaining to a denomination, the fabulous ways being only from thence expected; for, the Lord forbid, that we should make use of any fables in this a so very veritable history, is this herb called Pantagruelion; for Pantagruel was the inventor thereof. I do not say of the plant itself, but of a certain use which it serves for, exceeding odious and hateful to thieves and robbers, unto whom it is more contrarious and hurtful than the strangleweed and choke-fitch is to the flax, the cats-tail to the brakes, the sheave-grass to the mowers of hay, the fitches to the chickney-peas, the darnel to barley, the hatchet-fitch to the lentil-pulse, the antramium to the beans, tares to wheat, ivy to walls, the water-lily to lecherous monks, the birchenrod to the scholars of the college of Navarre in Paris, colewort to the vine-tree, garlic to the load-stone, onions to the sight, fern-seed to women with child, willow-grain to vicious nuns, the yew-tree shade to those that sleep under it, wolfs-bane to wolves and libbards, the smell of fig-tree to mad bulls, hemlock to goslings, purslane to the teeth, or oil to trees. For we have seen many of those rogues, by virtue and right applica-tion of this herb, finish their lives short and long, after the manner of Phyllis Queen of Thracia, of Benosus, Emperor of Rome, of Amata, King Latinus's wife, of Iphis, Autolycus, Lycambes, Arachne, Phædra, Leda, Achius, King of Lydia, and many thousands more; who were chiefly angry and vexed at this disaster therein, that, without being otherwise sick or evil disposed in their bodies, by a touch only of the Pantagruelion, they came on a sudden to have the passage obstructed, and their pipes, through which were wont to bolt so many jolly sayings, and to enter so many luscious morsels, stopped, more cleverly, than ever could have done the squinancy.

Others have been heard most woefully to lament at the very instant when Atropos was about to cut the thread of their life, that Pantagruel held them by the gorge. But, well-a-day, it was not Pantagruel; he never was an executioner. It was the Pantagruelion, manufactured and fashioned into an halter, and serving in the place and office of a cravat. In that, verily, they solecized and spoke improperly, unless you would excuse them by a trope, which alloweth us to posit the inventor in the place of the thing invented; as when Ceres is taken for bread, and Bacchus put instead of wine. I swear to you here, by the good and frolic words which are to issue out of that wine-bottle, which is a-cooling below in the copper vessel full of fountain water, that the noble Pantagruel never snatched any man by the throat, unless it was such a one as was altogether careless and neglective of those obviating remedies, which were preventive of the thirst to come.

It is also termed Pantagruelion by a similitude. For Panta-gruel, at the very first minute of his birth, was no less tall than this herb is long, whereof I speak unto you,—his measure having been then taken the more easy, that he was born in the season of the great drought, when they were busiest in the gathering of the said herb, to wit, at that time when Icarus's dog, with his fiery bawling and barking at the sun, maketh the whole world troglodytic, and enforceth people everywhere to hide themselves in dens and subterranean caves. It is likewise called Pantagruelion, because of the notable and singular qualities, virtues, and properties thereof. For as Pantagruel hath been the idea, pattern, prototype, and exemplary of all jovial perfection and accomplishment—in the truth whereof I believe there is none of you, gentlemen drinkers, that putteth any question—so in this Pantagruelion have I found so much efficacy and energy, so much completeness and excellency, so much exquisiteness and rarity, and so many admirable effects and operations of a transcendent nature, that, if the worth and virtue thereof had been known, when those trees, by the relation of the prophet, made election of a wooden king to rule and govern over them, it without doubt would have carried away from all the rest the plurality of votes and suffrages.

Shall I yet say more? If Oxilus, the son of Orius, had begotten this plant upon his sister Hamadryas, he had taken more delight in the value and perfection of it alone, than in all his eight children, so highly renowned by our ablest mythologians, that they have sedulously recommended their names to the never-failing tuition of an eternal remembrance. The eldest child was a daughter, whose name was Vine; the next born was a boy, and his name was Fig-tree; the third was called Walnut-tree; the fourth Oak; the fifth Sorbapple-tree; the sixth Ash; the seventh Poplar; and the last had the name of Elm, who was the greatest surgeon in his time. I shall forbear to tell you, how the juice or sap thereof, being poured and distilled within the ears, killeth every kind of vermin, that by any manner of putrefaction cometh to be bred and engendered there, and destroyeth also any whatsoever other animal that shall have entered in thereat. If, likewise, you put a little of the said juice with a pail or bucket full of water, you shall see the water instantly turn and grow thick therewith, as if it were milk curds, whereof the virtue is so great, that the water thus curded is a present remedy for horses subject to the cholic, and such as strike at their own flanks. The root thereof well boiled mollifieth the joints, softeneth the hardness of shrunk-in sinews, is every way comfortable to the nerves, and good against all cramps and convulsions, as likewise all cold and knotty gouts. If you would speedily heal a burning, whether occasioned by water or fire, apply thereto a little raw Pantagruelion, that is to say, take it so as it cometh out of the ground, without bestowing any other preparation or composition upon it; but have a special care to change it for some fresher, in lieu thereof, as soon as you shall find it waxing dry upon the sore.

Without this herb, kitchens would be detested, the tables of dining-rooms abhorred, although there were great plenty and variety of most dainty and sumptuous dishes of meat set down upon them—and the choicest beds also, how richly soever adorned with gold, silver, amber, ivory, porphyry, and the mixture of most precious metals, would without it yield no delight or pleasure to the reposers in them. Without it millers could neither carry wheat, nor any other kind of corn, to the mill, nor would they be able to bring back from thence flour, or any other sort of meal whatsoever. Without it, how could the papers and writs of lawyers' clients be brought to the bar? Seldom is the mortar, lime, or plaister brought to the workhouse without it. Without it, how should the water be got out of a draw-well; in what case would tabellions, notaries, copyists, makers of counterpanes, writers, clerks, secretaries, scriveners, and such-like persons be without it? Were it not for it, what would become of the toll-rates and rent-rolls? Would not the noble art of printing perish without it? Whereof could the chassis or paper windows be made? How should the bells be rung? The altars of Isis are adorned therewith, the Pastophorian priests are therewith clad and accoutred, and whole human nature covered and wrapped therein, at its first position and production in and into this world. All the lanific trees of Seres, the bumbast and cotton bushes in the territories near the Persian sea, and Gulf of Bengala; the Arabian swans, together with the plants of Malta, do not all of them clothe, attire, and apparel so many persons as this one herb alone. Soldiers are now-a-days much better sheltered under it, than they were in former times, when they lay in tents covered with skins. It overshadows the theatres and amphitheatres from the heat of a scorching sun. It begirdeth and encompasseth forests, chases, parks, copses, and groves, for the pleasure of hunters. It descendeth into the salt and fresh of both sea and river waters, for the profit of fishers. By it are boots of all sizes, buskins, gamashes, brodkins, gambados, shoes, pumps, slippers, and every cobbled ware wrought and made steadable for the use of man. By it the butt and rover bows are strung, the cross-bows bended, and the slings made fixed. And, as if it were an herb every whit as holy as the vervain, and reverenced by ghosts, spirits, hobgoblins, fiends, and phantoms, the bodies of deceased men are never buried without it.

I will proceed yet further. By the means of this fine herb, the invisible substances are visibly stopped, arrested, taken, detained, and prisoner-like committed to their receptive gaols. Heavy and ponderous weights are by it heaved, lifted up, turned, veered, drawn, carried, and every way moved quickly, nimbly and easily, to the great profit and emolument of human kind. When I perpend with myself these and such like marvellous effects of this wonderful herb, it seemeth strange unto me, how the invention of so useful a practice did escape through so many by-past ages the knowledge of the ancient philosophers, considering the inestimable utility which from thence proceeded, and the immense labour, which, without it, they did undergo in their pristine lucubrations. By virtue thereof, through the retention of some aerial gusts, are the huge barges, mighty galleons, the large floats, the Chiliander, the Myriander ships launched from their stations, and set agoing at the pleasure and arbitrement of their rulers, conders, and steersmen. By the help thereof those remote nations, whom nature seemed so unwilling to have discovered to us, and so desirous to have kept them still *in abscondito* and hidden from us, that the ways through which their countries were to be reached unto, were not only totally unknown, but judged also to be altogether impermeable and inaccessible, are now arrived to us, and we to them.

Those voyages outreached the flights of birds, and far surpassed the scope of feathered fowls, how swift soever they had been on the wing, and notwithstanding that advantage which they have of us, in swimming through the air. Taproban hath seen the heaths of Lapland, and both the Javas, the Riphæan mountains; wide distant Phebol shall see Theleme, and the Islanders drink of the flood of Euphrates. By it the chill-mouthed Boreas hath surveyed the parched mansions of the torrid Auster, and Eurus visited the regions which Zephyrus hath under his command; yea, in such sort have interviews been made, by the assistance of this sacred herb, that, maugre longitudes and latitudes, and all the variations of the zones, the Peræcian people, and Anteocian, Amphiscian, Heteroscian, and Periscian have oft rendered and received mutual visits to and from other, upon all the climates. These strange exploits bred such astonishment to the celestial intelligences, to all the marine and terrestrial gods, that they were on a sudden all afraid. From which amazement, when they saw, how, by means of this blest Pantagruelion, the Arctic people looked upon the Antarctic,

scoured the Atlantic Ocean, passed the tropics, pushed through
the torrid zone, measured all the zodiac, sported under the
equinoctial, having both poles level with their horizon; they
judged it high time to call a council for their own safety and
preservation.

The Olympic gods, being all and each of them affrighted at
the sight of such achievements, said, Pantagruel hath shapen
work enough for us, and put us more to a plunge, and nearer
our wit's end, by this sole herb of his, than did of old the Aloidæ
by overturning mountains. He very speedily is to be married,
and shall have many children by his wife. It lies not in our
power to oppose this destiny; for it hath passed through the
hands and spindles of the Fatal Sisters, necessity's inexorable
daughters. Who knows but by his sons may be found out an
herb of such another virtue and prodigious energy, as that by
the aid thereof in using it aright according to their father's
skill, they may contrive a way for human kind to pierce into
the high aërian clouds, get up unto the spring-head of the hail,
take an inspection of the snowy sources, and shut and open as
they please the sluices from whence proceed the floodgates of
the rain; then prosecuting their etherial voyage, they may step
in unto the lightning workhouse and shop, where all the thunderbolts are forged, where, seizing on the magazine of heaven, and
storehouse of our warlike fire munition, they may discharge a
bouncing peal or two of thundering ordnance, for joy of their
arrival to these new supernal places; and, charging those
tonitrual guns afresh, turn the whole force of that artillery
wherein we most confided against ourselves. Then is it like,
they will set forward to invade the territories of the moon,
whence, passing through both Mercury and Venus, the Sun will
serve them for a torch, to show the way from Mars to Jupiter
and Saturn. We shall not then be able to resist the impetuosity
of their intrusion, nor put a stoppage to their entering in at all,
whatever regions, domiciles, or mansions of the spangled firmament they shall have any mind to see, to stay in, or to travel
through for their recreation. All the celestial signs together,
with the constellations of the fixed stars, will jointly be at their
devotion then. Some will take up their lodging at the Ram,
some at the Bull, and others at the Twins; some at the Crab,
some at the Lion Inn, and others at the sign of the Virgin;
some at the Balance, others at the Scorpion, and others will be
quartered at the Archer; some will be harboured at the Goat,
some at the Water-pourer's sign, some at the Fishes: some will

lie at the Crown, some at the Harp, some at the Golden Eagle
and the Dolphin; some at the Flying Horse, some at the Ship,
some at the great, some at the little Bear, and so throughout
the glistening hostelries of the whole twinkling asteristic welkin.
There will be sojourners come from the earth, who, longing after
the taste of the sweet cream, of their own skimming off, from
the best milk of all the dairy of the Galaxy, will set themselves
at table down with us, drink of our nectar and ambrosia, and
take to their own beds at night for wives and concubines, our
fairest goddesses, the only means whereby they can be deified.
A junto hereupon being convocated, the better to consult upon
the manner of obviating so dreadful a danger, Jove, sitting in
his presidential throne, asked the votes of all the other gods,
which, after a profound deliberation amongst themselves on
all contingencies, they freely gave at last, and then resolved
unanimously to withstand the shocks of all whatsoever sublunary assaults.

CHAPTER LII

*How a certain kind of Pantagruelion is of that nature that the
fire is not able to consume it*

I HAVE already related to you great and admirable things; but,
if you might be induced to adventure upon the hazard of believing some other divinity of this sacred Pantagruelion, I very
willingly would tell it you.   Believe it, if you will, or, otherwise,
believe it not, I care not which of them you do, they are both
alike to me.   It shall be sufficient for my purpose to have told
you the truth, and the truth I will tell you.   But to enter in
thereat, because it is of a knaggy, difficult, and rugged access,
this is the question which I ask of you.   If I had put within
this bottle two pints, the one of wine, and the other of water,
thoroughly and exactly mingled together, how would you unmix
them?   After what manner would you go about to sever them,
and separate the one liquor from the other, in such sort, that
you render me the water apart, free from the wine, and the
wine also pure, without the intermixture of one drop of water,
and both of them in the same measure, quantity, and taste,
that I had embottled them?   Or, to state the question otherwise.   If your carmen and mariners, entrusted for the provision of your houses with the bringing of a certain considerable

number of tuns, puncheons, pipes, barrels, and hogsheads of
Graves wine, or of the wine of Orleans, Beaune, and Mirevaux,
should drink out the half, and afterwards with water fill up the
other empty halves of the vessels as full as before; as the
Limosins use to do, in their carriages by wains and carts, of the
wines of Argenton and Sangaultier, after that, how would you
part the water from the wine, and purify them both in such a
case? I understand you well enough. Your meaning is, that
I must do it with an ivy funnel. That is written, it is true, and
the verity thereof explored by a thousand experiments; you have
learned to do this feat before, I see it. But those that have
never known it, nor at any time have seen the like, would hardly
believe that it were possible. Let us nevertheless proceed.

But put the case, we were now living in the age of Sylla,
Marius Cæsar, and other such Roman emperors, or that we
were in the time of our ancient Druids, whose custom was to
burn and calcine the dead bodies of their parents and lords,
and that you had a mind to drink the ashes or cinders of your
wives or fathers, in the infused liquor of some good white-
wine, as Artemisia drunk the dust and ashes of her husband
Mausolus; or, otherwise, that you did determine to have them
reserved in some fine urn, or reliquary pot; how would you save
the ashes apart, and separate them from those other cinders
and ashes into which the fuel of the funeral and bustuary fire
hath been converted? Answer, if you can. By my figgings,
I believe it will trouble you so to do.

Well, I will dispatch, and tell you, that, if you take of this
celestial Pantagruelion so much as is needful to cover the body
of the defunct, and after that you shall have enwrapped and
bound therein, as hard and closely as you can, the corps of
the said deceased person, and sewed up the folding-sheet,
with thread of the same stuff, throw it into the fire, how great
or ardent soever it be, it matters not a straw, the fire through
this Pantagruelion will burn the body and reduce to ashes the
bones thereof, and the Pantagruelion shall be not only not consumed nor burnt, but also shall neither lose one atom of the
ashes enclosed within it, nor receive one atom of the huge
bustuary heap of ashes resulting from the blazing conflagration
of things combustible laid round about it, but shall at last,
when taken out of the fire, be fairer, whiter, and much cleaner
than when you did put it in first. Therefore it is called Asbeston,
which is as much as to say incombustible. Great plenty is to
be found thereof in Caprasia, as likewise in the climate Dia

Cyenes, at very easy rates. O how rare and admirable a thing it is, that the fire, which devoureth, consumeth, and destroyeth all such things else, should cleanse, purge, and whiten this sole Pantagruelion Carpasian Asbeston! If you mistrust the verity of this relation, and demand for further confirmation of my assertion a visible sign, as the Jews, and such incredulous infidels use to do, take a fresh egg, and orbicularly, or rather, ovally, enfold it within this divine Pantagruelion. When it is so wrapped up, put it in the hot embers of a fire, how great or ardent soever it be, and, having left it there as long as you will, you shall at last, at your taking it out of the fire, find the egg roasted hard, and as it were burnt, without any alteration, change, mutation, or so much as a calefaction of the sacred Pantagruelion. For less than a million of pounds sterling, modified, taken down and amoderated to the twelfth part of one four pence half-penny farthing, you are to put it to a trial, and make proof thereof.

Do not think to overmatch me here, by paragoning with it in the way of a more eminent comparison the Salamander. That is a fib; for, albeit a little ordinary fire, such as is used in dining-rooms and chambers, gladden, cheer up, exhilarate and quicken it, yet may I warrantably enough assure, that in the flaming fire of a furnace it will, like any other animated creature, be quickly suffocated, choked, consumed, and destroyed. We have seen experiment thereof, and Galen many ages ago hath clearly demonstrated and confirmed it, lib. 3. *De Temperamentis*. and Dioscorides maintaineth the same doctrine, lib. 2. Do not here instance, in competition with this sacred herb, the feather alum, or the wooden tower of Piræus, which Lucius Sylla was never able to get burnt; for that Archelaus, governor of the town for Mithridates King of Pontus, had plastered it all over on the outside with the said allum. Nor would I have you to compare therewith the herb, which Alexander Cornelius called Eonem, and said, that it had some resemblance with that oak which bears the mistletoe, and that it could neither be consumed, nor receive any manner of prejudice by fire, nor by water, no more than the mistletoe, of which was built, said he, the so renowned ship Argos. Search where you please for those that will believe it. I in that point desire to be excused. Neither would I wish you to parallel therewith,—although I cannot deny, but that it is of a very marvellous nature,—that sort of tree which groweth along the mountains of Briançon and Ambrun, which produceth out of its root the good Agaric.

From its body it yieldeth unto us a so excellent rosin, that
Galen hath been bold to equal it unto the turpentine. Upon
the delicate leaves thereof it retaineth for our use that sweet
heavenly honey, which is called the manna; and, although it
be of a gummy, oily, fat and greasy substance, it is notwithstanding unconsumable by any fire. It is in the Greek and
Latin called Larix. The Alpinese name is Melze. The Anter-
norides and Venetians term it Larége; which gave occasion to
that castle in Piedmont to receive the denomination of Larignum,
by putting Julius Cæsar to a stand at his return from amongst
the Gauls.

Julius Cæsar commanded all the yeomen, boors, hinds, and
other inhabitants in, near unto, and about the Alps and Piedmont
to bring all manner of victuals and provision for an army to
those places, which on the military road he had appointed to
receive them for the use of his marching soldiery. To which
ordinance all of them were obedient, save only those as were
within the garrison of Larignum, who, trusting in the natural
strength of the place, would not pay their contribution. The
emperor, purposing to chastise them for their refusal, caused
his whole army to march straight towards that castle, before
the gate whereof was erected a tower built of huge big spars
and rafters of the larch tree, fast bound together with pins and
pegs of the same wood, and interchangeably laid on one another,
after the fashion of a pile or stack of timber, set up in the fabric
thereof to such an apt and convenient height that from the
parapet above the portcullis they thought with stones and
levers to beat off and drive away such as should approach
thereto.

When Cæsar had understood, that the chief defence of those
within the castle did consist in stones and clubs, and that it
was not an easy matter to sling, hurl, dart, throw, or cast them
so far as to hinder the approaches, he forthwith commanded
his men to throw great store of bavins, faggots, and fascines
round about the castle; and, when they had made the heap of
a competent height, to put them all in a fair fire, which was
thereupon incontinently done. The fire put amidst the faggots
was so great and so high, that it covered the whole castle, that
they might well imagine the tower would thereby be altogether
burnt to dust and demolished. Nevertheless, contrary to all
their hopes and expectations, when the flame ceased, and that
the faggots were quite burnt and consumed, the tower appeared
as whole, sound, and entire as ever. Cæsar, after a serious

consideration had thereof, commanded a compass to be taken without the distance of a stone's cast from the castle round about it; there, with ditches and entrenchments to form a blockade; which when the Larignans understood, they rendered themselves upon terms. And then, by a relation from them, it was, that Cæsar learned the admirable nature and virtue of this wood, which of itself produceth neither fire, flame, nor coal, and would, therefore, in regard of that rare quality of incombustibility, have been admitted into this rank and degree of a true Pantagruelion plant; and that so much the rather, for that Pantagruel directed that all the gates, doors, angiports, windows, gutters, frettized, and embowed ceilings, cans, and other whatsoever wooden furniture in the abbey of Theleme, should be all materiated of this kind of timber. He likewise caused to cover therewith the sterns, stems, cook-rooms or laps, hatchets, decks, courses, bends and walls of his carricks, ships, galleons, galleys, brigantines, foysts, frigates, crears, barks, floyts, pinks, pinnaces, hoys, catches, capers, and other vessels of his Thalassian arsenal; were it not that the wood or timber of the larch-tree being put within a large and ample furnace, full of huge vehemently flaming fire proceeding from the fuel of other sorts and kinds of wood, cometh at last to be corrupted, consumed, dissipated, and destroyed, as are stones in a lime-kiln. But this Pantagruelion Asbeston is rather by the fire renewed and cleansed, than by the flames thereof consumed or changed. Therefore,

> Arabians, Indians, Sabæans,
> Sing not, in hymns and Io Pæans,
> Your incense, myrrh, or ebony.
> Come here, a nobler plant to see,
> And carry home, at any rate,
> Some seed, that you may propagate.
> If in your soil it takes, to heaven
> A thousand thousand thanks be given;
> And say, with France it goodly goes,
> Where the Pantagruelion grows.

Sir Thomas Urquhart's part of the translation ends here, and that of Motteux begins.

BOOK IV

TREATING OF THE HEROIC DEEDS AND SAYINGS OF THE GOOD
PANTAGRUEL

THE AUTHOR'S EPISTLE DEDICATORY

TO THE MOST ILLUSTRIOUS PRINCE, AND MOST REVEREND LORD
ODET, CARDINAL DE CHASTILLON

You are not unacquainted, most illustrious prince, how often I have been, and am daily pressed and required by great numbers of eminent persons, to proceed in the Pantagruelian fables: they tell me that many languishing, sick and disconsolate persons, perusing them, have deceived their grief, passed their time merrily, and been inspired with new joy and comfort. I commonly answer, that I aimed not at glory and applause, when I diverted myself with writing; but only designed to give by my pen, to the absent who labour under affliction, that little help which at all times I willingly strive to give to the present that stand in need of my art and service. Sometimes I at large relate to them, how Hippocrates in several places, and particularly in *lib*. 6. *Epidem.*, describing the institution of the physician his disciple, and also Soranus of Ephesus, Oribasius, Galen, Hali Abbas, and other authors, have descended to particulars, in the prescription of his motions, deportment, looks, countenance, gracefulness, civility, cleanliness of face, clothes, beard, hair, hands, mouth, even his very nails; as if he were to play the part of a lover in some comedy, or enter the lists to fight some potent enemy. And indeed the practice of physic is properly enough compared by Hippocrates to a fight, and also to a farce acted between three persons, the patient, the physician, and the disease. Which passage has sometimes put me in mind of Julia's saying to Augustus her father.[1] One day she came before him in a very gorgeous, loose, lascivious dress, which very much displeased him, though he did not much discover his discontent. The next day she put on another, and in a modest garb, such as the chaste Roman ladies wore, came into his presence. The kind father could not then forbear expressing the pleasure which he took to see her so much altered, and said to her: Oh! how much more this garb becomes, and is commendable in the daughter of Augustus. But she, having her excuse ready, answered: This day, sir, I dressed myself to

---

[1] See Macrobius, l. 9, c. 5, of his *Saturnalia*.

please my father's eye; yesterday, to gratify that of my husband. Thus disguised in looks and garb, nay even, as formerly was the fashion, with a rich and pleasant gown with four sleeves, which was called *philonium* according to Petrus Alexandrinus in 6. *Epidem.*, a physician might answer to such as might find the metamorphosis indecent: Thus have I accoutred myself, not that I am proud of appearing in such a dress; but for the sake of my patient, whom alone I wholly design to please, and no ways offend or dissatisfy. There is also a passage in our father Hippocrates, in the book I have named, which causes some to sweat, dispute, and labour: not indeed to know whether the physician's frowning, discontented, and morose Catonian look render the patient sad, and his joyful, serene, and pleasing countenance rejoice him; for experience teaches us that this is most certain; but whether such sensations of grief, or pleasure, are produced by the apprehension of the patient observing his motions and qualities in his physician and drawing from thence conjectures of the end and catastrophe of his disease; as, by his pleasing look, joyful and desirable events, and by his sorrowful and unpleasing air, sad and dismal consequences; and whether those sensations be produced by a transfusion of the serene or gloomy, aerial or terrestrial, joyful or melancholic spirits of the physician, into the person of the patient, as is the opinion of Plato and Averroes.

Above all things, the fore-cited authors have given particular directions to physicians about the words, discourse, and con-verse, which they ought to have with their patients; every one aiming at one point, that is, to rejoice them without offending God, and in no ways whatsoever to vex or displease them. Which causes Herophilus much to blame the physician Callianax, who, being asked by a patient of his, Shall I die? impudently made him this answer:

> Patroclus died, whom all allow,
> By much a better man than you.

Another, who had a mind to know the state of his distemper, asking him, after our merry Patelin's way; Well, doctor, does not my water tell you I shall die? He foolishly answered, No; if Latona, the mother of those lovely twins, Phœbus and Diana, begot thee. Galen, *lib.* 4, *Comment.* 6. *Epidem.*, blames much also Quintus his tutor, who, a certain nobleman of Rome, his patient, saying to him, You have been at breakfast, my master, your breath smells of wine; answered arrogantly, Yours smells of fever: which is the better smell of the two, wine or a putrid fever? But the calumny of certain cannibals, misanthropes, perpetual eavesdroppers, has been so foul and excessive against me, that it had conquered my patience, and I had resolved not to write one jot more. For the least of their detractions were, that my books are all stuffed with various heresies, of which, nevertheless, they could not show one single instance: much, indeed, of comical and facetious fooleries, neither offending God nor the king; (and truly I own they are the only subject, and only theme of these books) but of heresy, not a word, unless they interpreted wrong, and against all use of reason, and common language, what I had rather suffer a thousand deaths, if it were possible than have thought: as you should make bread to be stone, a fish to be a serpent, and an egg to be a scorpion. This, my lord, emboldened me once to tell you, as I was complaining of it in your presence, that if I did not esteem myself a better Christian, than they show themselves towards me, and if my life, writings, words, nay thoughts, betrayed to me one single spark of heresy, or I should in a detestable manner fall into the snares of the spirit of detraction, Διάβολος, who, by their means, raises such crimes against me; I would then, like the phœnix, gather dry wood, kindle a fire, and burn myself in the midst of it. You were then pleased to say to me, that King Francis, of eternal memory, had been made sensible of those false accusations; and that having caused my books (mine, I say, because several, false and infamous, have been wickedly laid to me) to be carefully and distinctly read to him by the most learned and faithful anagnost in this kingdom, he had not found any passage suspicious; and that he abhorred a certain envious, ignorant, hypocritical informer, who grounded a mortal heresy on an *n* put instead of an *m* by the carelessness of the printers.

As much was done by his son, our most gracious, virtuous, and blessed sovereign, Henry, whom Heaven long preserve: so that he granted you his royal privilege, and particular protection for me, against my slandering adversaries.

You kindly condescended since, to confirm me these happy news at Paris; and also lately, when you visited my Lord Cardinal du Bellay, who, for the benefit of his health, after a lingering distemper, was retired to St. Maur, that place (or rather paradise) of salubrity, serenity, conveniency, and all desirable country pleasures.

Thus, my lord, under so glorious a patronage, I am emboldened once more to draw my pen, undaunted now and secure; with hopes that you will still prove to me, against the power of detraction, a second Gallic Hercules in learning, prudence, and eloquence; an Alexicacos in virtue, power, and authority: you, of whom I may truly say what the wise monarch Solomon saith of Moses, that great prophet and captain of Israel, *Ecclesiast*. 45. A man fearing and loving God, who found favour in the sight of all flesh, well-beloved both of God and man; whose memorial is blessed. God made him like to the glorious saints, and magnified him so, that his enemies stood in fear of him; and for him made wonders; made him glorious in the sight of kings, gave him a commandment for his people, and by him showed his light: he sanctified him in his faithfulness, and meekness, and chose him out of all men. By him he made us to hear his voice, and caused by him the law of life and knowledge to be given.

Accordingly, if I shall be so happy as to hear any one commend those merry composures, they shall be adjured by me to be obliged, and pay their thanks to you alone, as also to offer their prayers to Heaven, for the continuance and increase of your greatness; and to attribute no more to me, than my humble and ready obedience to your commands; for by your most honourable encouragement, you at once have inspired me with spirit, and with invention; and without you my heart had failed me, and the fountain-head of my animal spirits had been dry. May the Lord keep you in his blessed mercy.

My Lord,

Your Most Humble, and Most Devoted Servant,

FRANCIS RABELAIS, *Physician.*

Paris, this 28th of January, MDLII.

THE AUTHOR'S PROLOGUE

GOOD people. God save and keep you! Where are you? I can't see you: stay—I'll saddle my nose with spectacles—oh, oh! it will be fair anon, I see you. Well, you have had a good vintage, they say: this is no bad news to Frank, you may swear. You have got an infallible cure against thirst: rarely performed of you, my friends! You, your wives, children, friends, and families are in as good case as hearts can wish; it is well, it is as I would have it: God be praised for it, and if such be his will, may you long be so. For my part, I am thereabouts, thanks to his blessed goodness; and by the means of a little Pantagruelism, (which you know is a certain jollity of mind, pickled in the scorn of fortune,) you see me now hale and cheery, as sound as a bell, and ready to drink, if you will. Would you know why I'm thus, good people? I will even give you a positive answer—Such is the Lord's will, which I obey and revere; it being said in his word, in great derision to the physician neglectful of his own health, Physician, heal thyself.

Galen had some knowledge of the Bible, and had conversed with the Christians of his time, as appears *lib.* 11. *De Usu Partium: lib.* 2. *De Differentiis Pulsuum, cap.* 3, and *ibid. lib.* 3. *cap.* 2. *and lib. De Rerum Affectibus* (if it be Galen's). Yet it was not for any such veneration of holy writ that he took care of his own health. No, it was for fear of being twitted with the saying so well known among physicians.

> Ἰατρὸς ἄλλων αὐτὸς ἕλκεσι βρύων.
>
> He boasts of healing poor and rich,
> Yet is himself all over itch.

This made him boldly say, that he did not desire to be esteemed a physician, if from his twenty-eighth year to his old age he had not lived in perfect health, except some ephemerous fevers, of which he soon rid himself: yet he was not naturally of the soundest temper, his stomach being evidently bad. Indeed, as, he saith, *lib.* 5, *De Sanitate tuenda*, that physician will hardly be thought very careful of the health of others, who neglects his own. Asclepiades boasted yet more than this; for he said that he had articled with fortune not to be reputed a physician, if he could be said to have been sick, since he began to practise physic, to his latter age, which he reached, lusty in all his members, and victorious over fortune; till at last the old gentlemen unluckily tumbled down from the top of a certain ill-propt and rotten staircase, and so there was an end of him.

If by some disaster health is fled from your worships to the right or to the left, above or below, before or behind, within or without, far or near, on this side or the other side, wheresoever it be, may you presently, with the help of the Lord, meet with it. Having found it, may you immediately claim it, seize it, and secure it. The law allows it: the king would have it so: nay, you have my advice for it. Neither more not less than the law makers of old did fully impower a master to claim and seize his runaway servant, wherever he might be found. Odsbodikins, is it not written and warranted by the ancient customs of this so noble, so rich, so flourishing realm of France, that the dead seizes the quick? See what has been declared very lately in that point by that learned, wise, courteous, humane and just civilian, Andrew Tiraqueau, counsellor of the great victorious, and triumphant Henry II, in the most honourable court of Parliament at Paris. Health is our life, as Ariphron the Sicyonian wisely has it; without health life is not life, it is not living life: ᾽ΑΒΙ᾽ΟΣ ΒΙ᾽ΟΣ, ΒΙ᾽ΟΣ ᾽ΑΒΙ᾽ΩΤΟΣ. Without health life is only a languishment, and an image of death. Therefore, you that want your health, that is to say, that are dead, seize the quick; secure life to yourselves, that is to say, health.

I have this hope in the Lord, that he will hear our supplications, considering with what faith and zeal we pray, and that he will grant this our wish, because it is moderate and mean. Mediocrity was held by the ancient sages to be golden, that is to say precious, praised by all men, and pleasing in all places. Read the sacred Bible, you will find, the prayers of those who asked moderately were never unanswered. For example, little dapper Zaccheus, whose body and reliques the monks of St. Garlick, near Orleans, boast of having, and nicknamed him St. Sylvanus, he only wished to see our blessed Saviour near Jerusalem. It was but a small request and no more than anybody then might pretend to. But alas! he was but low-built; and one of so diminutive a size, among the crowd, could not so much as get a glimpse of him. Well then he struts, stands on tip-toes, bustles, and bestirs his stumps, shoves and makes way, and with much ado clambers up a sycamore

Upon this, the Lord, who knew his sincere affection, presented himself to his sight, and was not only seen by him, but heard also; nay, what is more, he came to his house, and blessed his family.

One of the sons of the prophets in Israel felling wood near the river Jordan, his hatchet forsook the helve, and fell to the bottom of the river: so he prayed to have it again, (it was but a small request, mark ye me,) and having a strong faith, he did not throw the hatchet after the helve, as some spirits of contradiction say by way of scandalous blunder, but the helve after the hatchet, as you all properly have it. Presently two great miracles were seen: up springs the hatchet from the bottom of the water, and fixes itself to its old acquaintance the helve. Now had he wished to coach it to heaven in a fiery chariot like Elias, to multiply in seed like Abraham, be as rich as Job, strong as Sampson, and beautiful as Absalom, would he have obtained it, do ye think? In troth, my friends, I question it very much.

Now I talk of moderate wishes in point of hatchet, (but harkee me, be sure you do not forget when we ought to drink,) I will tell you what is written among the apologues of wise Æsop the Frenchman. I mean the Phrygian and Trojan, as Max. Planudes makes him; from which people, according to the most faithful chronicles, the noble French are descended. Ælian writes that he was of Thrace; and Agathias, after Herodotus, that he was of Samos; it is all one to Frank.

In his time lived a poor honest country fellow of Gravot, Tom Wellhung by name, a wood-cleaver by trade, who in that low drudgery made shift so to pick up a sorry livelihood. It happened that he lost his hatchet. Now tell me who ever had more cause to be vexed than poor Tom? Alas, his whole estate and life depended on his hatchet; by his hatchet he earned many a fair penny of the best wood-mongers or log-merchants, among whom he went a jobbing; for want of his hatchet he was like to starve; and had death but met with him six days after without a hatchet, the grim fiend would have mowed him down in the twinkling of a bed-staff. In this sad case he began to be in a heavy taking, and called upon Jupiter with the most eloquent prayers—for you know necessity was the mother of eloquence. With the whites of his eyes turned up towards heaven, down on his marrow-bones, his arms reared high, his fingers stretched wide, and his head bare, the poor wretch without ceasing was roaring out, by way of litany, at every repetition of his supplications, My hatchet, lord Jupiter, my hatchet! my hatchet! only my hatchet, O Jupiter, or money to buy another, and nothing else! alas, my poor hatchet!

Jupiter happened then to be holding a grand council, about certain urgent affairs, and old gammer Cybele was just giving her opinion, or, if you would rather have it so, it was young Phœbus the beau; but, in short, Tom's outcries and lamentations were so loud, that they were heard with no small amazement at the council-board, by the whole consistory of the gods. What a devil have we below, quoth Jupiter, that howls so horridly? By the mud of Styx, have not we had all along, and have not we here still enough to do, to set to rights a world of damned puzzling businesses of consequence? We made an end of the fray between Presthan, King of Persia, and Soliman the Turkish Emperor; we have stopped up the passages between the Tartars and the Muscovites; answered the Xeriff's petition; done the same to that of Golgots Rays; the state of Parma's dispatched; so is that of Maydenburg, that of Mirandola, and that of Africa, that town on the Mediterranean which we call Aphrodisium; Tripoli by carelessness has got a new master; her hour was come.

Here are the Gascons cursing and damning, demanding the restitution of their bells.

In yonder corner are the Saxons, Easterlings, Ostrogoths, and Germans, nations formerly invincible, but now aberkeids, bridled, curbed, and brought under by a paltry diminutive crippled fellow: they ask us revenge, relief, restitution of their former good sense, and ancient liberty.

But what shall we do with this same Ramus and this Galland, with a pox to them, who, surrounded with a swarm of their scullions, blackguard ragamuffins, sizers, vouchers, and stipulators, set together by the ears the whole university of Paris? I am in a sad quandary about it, and for the heart's blood of me cannot tell yet with whom of the two to side.

Both seem to me notable fellows, and as true cods as ever pissed. The one has rose-nobles, I say fine and weighty ones; the other would gladly have some too. The one knows something; the other is no dunce. The one loves the better sort of men; the other is beloved by them. The one is an old cunning fox; the other with tongue and pen, tooth and nail, falls foul of the ancient orators and philosophers, and barks at them like a cur.

What thinkest thou of it, say, thou bawdy Priapus? I

have found thy council just before now, *et habet tua mentula mentem*.

King Jupiter, answered Priapus, standing up and taking off his cowl, his snout uncased and reared up, fiercely and stiffly propt, since you compare the one to a yelping snarling cur, and the other to sly Reynard the fox, my advice is, with submission, that without fretting or puzzling your brains any further about them, without any more ado, even serve them both as, in the days of yore, you did the dog and the fox. How? asked Jupiter; when? who were they? where was it? You have a rare memory, for aught I see, returned Priapus! This right worshipful father Bacchus, whom we have here nodding with his crimson phiz, to be revenged on the Thebans, had got a fairy fox, who whatever mischief he did, was never to be caught or wronged by any beast that wore a head.

The noble Vulcan here present had framed a dog of Monesian brass, and with long puffing and blowing, put the spirit of life into him: he gave it to you, you gave it your Miss Europa, Miss Europa gave it Minos, Minos gave it Procris, Procris gave it Cephalus. He was also of the fairy kind; so that, like the lawyers of our age, he was too hard for all other sorts of creatures; nothing could escape the dog. Now who should happen to meet but these two? What do you think they did? Dog by his destiny was to take fox, and fox by his fate was not to be taken.

The case was brought before your council: you protested that you would not act against the fates; and the fates were contradictory. In short, the end and result of the matter was, that to reconcile two contradictions was an impossibility in nature. The very pang put you into a sweat; some drops of which happening to light on the earth, produceth what the mortals call cabbage. All our noble consistory, for want of a categorical resolution, were seized with such a horrid thirst, that above seventy-eight hogsheads of nectar were swilled down at that sitting. At last you took my advice, and transmogrified them into stones; and immediately got rid of your perplexity, and a truce with thirst was proclaimed through this vast Olympus. This was the year of flabby cods, near Teumessus, between Thebes and Chalcis.

After this manner, it is my opinion, that you should petrify this dog and this fox. The metamorphosis will not be incongruous: for they both bear the name of Peter. And because, according to the Limosin proverb, to make an oven's mouth

there must be three stones, you may associate them with master
Peter du Coignet, whom you formerly petrified for the same
cause. Then those three dead pieces shall be put in an equilateral
trigone, somewhere in the great temple at Paris; in the middle
of the porch, if you will; there to perform the office of extin-
guishers, and with their noses put out the lighted candles,
torches, tapers, and flambeaux; since, while they lived, they
still lighted, ballock-like, the fire of faction, division, ballock
sects, and wrangling among those idle bearded boys, the students.
And this will be an everlasting monument to show, that those
puny self-conceited pedants, ballock-framers, were rather con-
temned than condemned by you. Dixi, I have said my say.

You deal too kindly by them, said Jupiter, for aught I see,
Monsieur Priapus. You do not use to be so kind to every
body, let me tell you; for as they seek to eternize their names,
it would be much better for them to be thus changed into hard
stones, than to return to earth and putrefaction. But now to
others matter. Yonder behind us, towards the Tuscan sea,
and the neighbourhood of Mount Apennine, do you see what
tragedies are stirred up by certain topping ecclesiastical bullies?
This hot fit will last its time, like the Limosins' ovens, and then
will be cooled, but not so fast.

We shall have sport enough with it; but I foresee one inconveniency: for methinks we have but little store of thunder
ammunition, since the time that you, my fellow gods, for your
pastime, lavished them away to bombard new Antioch, by my
particular permission; as since, after your example, the stout
champions, who had undertaken to hold the fortress of Din-
denarois against all comers, fairly wasted their powder with
shooting at sparrows; and then, not having wherewith to
defend themselves in time of need, valiantly surrendered to the
enemy, who were already packing up their awls, full of madness
and despair, and thought on nothing but a shameful retreat.
Take care this be remedied, son Vulcan: rouse up your drowsy
Cyclopes, Asteropes, Brontes, Arges, Polyphemus, Steropes,
Pyracmon, and so forth; set them at work, and make them
drink as they ought.

Never spare liquor to such as are at hot work. Now let us
dispatch this bawling fellow below. You Mercury, go see who
it is, and know what he wants. Mercury looked out at heaven's
trap-door, through which as I am told, they hear what is said
here below. By the way, one might well enough mistake it
for the scuttle of a ship; though Icaromenippus said it was like

the mouth of a well. The light-heeled deity saw that it was
honest Tom, who asked for his lost hatchet; and accordingly
he made his report to the synod. Marry, said Jupiter, we are
finely helped up, as if we had now nothing else to do here but
to restore lost hatchets. Well, he must have it then for all
this, for so it is written in the book of fate, (do you hear?)
as well as if it was worth the whole duchy of Milan. The truth
is, the fellow's hatchet is as much to him as a kingdom to a
king. Come, come, let no more words be scattered about it,
let him have his hatchet again.

Now, let us make an end of the difference betwixt the levites
and mole-catchers of Landerousse. Whereabouts were we?
Priapus was standing in the chimney-corner, and having heard
what Mercury had reported, said in a most courteous and jovial
manner: King Jupiter, while by your order and particular
favour, I was garden-keeper-general on earth, I observed that
this word hatchet is equivocal to many things: for it signifies
a certain instrument, by the means of which men fell and cleave
timber. It also signifies (at least I am sure it did formerly) a
female soundly and frequently thumpthumpriggletickletwiddle-
tobyed. Thus I perceived that every cock of the game used
to call his doxy his hatchet; for with that same tool (this he
said lugging out and exhibiting his nine-inch knocker) they so
strongly and resolutely shove and drive in their helves, that the
females remain free from a fear epidemical amongst their sex,
viz., that from the bottom of the male's belly the instrument
should dangle at his heel for want of such feminine props.
And I remember, for I have a member, and a memory too, ay,
and a fine memory, large enough to fill a butter-firkin:) I
remember, I say, that one day of tubilustre [horn-fair] at the
festivals of good-man Vulcan in May, I heard Josquin Des
Prez, Olkegan, Hobrethe, Agricola, Brumel, Camelin, Vigoris,
de la Fage, Bruyer, Prioris, Seguin, de la Rue, Midy, Moulu,
Mouton, Gascogne, Loyset, Compere, Penet, Fevin, Rousée,
Richard Fort, Rousseau, Consilion, Constantio Festi, Jacquet
Bercan, melodiously singing the following catch on a pleasant
green.

> Long John to bed went to his bride,
> And laid a mallet by his side:
> What means this mallet, John, saith she?
> Why! it is to wedge thee home, quoth he.
> Alas! cried she, the man's a fool:
> What need you use a wooden tool?
> When lusty John does to me come,
> He never shoves but with his bum.

Nine Olympiads, and an intercalary year after (I have a rare member, I would say memory; but I often make blunders in the symbolization and colligance of those two words) I heard Adrian Villart, Gombert, Janequin, Arcadet, Claudin, Certon, Manchicourt, Auxerre, Villiers, Sandrin, Sohier, Hesdin, Morales Passereau, Maille, Maillart, Jacotin, Heurteur, Vardelot, Carpentras, l'Heritier, Cadéac, Doublet, Vermont, Bouteiller, Lupi, Pagnier, Millet, du Moulin, Alaire, Maraut, Morpain, Gendre, and other merry lovers of music, in a private garden, under some fine shady trees, round about a bulwark of flagons, gammons, pasties, with several coated quails, and laced mutton, waggishly singing:

> Since tools without their hafts are useless lumber,
> And hatchets without helves are of that number;
> That one may go in t'other, and may match it,
> I'll be the helve, and thou shalt be the hatchet.

Now would I know what kind of hatchet this bawling Tom wants? This threw all the venerable gods and goddesses into a fit of laughter, like any microcosm of flies; and even set limping Vulcan a hopping and jumping smoothly three or four times for the sake of his dear. Come, come, said Jupiter to Mercury, run down immediately and cast at the poor fellow's feet three hatchets; his own, another of gold, and a third of massy silver, all of one size: then having left it to his will to take his choice, if he take his own, and be satisfied with it, give him the other two: if he take another, chop his head off with his own: and henceforth serve me all those losers of hatchets after that manner. Having said this, Jupiter, with an awkward turn of his head, like a jackanapes swallowing of pills, made so dreadful a phiz, that all the vast Olympus quaked again. Heaven's foot messenger, thanks to his low-crowned narrow-brimmed hat, his plume of feathers, heel-pieces, and running stick with pigeon wings, flings himself out of heaven's wicket, through the empty deserts of the air, and in a trice nimbly alights on the earth, and throws at friend Tom's feet the three hatchets, saying unto him; Thou hast bawled long enough to be a-dry: thy prayers and request are granted by Jupiter; see which of these three is thy hatchet, and take it away with thee. Wellhung lifts up the golden hatchet, peeps upon it, and finds it very heavy: then staring on Mercury, cries, Codszouks this is none of mine; I will not have it: the same he did with the silver one, and said, it is not this neither, you may even take them again. At last, he takes up his own hatchet, examines the end of the helve, and finds his mark there; then, ravished with joy, like a fox that meets some straggling poultry, and sneering from the tip of his nose, he cried, By the mass, this is my hatchet, master god; if you will leave it me, I will sacrifice to you a very good and huge pot of milk, brim full, covered with fine strawberries, next ides, i.e. the 15th of May.

Honest fellow, said Mercury, I leave it thee; take it; and because thou hast wished and chosen moderately, in point of hatchet, by Jupiter's command, I give thee those two others; thou hast now wherewith to make thyself rich: be honest. Honest Tom gave Mercury a whole cartload of thanks, and revered the most great Jupiter. His old hatchet he fastens close to his leathern girdle, and girds it above his breech like Martin of Cambray: the two others, being more heavy, he lays on his shoulder.   Thus he plods on, trudging over the fields, keeping a good countenance amongst his neighbours and fellow-parishioners, with one merry saying or other after Patelin's way. The next day, having put on a clean white jacket, he takes on his back the two precious hatchets, and comes to Chinon, the famous city, noble city, ancient city, yea the first city in the world, according to the judgment and assertion of the most learned massorets.   At Chinon he turned his silver hatchet into fine testons, crown-pieces, and other white cash; his golden hatchet into fine angels, curious ducats, substantial ridders, spankers, and rose nobles: then with them purchases a good number of farms, barns, houses, out-houses, thatched-houses, stables, meadows, orchards, fields, vineyards, woods, arable lands, pastures, ponds, mills, gardens, nurseries, oxen, cows, sheep, goats, swine, hogs, asses, horses, hens, cocks, capons, chickens, geese, ganders, ducks, drakes, and a world of all other necessaries, and in a short time became the richest man in the country, nay even richer than that limping scrape-good Maulevrier. His brother bumpkins, and the other yeomen and country-puts thereabouts, perceiving his good fortune, were not a little amazed, insomuch that their former pity of Tom was soon changed into an envy of his so great and unex-pected rise; and as they could not for their souls devise how this came about, they made it their business to pry up and down, and lay their heads together, to inquire, seek, and inform themselves by what means, in what place, on what day, what hour, how, why, and wherefore, he had come by his great treasure.

At last, hearing it was by losing his hatchet, Ha, ha! said

they, was there no more to do but to lose a hatchet to make us rich? Mum for that; it is as easy as pissing a bed, and will cost but little. Are then at this time the revolutions of the heavens, the constellations of the firmament and aspects of the planets such, that whosoever shall lose a hatchet, shall immediately grow rich? Ha, ha, ha! by Jove, you shall even be lost, and it please you, my dear hatchet. With this they all fairly lost their hatchets out of hand. The devil of one that had a hatchet left: he was not his mother's son, that did not lose his hatchet. No more was wood felled or cleaved in that country, through want of hatchets. Nay, the Æsopian apologue even saith, that certain petty country gents, of the lower class, who had sold Wellhung their little mill and little field, to have wherewithal to make a figure at the next muster, having been told that his treasure was come to him by this only means, sold the only badge of their gentility, their swords, to purchase hatchets to go lose them, as the silly clodpates did, in hopes to gain store of chink by that loss.

You would have truly sworn they had been a parcel of your petty spiritual usurers, Rome-bound, selling their all, and borrowing of others to buy store of mandates, a pennyworth of a new-made pope.

Now they cried out and brayed, and prayed and bawled, and invoked Jupiter: My hatchet! my hatchet! Jupiter, my hatchet! on this side, my hatchet! on that side, my hatchet! ho, ho, ho, ho, Jupiter, my hatchet! The air round about rung again with the cries and howlings of these rascally losers of hatchets.

Mercury was nimble in bringing them hatchets; to each offering that which he had lost, as also another of gold, and a third of silver.

Every he still was for that of gold, giving thanks in abundance to the great giver, Jupiter; but in the very nick of time, that they bowed and stooped to take it from the ground, whip, in a trice, Mercury lopped off their heads, as Jupiter had commanded; and of heads, thus cut off, the number was just equal to that of the lost hatchets.

You see how it is now; you see how it goes with those, who in the simplicity of their hearts wish and desire with moderation. Take warning by this, all you greedy, fresh-water shirks, who scorn to wish for anything under ten thousand pounds: and do not for the future run on impudently, as I have sometimes heard you wishing, Would to God, I had now one hundred seventy-eight millions of gold! Oh! how I should tickle it off.

The deuce on you, what more might a king, an emperor, a pope wish for? For that reason, indeed, you see that after you have made such hopeful wishes, all the good that comes to you of it is the itch or the scab, and not a cross in your breeches to scare the devil that tempts you to make these wishes: no more than those two mumpers, wishers after the custom of Paris; one of whom only wished to have in good old gold as much as hath been spent, bought, and sold in Paris, since its first founda-tions were laid, to this hour; all of it valued at the price, sale, and rate of the dearest year in all that space of time. Do you think the fellow was bashful? Had he eaten sour plums un-peeled? Were his teeth on edge, I pray you? The other wished our lady's church brim-full of steel needles, from the floor to the top of the roof, and to have as many ducats as might be crammed into as many bags as might be sewed with each and every one of these needles, till they were all either broke at the point or eye. This is to wish with a vengeance! What think you of it? What did they get by it, in your opinion? Why at night both my gentlemen had kibed-heels, a tetter in the chin, a church-yard cough in the lungs, a catarrh in the throat, a swingeing boil at the rump, and the devil of one musty crust of a brown george the poor dogs had to scour their grinders with. Wish therefore for mediocrity, and it shall be given unto you, and over and above yet; that is to say, provided you bestir yourself manfully, and do your best in the meantime.

Ay, but say you, God might as soon have given me seventy-eight thousand as the thirteenth part of one half: for he is omnipotent, and a million of gold is no more to him than one farthing. Oh, oh! pray tell me who taught you to talk at this rate of the power and predestination of God, poor silly people? Peace, tush, st, st, st! fall down before his sacred face, and own the nothingness of your nothing.

Upon this, O ye that labour under the affliction of the gout, I ground my hopes; firmly believing, that if it so pleases the divine goodness, you shall obtain health; since you wish and ask for nothing else, at least for the present. Well, stay yet a little longer with half an ounce of patience.

The Genose do not use, like you, to be satisfied with wishing health alone, when after they have all the live-long morning been in a brown study, talked, pondered, ruminated, and resolved in the counting-house, of whom and how they may squeeze the ready, and who by their craft must be hooked in, wheedled, bubbled, sharped, over-reached, and choused; they go to the exchange, and greet one another with a *Sanità et guadagno messer*; health and gain to you, sir. Health alone will not go down with the greedy curmudgeons: they over and above must wish for gain, with a pox to them; ay, and for the fine crowns, or *scudi di Guadaigne*: whence, heaven be praised, it happens many a time, that the silly wishers and woulders are baulked, and get neither.

Now, my lads, as you hope for good health, cough once aloud with lungs of leather; take me off three swingeing bumpers; prick up your ears; and you shall hear me tell wonders of the noble and good Pantagruel.

CHAPTER I

How Pantagruel went to sea to visit the oracle of Bacbuc, alias the Holy Bottle

In the month of June on Vesta's Holiday, the very numerical day on which Brutus, conquering Spain, taught its strutting dons to truckle under him, and that niggardly miser Crassus was routed and knocked on the head by the Parthians, Pantagruel took his leave of the good Gargantua, his royal father. The old gentleman, according to the laudable custom of the primitive Christians, devoutly prayed for the happy voyage of his son and his whole company, and then they took shipping at the port of Thalassa. Pantagruel had with him Panurge, Friar John des Entomeures, alias of the funnels, Epistemon, Gymnast, Eusthenes, Rhizotomus, Carpalim, *cum multis aliis*, his ancient servants and domestics: also Xenomanes, the great traveller, who had crossed so many dangerous roads, dikes, ponds, seas, and so forth, and was come some time before, having been sent for by Panurge.

For certain good causes and considerations him thereunto moving, he had left with Gargantua, and marked out, in his great and universal hydrographical chart, the course which they were to steer to visit the Oracle of the Holy Bottle Bacbuc. The number of ships were such as I described in the third book, convoyed by a like number of triremes, men of war, galleons, and feluccas, well-rigged, caulked, and stored with a good quantity of Pantagruelion.

All the officers, dragomen, (interpreters,) pilots, captains, mates, boatswains, midshipmen, quartermasters, and sailors, met in the *Thalamege*, Pantagruel's principle flag-ship, which had in her stern, for her ensign, a huge large bottle, half silver, well polished, the other half gold, enamelled with carnation; whereby it was easy to guess that white and red were the colours of the noble travellers, and that they went for the word of the Bottle.

On the stern of the second was a lantern, like those of the ancients, industriously made with diaphanous stone, implying that they were to pass by Lanternland. The third ship had for her device a fine deep China ewer. The fourth, a double-handed jar of gold, much like an ancient urn. The fifth, a famous can made of sperm of emerald. The sixth, a monk's mumping bottle made of the four metals together. The seventh, an ebony funnel, all embossed and wrought with gold after the tauchic manner. The eighth, an ivy goblet, very precious, inlaid with gold. The ninth a cup of fine obriz gold. The tenth, a tumbler of aromatic agoloch (you call it lignum aloes) edged with Cyprian gold, after the Azemine make. The eleventh, a golden vine-tub of mosaic work. The twelfth, a runlet of unpolished gold, covered with a small vine of large Indian pearl of topiarian work. Insomuch that there was not a man, however in the dumps, musty, sourlooked, or melancholic he were, not even excepting that blubbering whiner Heraclitus, had he been there, but seeing this noble convoy of ships and their devices, must have been seized with present gladness of heart, and smiling at the conceit, have said, that the travellers were all honest topers, true-pitcher men; and have judged by a most sure prognostication, that their voyage both outward and homeward-bound, would be performed in mirth and perfect health.

In the *Thalamege*, where was the general meeting, Pantagruel made a short but sweet exhortation, wholly backed with authorities from Scripture upon navigation; which being ended, with an audible voice prayers were said in the presence and hearing of all the burghers of Thalassa, who had flocked to the mole to see them take shipping. After the prayers, was melodiously sung a psalm of the holy King David, which begins, *When Israel went out of Egypt*; and that being ended, tables were placed upon deck, and a feast speedily served up. The Thalassians, who had also borne a chorus in the psalm, caused store of bellytimber and vinegar to be brought out of their houses. All drank to them: they drank to all: which was the cause that none of the whole company gave up what they had eaten, nor were sea-sick, with a pain at the head and stomach; which inconveniency they could not so easily have prevented by drinking, for some time before, salt water, either alone or mixed with wine; using quinces, citron peel, juice of pomegranates, sourish sweet-meats, fasting a long time, covering their stomachs with paper, or following such other idle remedies, as foolish physicians prescribe to those that go to sea.

Having often renewed their tipplings, each mother's son retired on board his own ship, and set sail all so fast with a merry gale at south east; to which point of the compass the chief pilot, James Brayer by name, had shaped his course, and fixed all things accordingly. For seeing that the Oracle of the Holy Bottle lay near Cathay, in the Upper India, his advice, and that of Xenomanes also, was not to steer the course which the Portuguese use, while sailing through the torrid zone, and Cape Bona Speranza, at the south point of Africa, beyond the equinoctial line, and losing sight of the northern pole, their guide, they make a prodigious long voyage; but rather to keep as near the parallel of the said India as possible, and to tack to the westward of the said pole, so that winding under the north, they might find themselves in the latitude of the port of Olone, without coming nearer it for fear of being shut up in the frozen sea; whereas, following this canonical turn, by the said parallel, they must have that on the right to the eastward, which at their departure was on their left.

This proved a much shorter cut; for without shipwreck, danger, or loss of men, with uninterrupted good weather, except one day near the island of the Macreons, they performed in less than four months the voyage of Upper India, which the Portuguese, with a thousand inconveniences and innumerable dangers, can hardly complete in three years. And it is my opinion, with submission to better judgments, that this course was perhaps steered by those Indians who sailed to Germany, and were honourably received by the King of the Swedes, while Quintus Metellus Celer was proconsul of the Gauls; as Cornelius Nepos, Pomponius Mela, and Pliny after them tell us.

CHAPTER II

How Pantagruel bought many rarities in the island of Medamothy

THAT day and the two following they neither discovered land nor anything new; for they had formerly sailed that way: but on the fourth they made an island called Medamothy, of a fine and delightful prospect, by reason of the vast number of light-houses, and high marble towers in its circuit, which is not less than that of Candia. Pantagruel, inquiring who governed there, heard that it was King Philophanes, absent at that time upon account of the marriage of his brother Philotheamon with the infanta of the kingdom of Engys.

Hearing this, he went ashore in the harbour, and while every ship's crew watered, passed his time in viewing divers pictures, pieces of tapestry, animals, fishes, birds, and other exotic and foreign merchandises, which were along the walks of the mole, and in the markets of the port. For it was the third day of the great and famous fair of the place, to which the chief merchants of Africa and Asia resorted. Out of these Friar John bought him two rare pictures; in one of which, the face of a man that brings in an appeal (or that calls out to another) was drawn to the life; and in the other a servant that wants a master, with every needful particular, action, countenance, look, gait, feature, and deportment, being an original, by Master Charles Charmois, principal painter to King Megistus; and he paid for them in the court fashion, with *congé* and grimace. Panurge bought a large picture, copied and done from the needle-work formerly wrought by Philomela, showing to her sister Progne how her brother-in-law Tereus had by force hand-selled her copyhold, and then cut out her tongue, that she might not (as women will) tell tales. I vow and swear by the handle of my paper lantern, that it was a gallant, a mirific, nay, a most admirable piece. Nor do you think, I pray you, that in it was the picture of a man playing the beast with two backs with a female; this had been too silly and gross: no, no; it was another-guise thing, and much plainer. You may, if you please, see it at Theleme, on the left hand, as you go into the high gallery. Epistemon bought another, wherein were painted to the life, the ideas of Plato, and the atoms of Epicurus. Rhizotomus purchased another, wherein Echo was drawn to the life. Pantagruel caused to be bought, by Gymnast, the life and deeds of Achilles, in seventy-eight pieces of tapestry, four fathoms long, and three fathoms broad, all of Phrygian silk, embossed with gold and silver; the work beginning of the nuptials of Peleus and Thetis, continuing to the birth of Achilles: his youth, described by Statius Papinius; his warlike achievements, celebrated by Homer; his death and obsequies, written by Ovid and Quintus Calaber; and ending at the appearance of his ghost, and Polyxena's sacrifice, rehearsed by Euripides.

He also caused to be bought three fine young unicorns; one of them a male of a chesnut colour, and two grey dappled females; also a tarand, whom he bought of a Scythian of the Gelone's country.

A tarand is an animal as big as a bullock, having a head like a stag, or a little bigger, two stately horns with large branches, cloven feet, hair long like that of a furred Muscovite, I mean a bear, and a skin almost as hard as steel armour. The Scythian said that there are but few tarands to be found in Scythia, because it varieth its colour according to the diversity of the places where it grazes and abides, and represents the colour of the grass, plants, trees, shrubs, flowers, meadows, rocks, and generally of all things near which it comes. It hath this common with the sea-pulp, or polypus, with the thoes, with the wolves of India, and with the chameleon; which is a kind of a lizard so wonderful, that Democritus hath written a whole book of its figure, and anatomy, as also of its virtue and property in magic. This I can affirm, that I have seen it change its colour, not only at the approach of things that have a colour, but by its own voluntary impulse, according to its fear or other affections: as for example, upon a green carpet, I have certainly seen it become green; but having remained there some time, it turned yellow, blue, tanned, and purple, in course, in the same manner as you see a turkey-cock's comb change colour according to its passions. But what we find most surprising in this tarand is, that not only its face and skin, but also its hair could take whatever colour was about it. Near Panurge with his kersey coat, its hair used to turn gray: near Pantagruel with his scarlet mantle, its hair and skin grew red; near the pilot, dressed after the fashion of the Isiaci of Anubis, in Egypt, its hair seemed all white; which two last colours the chameleon cannot borrow.

When the creature was free from any fear or affection, the colour of its hair was just such as you see that of the asses of Meung.

CHAPTER III

How Pantagruel received a letter from his father Gargantua, and of the strange way to have speedy news from far distant places

WHILE Pantagruel was taken up with the purchase of these foreign animals, the noise of ten guns and culverins, together with a loud and joyful cheer of all the fleet, was heard from the mole. Pantagruel looked towards the haven, and perceived that this was occasioned by the arrival of one of his father Gargantua's celoces, or advice-boats, named the *Chelidonia*; because on the stern of it was carved in Corinthian brass, a sea swallow; which is a fish as large as a dare-fish of Loire, all flesh, without scale, with cartilaginous wings, (like a bat's,)

very long and broad, by the means of which, I have seen them
fly a fathom above water, about a bow-shot. At Marseilles
this flying fish is called lendole. And indeed that ship was as
light as a swallow; so that it rather seemed to fly on the sea
than to sail. Malicorne, Gargantua's esquire carver, was come
in her, being sent expressly by his master to have an account
of his son's health and circumstances, and to bring him
credentials. When Malicorne had saluted Pantagruel, and
the prince had embraced him about the neck, and showed him
a little of the cap-courtesy, before he opened the letters, the
first thing he said to him was, Have you here the Gozal, the
heavenly messenger? Yes, sir, said he, here it is swaddled up
in this basket. It was a grey pigeon, taken out of Gargantua's
dove-house, whose young ones were just hatched when the
advice-boat was going off.

If any ill fortune had befallen Pantagruel, he would have
fastened some black riband to his feet; but because all things
had succeeded happily hitherto, having, caused it to be undressed,
he tied to its feet a white riband, and, without any further delay,
let it loose. The pigeon presently flew away, cutting the air
with an incredible speed; as you know that there is no flight
like a pigeon's, especially when it hath eggs or young ones,
through the extreme care which nature hath fixed in it to relieve
and be with its young; insomuch, that in less than two hours
it compassed in the air the long tract which the advice-boat,
with all her diligence, with oars and sails, and a fair wind,
could not go through in less than three days and three nights,
and was seen as it was going into the dove-house to its nest.
Whereupon the worthy Gargantua, hearing that it had the
white riband on, was joyful and secure of his son's welfare.
This was the custom of the noble Gargantua and Pantagruel,
when they would have speedy news of something of great
concern; as the event of some battle, either by sea or land;
the surrendering or holding out of some strong place; the
determination of some difference of moment; the safe or unhappy
delivery of some queen or great lady; the death or recovery
of their sick friends or allies, and so forth. They used to take
the gozal, and had it carried from one to another by the post,
to the places whence they desired to have news. The gozal,
bearing either a black or white riband, according to the occur-
rences and accidents, used to remove their doubts at its return,
making, in the space of one hour, more way through the air,
than thirty post-boys could have done in one natural day.

May not this be said to redeem and gain time with a vengeance, think you? For the like service, therefore, you may believe, as a most true thing, that, in the dove-houses of their farms, there were to be found, all the year long, store of pigeons hatching eggs, or rearing their young. Which may be easily done in aviaries and voleries, by the help of saltpetre and the sacred herb vervain.

The gozal being let fly, Pantagruel perused his father Gargantua's letter, the contents of which were as followeth:

My dearest Son,—The affection that naturally a father bears to a beloved son, is so much increased in me, by reflecting on the particular gifts which by the divine goodness have been heaped on thee, that since thy departure it hath often banished all other thoughts out of my mind; leaving my heart wholly possessed with fear, lest some misfortune has attended thy voyage: for thou knowest that fear was ever the attendant of true and sincere love. Now because, as Hesiod sayeth, A good beginning of any thing is the half of it; or, Well begun is half done, according to the old saying; to free my mind from this anxiety, I have expressly dispatched Malicorne, that he may give me a true account of thy health at the beginning of thy voyage. For if it be good, and such as I wish it, I shall easily foresee the rest.

I have met with some diverting books, which the bearer will deliver thee; thou mayest read them when thou wantest to unbend and ease thy mind from thy better studies. He will also give thee at large the news at court. The peace of the Lord be with thee. Remember me to Panurge, Friar John, Epistemon, Xenomanes, Gymnast, and the other principal domestics, my good friends. Dated at our paternal seat, this 13th day of June.

Thy father and friend, Gargantua.

CHAPTER IV

How Pantagruel writ to his father Gargantua, and sent him several curiosities

Pantagruel, having perused the letter, had a long conference with the esquire Malicorne; insomuch, that Panurge at last interrupting them, asked him, Pray, sir, when do you design to drink? when shall we drink? When shall the worshipful esquire drink? What a devil! have you not talked long enough to drink? It is a good motion, answered Pantagruel; go, get us something ready at the next inn; I think it is the Satyr on horseback. In the meantime he writ to Gargantua as followeth, to be sent by the aforesaid esquire.

Most gracious Father,—As our senses and animal faculties are more discomposed at the news of events unexpected, though desired (even to an immediate dissolution of the soul from the body), than if those accidents had been foreseen; so the coming of Malicorne hath much surprised and disordered me. For I had no hopes to see any of your servants, or to hear from you, before I had finished our voyage; and contented myself with the dear remembrance of your august majesty, deeply impressed in the hindmost ventricle of my brain, often representing you to my mind.

But since you have made me happy beyond expectation, by the perusal of your gracious letter, and the faith I have in your esquire faith revived my spirits by the news of your welfare; I am, as it were, compelled to do what formerly I did freely, that is, first to praise the Blessed Redeemer, who by his divine goodness preserves you in this long enjoyment of perfect health; then to return you eternal thanks for the fervent affection which you have for me your most humble son and unprofitable servant.

Formerly a Roman, named Furnius, said to Augustus, who had received his father into favour, and pardoned him after he had sided with Anthony, that by that action the emperor had reduced him to this extremity, that for want of power to be grateful, both while he lived and after it, he should be obliged to be taxed with ingratitude. So I may say, that the excess of your fatherly affection drives me into such a straight, that I should be forced to live and die ungrateful; unless that crime be redressed by the sentence of the stoics, who say, that there are three parts in a benefit, the one of the giver, the other of the receiver, the third of the remunerator; and that the receiver rewards the giver, when he freely receives the benefit, and always remembers it; as on the contrary, that man is most ungrateful who despises and forgets a benefit. Therefore, being overwhelmed with infinite favours, all proceeding from your extreme goodness, and on the other side wholly incapable of making the smallest return, I hope, at least, to free myself from the imputation of ingratitude, since they can never be blotted out of my mind; and my tongue shall never cease to own, that, to thank you as I ought, transcends my capacity.

As for us, I have this assurance in the Lord's mercy and help, that the end of our voyage will be answerable to its beginning, and so it will be entirely performed in health and mirth. I will not fail to set down in a journal a full account of our navigation, that, at our return, you may have an exact relation of the whole.

I have found here a Scythian tarand, an animal strange and wonderful for the variations of colour on its skin and hair, according to the distinction of neighbouring things: it is as tractable and easily kept as a lamb; be pleased to accept of it.

I also send you three young unicorns, which are the tamest of creatures. I have conferred with the esquire, and taught him how they must be fed. These cannot graze on the ground, by reason of the long horn on their forehead, but are forced to browse on fruit trees, or on proper racks, or to be fed by hand, with herbs, sheaves, apples, pears, barley, rye, and other fruits and roots, being placed before them.

I am amazed that ancient writers should report them to be so wild, furious, and dangerous, and never seen alive: far from it, you will find that they are the mildest things in the world, provided they are not maliciously offended. Likewise I send you the life and deeds of Achilles, in curious tapestry; assuring you whatever rarities of animals, plants, birds, or precious stones, and others, I shall be able to find and purchase in our travels, shall be brought to you, God willing, whom I beseech, by his blessed grace, to preserve you.

From Medamothy, this 15th of June. Panurge, Friar John, Epistemon, Xenomanes, Gymnast, Eusthenes, Rhizotomus, and Carpalim, having most humbly kissed your hand, return your salute a thousand times.

Your most dutiful son and servant, PANTAGRUEL.

While Pantagruel was writing this letter, Malicorne was made welcome with a thousand goodly good-morrows and howd'ye's:

they clung about him so, that I cannot tell you how much they made of him, how many humble services, how many from my love and to my love were sent with him. Pantagruel, having writ his letters, sat down at table with him, and afterwards presented him with a large chain of gold, weighing eight hundred crowns; between whose septenary links, some large diamonds, rubies, emeralds, turquoise stones, and unions were alternately set in. To each of his bark's crew, he ordered to be given five hundred crowns. To Gargantua, his father, he sent the tarand covered with a cloth of satin, brocaded with gold: and the tapestry containing the life and deeds of Achilles, with the three unicorns in frized cloth of gold trappings: and so they left Medamothy; Malicorne, to return to Gargantua; and Pantagruel, to proceed in his voyage: during which, Epistemon read to him the books which the esquire had brought; and because he found them jovial and pleasant, I shall give you an account of them, if you earnestly desire it.

CHAPTER V

How Pantagruel met a ship with passengers returning from Lanternland

On the fifth day, beginning already to wind by little and little about the pole, going still farther from the equinoctial line, we discovered a merchant-man to the windward of us. The joy for this was not small on both sides; we in hopes to hear news from sea, and those in the merchantman from land. So we bore upon them, and coming up with them we hailed them: and finding them to be Frenchmen of Xaintonge, backed our sails and lay by to talk to them. Pantagruel heard that they came from Lanternland; which added to his joy, and that of the whole fleet. We inquired about the state of that country, and the way of living of the Lanterns: and were told, that about the latter end of the following July, was the time prefixed for the meeting of the general chapter of the Lanterns; and that if we arrived there at that time, as we might easily, we should see a handsome, honourable, and jolly company of Lanterns; and that great preparations were making, as if they intended to lanternise there to the purpose. We were told also, that if we touched at the great kingdom of Gebarim, we should be honourably received and treated by the sovereign of that country, King Ohabé, who, as well as all his subjects, speaks Touraine French.

While we were listening to this news, Panurge fell out with one Dingdong, a drover or sheep merchant of Taillebourg. The occasion of the fray was thus.

This same Dingdong, seeing Panurge without a codpiece, with his spectacles fastened to his cap, said to one of his comrades, Prithee, look, is there not a fine medal of a cuckold? Panurge, by reason of his spectacles, as you may well think, heard more plainly by half with his ears than usually; which caused him (hearing this) to say to the saucy dealer in mutton, in a kind of a pet:

How the devil should I be one of the hornified fraternity, since I am not yet a brother of the marriage-noose, as thou art; as I guess by thy ill-favoured phiz?

Yea, verily, quoth the grazier, I am married, and would not be otherwise for all the pairs of spectacles in Europe; nay, not for all the magnifying gim-cracks in Africa; for I have got me the cleverest, prettiest, handsomest, properest, neatest, tightest, honestest, and soberest piece of woman's flesh for my wife, that is in all the whole country of Xaintonge; I will say that for her, and a fart for all the rest. I bring her home a fine eleven-inch-long branch of red coral for her Christmas-box. What hast thou to do with it? what is that to thee? who art thou? whence comest thou, O dark lanthorn of antichrist. Answer, if thou art of God. I ask thee, by the way of question, said Panurge to him very seriously, if with the consent and countenance of all the elements, I had gingumbob'd, codpieced, and thump-thumpriggledtickledtwiddled thy so clever, so pretty, so handsome, so proper, so neat, so tight, so honest, and so sober female importance, insomuch that the stiff deity that has no forecast, Priapus, (who dwells here at liberty, all subjection of fastened codpieces, or bolts, bars, and locks, abdicated,) remained sticking in her natural Christmas-box in such a lamentable manner, that it were never to come out, but eternally should stick there, unless thou didst pull it out with thy teeth; what wouldst thou do? Wouldst thou everlastingly leave it there, or wouldst thou pluck it out with thy grinders? Answer me, O thou ram of Mahomet, since thou art one of the devil's gang. I would, replied the sheepmonger, take thee such a woundy cut on this spectacle-bearing lug of thine, with my trusty bilbo, as would smite thee dead as a herring. Thus, having taken pepper in the nose, he was lugging out his sword, but alas! cursed cows have short horns; it stuck in the scabbard; as you know that at sea, cold iron will easily take rust, by reason of the excessive and nitrous moisture. Panurge, so smitten with terror, that his heart sunk down to his midriff, scoured off to Pantagruel for help: but Friar John laid hand on his flashing scymitar that was new ground, and would certainly have dispatched Dingdong to rights, had not the skipper, and some of his passengers, beseeched Pantagruel not to suffer such an outrage to be committed on board his ship. So the matter was made up, and Panurge and his antagonist shaked fists, and drank in course to one another, in token of a perfect reconciliation.

CHAPTER VI

How the fray being over, Panurge cheapened one of Dingdong's sheep

THIS quarrel being hushed, Panurge tipped the wink upon Epistemon and Friar John, and taking them aside,—Stand at some distance out of the way, said he, and take your share of the following scene of mirth: you shall have rare sport anon, if my cake be not dough, and my plot do but take. Then addressing himself to the drover, he took off to him a bumper of good lantern wine. The other pledged him briskly and courteously. This done, Panugre earnestly entreated him to sell him one of his sheep.

But the other answered him, Is it come to that, friend and neighbour? Would you put tricks upon travellers? Alas, how finely you love to play upon poor folk! Nay, you seem a rare chapman, that is the truth on it. Oh what a mighty sheep merchant you are! In good faith, you look liker one of the diving trade, than a buyer of sheep. Adzookers, what a blessing it would be to have one's purse, well lined with chink, near your worship at a tripe-house, when it begins to thaw! Humph, humph, did not we know you well, you might serve one a slippery trick! Pray do but see, good people, what a mighty conjuror the fellow would be reckoned. Patience, said Panurge: but waving that, be so kind as to sell me one of your sheep. Come, how much? What do you mean, master of mine? answered the other. They are long-woolled sheep: from these did Jason take his golden fleece. The order of the house of Burgundy was drawn from them. Zwoons, man, they are

oriental sheep, topping sheep, fatted sheep, sheep of quality.
Be it so, said Panurge: but sell me one of them, I beseech you,
and that for a cause, paying you ready money upon the nail,
in good and lawful occidental current cash. Wilt say how
much? Friend, neighbour, answered the seller of mutton,
hark ye me a little, on the ear.

Panurge. On which side you please; I hear you.

Dingdong. You are going to Lantern-land, they say.

Pan. Yea, verily.

Ding. To see fashions?

Pan. Yea, verily.

Ding. And be merry?

Pan. Yea, verily.

Ding. Your name is, as I take it, Robin Mutton?

Pan. As you please for that, sweet sir.

Ding. Nay, without offence.

Pan. So I understand it.

Ding. You are, as I take it, the king's jester; are not you?

Pan. Yea, verily.

Ding. Give me your hand—humph, humph, you go to see
fashions, you are the king's jester, your name is Robin Mutton!
Do you see this same ram? His name, too, is Robin. Here
Robin, Robin, Robin! Baea, baea, baea. Hath he not a
rare voice?

Pan. Ay, marry has he, a very fine and harmonious voice.

Ding. Well, this bargain shall be made between you and
me, friend and neighbour; we will get a pair of scales, then you
Robin Mutton shall be put into one of them, and Tup Robin
into the other. Now I will hold you a peck of Busch oysters,
that in weight, value, and price, he shall outdo you, and you
shall be found light in the very numerical manner, as when you
shall be hanged and suspended.

Patience, said Panurge: but you would do much for me,
and your whole posterity, if you would chaffer with me for him,
or some other of his inferiors. I beg it of you; good your worship, be so kind. Hark ye, friend of mine, answered the other,
with the fleece of these, your fine Rouen cloth is to be made;
your Leominster superfine wool is mine arse to it; mere flock
in comparison. Of their skins the best cordovan will be made,
which shall be sold for Turkey and Montelimart, or for Spanish
leather at least. Of the guts shall be made fiddle and harp
strings, that will sell as dear as if they came from Munican or
Aquileia. What do you think of it, hah? If you please, sell

me one of them, said Panurge, and I will be yours for ever. Look, here is ready cash. What's the price? This he said, exhibiting his purse stuffed with new Henricuses.

CHAPTER VII

Which if your read, you will find how Panurge bargained with Dingdong

NEIGHBOUR, my friend, answered Dingdong, they are meat for none but kings and princes: their flesh is so delicate, so savoury, and so dainty, that one would swear it melted in the mouth. I bring them out of a country where the very hogs, God be with us, live on nothing but myrobalans. The sows in the styes, when they lie-in (saving the honour of this good company) are fed only with orange-flowers. But, said Panurge, drive a bargain with me for one of them, and I will pay you for it like a king, upon the honest word of a true Trojan: come, come, what do you ask? Not so fast, Robin, answered the trader, these sheep are lineally descended from the very family of the ram that wafted Phryxus and Helle over the sea, since called the Hellespont. A pox on it, said Panurge, you are *clericus vel addiscens!* *Ità* is a cabbage, and *verè* a leek, answered the merchant. But rr, rrr, rrrr, rrrrr, hoh Robin, rr, rrrrrrr, you do not understand that gibberish, do you? Now I think of it, over all the fields, where they piss, corn grows as fast as if the Lord had pissed there; they need neither be tilled nor dunged. Besides, man, your chemists extract the best saltpetre in the world out of their urine. Nay, with their very dung (with reverence be it spoken) the doctors in our country make pills that cure seventy-eight kinds of diseases, the least of which is the evil of St. Eutropius of Xaintes, from which, good Lord deliver us! Now what do you think on't, neighbour, my friend? The truth is, they cost me money, that they do. Cost what they will, cried Panurge, trade with me for one of them, paying you well. Our friend, quoth the quack-like sheep man, do but mind the wonders of nature that are found in those animals, even in a member which one would think were of no use. Take me but these horns, and bray them a little with an iron pestle, or with an andiron, which you please, it is all one of me; then bury them wherever you will, provided it be where the sun may shine, and water them frequently; in a few months I will engage you will have the best asparagus in the world not even excepting those of Ravenna. Now, come and tell me whether the horns of you other knights of the bull's feather have such a virtue and wonderful propriety?

Patience, said Panurge. I do not know whether you be a scholar or no, pursued Dingdong: I have seen a world of scholars, I say great scholars, that were cuckolds, I'll assure you. But hark you me, if you were a scholar, you should know that in the most inferior members of those animals—which are the feet—there is a bone—which is the heel—the astragalus, if you will have it so, wherewith, and with that of no other creature breathing, except the Indian ass, and the dorcades of Libya, they used in old times to play at the royal game of dice, whereat Augustus the emperor won above fifty thousand crowns one evening. Now such cuckolds as you will be hanged ere you get half so much at it. Patience, said Panurge; but let us dispatch. And when, my friend and neighbour, continued the canting sheep-seller, shall I have duly praised the inward members, the shoulders, the legs, the knuckles, the neck, the breast, the liver, the spleen, the tripes, the kidneys, the bladder, wherewith they make footballs; the ribs, which serve in Pigmyland to make little cross-bows, to pelt the cranes with cherry-stones; the head, which with a little brimstone serves to make a miraculous decoction to loosen and ease the belly of costive dogs? A turd on it, said the skipper to his preaching passenger, what a fiddle-faddle have we here? There is too long a lecture by half: sell him if thou wilt; if thou wilt not, do not let the man lose more time. I hate a gibble-gabble, and a rimble-ramble talk. I am for a man of brevity. I will, for your sake, replied the holder forth; but then he shall give me three livres, French money, for each pick and choose. It is a woundy price, cried Panurge; in our country, I could have five, nay six, for the money: see that you do not overreach me, master. You are not the first man whom I have known to have fallen, even sometimes to the endangering, if not breaking, of his own neck, for endeavouring to rise all at once. A murrain seize thee for a blockheaded booby, cried the angry seller of sheep; by the worthy vow of our lady of Charroux, the worst in this flock is four times better than those which in days of yore the Coraxians in Tuditania, a country of Spain, used to sell for a gold talent each; and how much dost thou think, thou Hibernian fool, that a talent of gold was worth? Sweet sir, you fall into a passion, I see, returned Panurge: well hold, here is your money.

Panurge, having paid his money, chose him out of all the flock a fine topping ram; and as he was hauling it along, crying out and bleating, all the rest, hearing and bleating in concert, stared to see whither their brother ram should be carried. In the meanwhile the drover was saying to his shepherds: Ah! how well the knave could choose him out a ram; the whoreson has skill in cattle. On my honest word, I reserved that very piece of flesh for the Lord of Cancale, well knowing his disposition: for the good man is naturally overjoyed when he holds a goodsized handsome shoulder of mutton instead of a left-handed racket, in one hand, with a good sharp carver in the other: got wot how he bestirs himself then.

CHAPTER VIII

How Panurge caused Dingdong and his sheep to be drowned in the sea

ON a sudden, you would wonder how the thing was so soon done; for my part I cannot tell you, for I had not leisure to mind it; our friend Panurge, without any further tittle-tattle, throws you his ram overboard into the middle of the sea, bleating and making a sad noise. Upon this all the other sheep in the ship, crying and bleating in the same tone, made all the haste they could to leap nimbly into the sea, one after another; and great was the throng who should leap in first after their leader. It was impossible to hinder them: for you know that it is the nature of sheep always to follow the first, wheresoever it goes; which makes Aristotle, *lib.* 9. *De Hist. Animal.*, mark them for the most silly and foolish animals in the world. Dingdong, at his wit's end, and stark staring mad, as a man who saw his sheep destroy and drown themselves before his face, strove to hinder and keep them by might and main; but all in vain: they all, one after the other frisked and jumped into the sea, and were lost. At last he laid hold on a huge sturdy one by the fleece, upon the deck of the ship, hoping to keep it back, and so save that and the rest; but the ram was so strong that it proved too hard for him, and carried its master into the herring pond in spite of his teeth; where it is supposed he drank somewhat more than his fill; so that he was drowned, in the same manner as one-eyed Polyphemus' sheep carried out of the den Ulysses and his companions. The like happened to the shepherds and all their gang, some laying hold on their beloved tup, this by the horns, the other by the legs, a third by the rump, and others by the fleece; till in fine they were all of them forced to sea, and drowned like so many rats. Panurge on the gunnel of the ship, with an oar in his hand, not to help them you may swear, but to keep them from swimming to the ship, and saving themselves from drowning, preached and canted to them all the while, like any little Friar Oliver Maillard, or another Friar John Burgess; laying before them rhetorical common-places concerning the miseries of this life, and the blessings and felicity of the next; assuring them that the dead were much happier than the living in this vale of misery, and promising to erect a stately cenotaph and honorary tomb to every one of them, on the highest summit of Mount Cenis, at his return from Lantern-land; wishing them, nevertheless, in case they were not disposed to shake hands with this life, and did not like their salt liquor, they might have the good luck to meet with some kind whale which might set them ashore safe and sound, on some land of Gotham, after a famous example.

The ship being cleared of Dingdong and his tups: Is there ever another sheepish soul left lurking on board? cried Panurge. Where are those of Toby Lamb, and Robin Ram, that sleep whilst the rest are a feeding? Faith I cannot tell myself. This was an old coaster's trick. What thinkest of it, Friar John, hah? Rarely performed, answered Friar John: only methinks that as formerly in war, on the day of battle, a double pay was commonly promised the soldiers for that day: for if they overcome, there was enough to pay them; and if they lost, it would have been shameful for them to demand it, as the cowardly foresters did after the battle of Cerizoles: so like-wise, my friend, you ought not to have paid your man, and the money had been saved. A fart for the money, said Panurge: have I not had above fifty thousand pounds worth of sport? Come now, let us be gone; the wind is fair. Hark you me, my friend John: never did man do me a good turn, but I returned, or at least acknowledged it; no, I scorn to be ungrateful; I never was, nor ever will be: never did man do me an ill one without rueing the day that he did it, either in this world or the next. I am not yet so much a fool neither. Thou damnest thyself like any old devil, quoth Friar John: it is written, *Mihi vindictam, &c.* Matter of breviary, mark ye me.

CHAPTER IX

*How Pantagruel arrived at the island of Ennasin, and of the
strange ways of being akin in that country*

WE had still the wind at south south west, and had been a whole
day without making land. On the third day, at the flies up
rising, (which, you know, is some two or three hours after the
sun's,) we got sight of a triangular island, very much like Sicily
for its form and situation. It was called the Island of Alliances.

The people there are much like your carrot-pated Poitevins,
save only that all of them, men, women, and children, have
their noses shaped like an ace of clubs. For that reason the
ancient name of the country was Ennasin. They were all akin,
as the mayor of the place told us, at least they boasted so.

You people of the other world esteem it a wonderful thing,
that, out of the family of the Fabii at Rome, on a certain day,
which was the 13th of February, at a certain gate, which was
the Porta Carmentalis, since named Scelerata, formerly situated
at the foot of the Capitol, between the Tarpeian rock and the
Tiber, marched out against the Veientes of Etruria, three hundred
and six men bearing arms, all related to each other, with five
thousand other soldiers, every one of them their vassals, who
were all slain near the river Cremera, that comes out of the lake
of Beccano. Now from this same country of Ennasin, in case
of need, above three hundred thousand, all relations, and of
one family, might march out. Their degrees of consanguinity
and alliance are very strange: for being thus akin and allied
to one another, we found that none was either father or mother,
brother or sister, uncle or aunt, nephew or niece, son-in-law,
or daughter-in-law, godfather or godmother, to the other;
unless, truly, a tall flat-nosed old fellow, who, as I perceived,
called a little shitten arsed girl, of three or four years old,
father, and the child called him daughter.

Their distinction of degrees of kindred was thus: a man used
to call a woman, my lean bit; the woman called him, my por-
poise. Those, said Friar John, must needs stink damnably of
fish, when they have rubbed their bacon one with the other.
One smiling on a young buxom baggage, said, Good morrow,
dear currycomb. She, to return him his civility, said, The
like to you, my steed. Ha! ha! ha! said Panurge, that is pretty
well in faith; for indeed it stands her in good stead to curry-
comb this steed. Another greeted his buttock with a Farewell,

my case. She replied, Adieu, trial. By St. Winifred's placket, cried Gymnast, this case has been often tried. Another asked a she-friend of his, How is it, hatchet? She answered him, At your service, dear helve. Odds belly, saith Carpalim, this helve and this hatchet are well matched. As we went on, I saw one who, calling his she-relation, styled her my crum, and she called him, my crust.

Quoth one to a brisk, plump, juicy female, I am glad to see you, dear tap. So am I to find you so merry, sweet spiggot, replied she. One called a wench, his shovel; she called him, her peal: one named his, my slipper: and she my foot: another, my boot; she, my shasoon.

In the same degree of kindred, one called his, my butter; she called him, my eggs; and they were akin just like a dish of buttered eggs. I heard one call his, my tripe, and she called him, my faggot. Now I could not, for the heart's blood of me, pick out or discover what parentage, alliance, affinity, or consanguinity was between them, with reference to our custom; only they told us that she was faggot's tripe. (*Tripe de fagot*, means the smallest sticks in a faggot.) Another complimenting his convenient, said, Yours, my shell: she replied, I was yours before, sweet oyster. I reckon, said Carpalim, she hath gutted his oyster. Another long-shanked ugly rogue, mounted on a pair of high-heeled wooden slippers, meeting a strapping, fusty, squobbed dowdy, says he to her, How is it, my top? She was short upon him, and arrogantly replied, Never the better for you, my whip. By St. Anthony's hog, said Xenomanes, I believe so; for how can this whip be sufficient to lash this top?

A college professor, well provided with cod, and powdered and prinked up, having a while discoursed with a great lady, taking his leave, with these words, Thank you, sweet-meat; she cried, There needs no thanks, sour-sauce. Saith Pantagruel, This is not altogether incongruous, for sweet meat must have sour sauce. A wooden loggerhead said to a young wench, It is long since I saw you, bag: All the better, cried she, pipe. Set them together, said Panurge, then blow in their arses, it will be a bagpipe. We saw, after that, a diminutive hump-back gallant, pretty near us, taking leave of a she relation of his, thus: Fare thee well, friend hole: she reparteed, Save thee, friend peg. Quoth Friar John, What could they say more, were he all peg and she all hole? But now would I give something to know if every cranny of the hole can be stopped up with that same peg.

A bawdy bachelor, talking with an old trout, was saying, Remember, rusty gun. I will not fail, said she, scourer. Do you reckon these two to be akin? said Pantagruel to the mayor: I rather take them to be foes: in our country a woman would take this as a mortal affront. Good people of the other world, replied the mayor, you have few such and so near relations as this gun and scourer are to one another; for they both come out of one shop. What, was the shop their mother? quoth Panurge. What mother, said the mayor, does the man mean? That must be some of your world's affinity; we have here neither father nor mother: your little paltry fellows, that live on the other side the water, poor rogues, booted with whisps of hay, may indeed have such; but we scorn it. The good Pantagruel stood gazing and listening; but at those words he had like to have lost all patience.

Having very exactly viewed the situation of the island, and the way of living of the Ennaséd nation, we went to take a cup of the creature at a tavern, where there happened to be a wedding after the manner of the country. Bating that shocking custom, there was special good cheer.

While we were there, a pleasant match was struck up betwixt a female called Pear (a tight thing, as we thought, but by some who knew better things, said to be quaggy and flabby,) and a young soft male, called Cheese, somewhat sandy. (Many such matches have been, and they were formerly much commended.) In our country we say, *Il ne fut ocques tel mariage, qu'est de la poire et du fromage;* there is no match like that made between the pear and the cheese: and in many other places good store of such bargains have been driven. Besides, when the women are at their last prayers, it is to this day a noted saying, that after cheese comes nothing.

In another room I saw them marrying an old greasy boot to a young pliable buskin. Pantagruel was told, that young buskin took old boot to have and to hold, because she was of special leather, in good case, and waxed, seared, liquored, and greased to the purpose, even though it had been for the fisherman that went to bed with his boots on. In another room below, I saw a young brogue taking a young slipper for better for worse: which, they told us, was neither for sake of her piety, parts, or person, but for the fourth comprehensive p, portion; the spankers, spur-royals, rose-nobles, and other coriander seed with which she was quilted all over.

CHAPTER X

*How Pantagruel went ashore at the island of Chely, where he saw
King St. Panigon*

WE sailed right before the wind, which we had at west, leaving
those odd alliancers with their ace-of-clubs snouts, and having
taken height by the sun, stood in for Chely, a large, fruitful,
wealthy, and well-peopled island. King St. Panigon, first of
the name, reigned there, and, attended by the princes, his sons,
and the nobles of his court, came as far as the port to receive
Pantagruel, and conducted him to his palace; near the gate of
which, the queen, attended by the princesses her daughters,
and the court ladies, received us. Panigon directed her and
all her retinue to salute Pantagruel and his men with a kiss;
for such was the civil custom of the country: and they were all
fairly bussed accordingly, except Friar John, who stepped aside,
and sneaked off among the king's officers. Panigon used all
the entreaties imaginable to persuade Pantagruel to tarry there
that day and the next: but he would needs be gone, and excused
himself upon the opportunity of wind and weather, which being
oftener desired then enjoyed, ought not to be neglected when
it comes. Panigon, having heard these reasons, let us go, but
first made us take off some five and twenty or thirty bumpers
each.

Pantagruel, returning to the port, missed Friar John, and
asked why he was not with the rest of the company? Panurge
could not tell how to excuse him, and would have gone back to
the palace to call him, when Friar John overtook them, and
merrily cried, Long live the noble Panigon! As I love my belly,
he minds good eating, and keeps a noble house and a dainty
kitchen. I have been there, boys. Every thing goes about by
dozens. I was in good hopes to have stuffed my puddings there
like a monk. What! always in a kitchen, friend? said Pantagruel.
By the belly of St. Crampacon, quoth the Friar, I understand
the customs and ceremonies which are used there, much better
than all the formal stuff, antic postures, and nonsensical fiddle-
faddle that must be used with those women, *magni magna,
shitten cumshita,* cringes, grimaces, scrapes, bows, and congees;
double honours this way, triple salutes that way, the embrace,
the grasp, the squeeze, the hug, the leer, the smack, *beso las
manos de vostra mercé, de vostra maestá.* You are most *tarabin,*

tarabas, Stront; that is downright Dutch. Why all this ado?
I do not say but a man might be for a bit by the bye and away,
to be doing as well as his neighbours; but this little nasty
cringing and courtesying made me as mad as any March devil.
You talk of kissing ladies; by the worthy and sacred frock I
wear, I seldom venture upon it, lest I be served as was the Lord
of Guyercharois.   What was it? said Pantagruel; I know him;
he is one of the best friends I have.

   He was invited to a sumptuous feast, said Friar John, by a
relation and neighbour of his, together with all the gentlemen
and ladies in the neighbourhood.   Now some of the latter [the
ladies] expecting his coming, dressed the pages in women's
clothes, and finified them like any babies; then ordered them
to meet my lord at his coming near the draw-bridge; so the
complimenting monsieur came, and there kissed the petti-
coated lads with great formality.   At last the ladies, who minded
passages in the gallery, burst out with laughing, and made signs
to the pages to take off their dress; which the good lord having
observed, the devil a bit he durst make up to the true ladies to
kiss them, but said, that since they had disguised the pages,
by his great grandfather's helmet, these were certainly the very
footmen and grooms still more cunningly disguised.   Odds fish,
da jurandi, why do not we rather remove our humanities into
some good warm kitchen of God, that noble laboratory; and
there admire the turning of the spits, the harmonious rattling
of the jacks and fenders, criticise on the position of the lard,
the temperature of the pottages, the preparation for the dessert,
and the order of the wine service?   *Beati immaculati in via.*
Matter of breviary, my masters.

CHAPTER XI

Why monks love to be in kitchens

THIS, said Epistemon, is spoke like a true monk: I mean like
a right monking monk, not a bemonked monastical monkling.
Truly you put me in mind of some passages that happened at
Florence, some twenty years ago, in a company of studious
travellers, fond of visiting the learned, and seeing the antiquities
of Italy, among whom I was.   As we viewed the situation and
beauty of Florence, the structure of the dome, the magnificence
of the churches and palaces, we strove to outdo one another

in giving them their due; when a certain monk of Amiens, Bernard Lardon by name, quite angry, scandalized, and out of all patience, told us, I do not know what the devil you can find in this same town, that is so much cried up: for my part I have looked and pored and stared as well as the best of you; I think my eyesight is as clear as another body's; and what can one see after all? There are fine houses, indeed, and that is all. But the cage does not feed the birds. God and Monsieur St. Bernard, our good patron, be with us! in all this same town I have not seen one poor lane of roasting cooks; and yet I have not a little looked about, and sought for so necessary a part of a commonwealth: ay, and I dare assure you that I have pried up and down with the exactness of an informer; as ready to number both to the right and left, how many, and on what side, we might find most roasting cooks, as a spy would be to reckon the bastions of a town. Now at Amiens, in four, nay five times less ground than we have trod in our contemplations, I could have shown you above fourteen streets of roasting cooks, most ancient, savoury, and aromatic. I cannot imagine what kind of pleasure you can have taken in gazing on the lions and Africans, (so methinks you call their tigers,) near the belfry; or in ogling the porcupines and ostriches in the Lord Philip Strozzi's palace. Faith and truth I had rather see a good fat goose at the spit. This porphyry, those marbles are fine; I say nothing to the contrary: but our cheesecakes at Amiens are far better in my mind. These ancient statues are well made; I am willing to believe it: but by St. Ferreol of Abbeville, we have young wenches in our country, which please me better a thousand times.

What is the reason, asked Friar John, that monks are always to be found in kitchens; and kings, emperors, and popes are never there? Is there not, said Rhizotomus, some latent virtue and specific property hid in the kettles and pans, which, as the loadstone attracts iron, draws the monk there, and cannot attract emperors, popes, or kings? Or is it a natural induction and inclination, fixed in the frocks and cowls, which of itself leads and forceth those good religious men into kitchens, whether they will or no? He means, forms, following matter, as Averroës calls them, answered Epistemon. Right, said Friar John.

I will not offer to solve this problem, said Pantagruel; for it is somewhat ticklish, and you can hardly handle it without coming off scurvily; but I will tell you what I have heard.

Antigonus, King of Macedon, one day coming to one of his

tents, where his cooks used to dress his meat, and finding there poet Antagoras frying a conger, and holding the pan himself, merrily asked him, Pray, Mr. Poet, was Homer frying congers when he wrote the deeds of Agamemnon? Antagoras readily answered, But do you think, sir, that when Agamemnon did them, he made it his business to know if any in his camp were frying congers? The king thought it an indecency that a poet should be thus a frying in a kitchen; and the poet let the king know, that it was a more indecent thing for a king to be found in such a place. I will clap another story upon the neck of this, quoth Panurge, and will tell you what Breton Villandry answered one day to the Duke of Guise.

They were saying that at a certain battle of King Francis, against the Emperor, Charles the Fifth, Breton, armed cap-a-pé to the teeth, and mounted like St. George; yet sneaked off, and played least in sight during the engagement. Blood an'ouns, answered Breton, I was there, and can prove it easily; nay, even where you, my lord, dared not have been. The duke began to resent this as too rash and saucy: but Breton easily appeased him, and set them all a laughing. I gad, my lord, quoth he, I kept out of harm's way; I was all the while with your page Jack, skulking in a certain place where you had not dared hide your head, as I did. Thus discoursing, they got to their ships, and left the island of Chely.

CHAPTER XII

How Pantagruel passed through the land of Pettifogging, and of the strange way of living among the Catchpoles

STEERING our course forwards the next day, we passed through Pettifogging, a country all blurred and blotted, so that I could hardly tell what to make on it. There we saw some pettifoggers and catchpoles, rogues that will hang their father for a groat. They neither invited us to eat or drink; but, with a multiplied train of scrapes and cringes, said they were all at our service, for a consideration.

One of our interpreters related to Pantagruel their strange way of living, diametrically opposite to that of our modern Romans; for at Rome a world of folks get an honest livelihood by poisoning, drubbing, lambasting, stabbing, and murdering; but the catchpoles earn theirs by being thrashed; so that if they were long without a tight lambasting, the poor dogs with their wives and children would be starved. This is just, quoth Panurge, like those who, as Galen tells us, cannot erect the cavernous nerve towards the equinoctial circle, unless they are soundly flogged. By St. Patrick's slipper, whoever should jirk me so, would soon, instead of setting me right, throw me off the saddle, in the devil's name.

The way is this, said the interpreter. When a monk, levite, close-fisted usurer, or lawyer owes a grudge to some neighbouring gentleman, he sends to him one of those catchpoles, or apparitors, who nabs, or at least cites him, serves a writ or warrant upon him, thumps, abuses, and affronts him impudently by natural instinct, and according to his pious instructions: insomuch, that if the gentleman hath but any guts in his brains, and is not more stupid than a gyrin frog, he will find himself obliged either to apply a faggot-stick or his sword to the rascal's jobbernol, give him the gentle lash, or make him cut a caper out of the window, by way of correction. This done, Catchpole is rich for four months at least, as if bastinadoes were his real harvest: for the monk, levite, usurer, or lawyer, will reward him roundly; and my gentleman must pay him such swingeing damages, that his acres must bleed for it, and he be in danger of miserably rotting within a stone doublet, as if he had struck the king.

Quoth Panurge, I know an excellent remedy against this; used by the Lord of Basché. What is it? said Pantagruel. The Lord of Basché, said Panurge, was a brave, honest, noble-spirited gentleman, who, at his return from the long war, in which the Duke of Ferrara, with the help of the French, bravely defended himself against the fury of Pope Julius the Second, was every day cited, warned, and prosecuted at the suit, and for the sport and fancy of the fat prior of St. Louant.

One morning as he was at breakfast with some of his domestics (for he loved to be sometimes among them) he sent for one Loire his baker, and his spouse, and for one Oudart, the vicar of his parish, who was also his butler, as the custom was then in France; then said to them before his gentleman and other servants: You all see how I am daily plagued with these rascally catchpoles: truly if you do not lend me your helping hand, I am finally resolved to leave the country, and go fight for the sultan, or the devil, rather than be thus eternally teazed. Therefore to be rid of their damned visits, hereafter, when any of them come here, be ready you baker and your wife, to make your personal appearance in my great hall, in your wedding clothes, as if you were going to be affianced. Here take these ducats, which I give you to keep you in a fitting garb. As for you, Sir Oudart, be sure you make your personal appearance there in your fair surplice and stole, not forgetting your holy water, as if you were to wed them. Be you there also, Trudon, said he to his drummer, with your pipe and tabour. The form of matrimony must be read, and the bride kissed at the beat of the tabour; then all of you, as the witnesses used do in this country, shall give one another the remembrance of the wedding, —which you know is to be a blow with your fist, bidding the party struck, remember the nuptials by that token. This will but make you have the better stomach to your supper; but when you come to the catchpole's turn, thrash him thrice and three-fold, as you would a sheaf of green corn; do not spare him; maul him, drub him, lambast him, swinge him off, I pray you. Here, take these steel gauntlets, covered with kid. Head, back, belly, and sides, give him blows innumerable: he that gives him most, shall be my best friend. Fear not to be called to an account about it; I will stand by you: for the blows must seem to be given in jest, as it is customary among us at all weddings.

Ay, but how shall we know the catchpole, said the man of God? All sorts of people daily resort to this castle. I have taken care of that, replied the lord. When some fellow, either on foot, or on a scurvy jade, with a large broad silver ring on his thumb, comes to the door, he is certainly a catchpole: the porter, having civilly let him in, shall ring the bell; then be all ready, and come into the hall, to act the tragi-comedy, whose plot I have now laid for you.

That numerical day, as chance would have it, came an old fat ruddy catchpole. Having knocked at the gate, and then pissed, as most men will do, the porter soon found him out, by his large greasy spatterdashes, his jaded hollow-flanked mare, his bag full of writs and informations dangling at his girdle, but, above all, by the large silver hoop on his left thumb.

The porter was civil to him, admitted him kindly, and rung the bell briskly. As soon as the baker and his wife heard it, they clapped on their best clothes, and made their personal appearance in the hall, keeping their gravities like a new-made judge. The dominie put on his surplice and stole, and as he came out of his office, met the catchpole, had him in there, and made him suck his face a good while, while the gauntlets were drawing on all hands; and then told him, You are come just in pudding-time; my lord is in his right cue: we shall feast

like kings anon, here is to be swingeing doings; we have a
wedding in the house; here, drink and cheer up; pull away.

While these two were at hand-to-fist, Basché, seeing all his
people in the hall in their proper equipages, sends for the vicar.
Oudart comes with the holy water pot, followed by the catchpole, who, as he came into the hall, did not forget to make
good store of awkward cringes, and then served Basché with a
writ. Basché gave him grimace for grimace, slipped an angel
into his mutton fist, and prayed him to assist at the contract
and ceremony: which he did. When it was ended, thumps
and fisticuffs began to fly about among the assistants; but when
it came to the catchpole's turn, they all laid on him so unmercifully with their gauntlets, that they at last settled him, all
stunned and battered, bruised and mortified, with one of his
eyes black and blue, eight ribs bruised, his brisket sunk in, his
omoplates in four quarters, his under jawbone in three pieces;
and all this in jest, and no harm done. God wot how the levite
belaboured him, hiding within the long sleeve of his canonical
shirt his huge steel gauntlet lined with ermine: for he was a
strong built ball, and an old dog at fisticuffs. The catchpole,
all of a bloody tiger-like stripe, with much ado crawled home to
L'Isle Bouchart, well pleased and edified however with Basché's
kind reception; and, with the help of the good surgeons of the
place, lived as long as you would have him. From that time
to this, not a word of the business; the memory of it was lost
with the sound of the bells that rung with joy at his funeral.

CHAPTER XIII

*How, like Master Francis Villon, the Lord of Basché commended
his servants*

THE catchpole being packed off on blind Sorrel,—so he called
his one-eyed-mare,—Basché sent for his lady, her women, and
all his servants, into the arbour of his garden; had wine brought,
attended with good store of pasties, hams, fruit, and other
table-ammunition, for a nunchion; drank with them joyfully,
and then told them this story.

Master Francis Villon, in his old age, retired to St. Maxent,
in Poictou, under the patronage of a good honest abbot of the
place. There to make sport for the mob, he undertook to get
"The Passion" acted, after the way, and in the dialect of the

country. The parts being distributed, the play having been
rehearsed, and the stage prepared, he told the mayor and alder-
men, that the mystery would be ready after Niort fair, and that
there only wanted properties and necessaries, but chiefly clothes
fit for the parts: so the mayor and his brethren took care to
get them.

Villon, to dress an old clownish father grey-beard, who was
to represent G—d the father, begged of Friar Stephen Tickletoby,
sacristan to the Franciscan friars of the place, to lend him a
cope and a stole. Tickletoby refused him, alleging, that by their
provincial statutes, it was rigorously forbidden to give or lend
anything to players. Villon replied, that the statute reached
no farther than farces, drolls, antics, loose and dissolute games,
and that he asked no more than what he had seen allowed at
Brussels and other places. Tickletoby, notwithstanding, peremptorily bid him provide himself elsewhere if he would, and
not to hope for any thing out of his monastical wardrobe. Villon
gave an account of this to the players, as of a most abominable
action; adding, that God would shortly revenge himself, and
make an example of Tickletoby.

The Saturday following, he had notice given him, that Tickletoby, upon the filly of the convent — so they call a young
mare that was never leaped yet—was gone a mumping to St.
Ligarius, and would be back about two in the afternoon. Knowing this, he made a cavalcade of his devils of "The Passion"
through the town. They were all rigged with wolves', calves',
and rams' skins, laced and trimmed with sheep's heads, bulls'
feathers, and large kitchen tenterhooks, girt with broad leathern
girdles; whereat hanged dangling huge cow-bells and horse-
bells, which made a horrid din. Some held in their claws
black sticks full of squibs and crackers: others had long lighted
pieces of wood, upon which, at the corner of every street, they
flung whole handfuls of rosin-dust, that made a terrible fire and
smoke. Having thus led them about, to the great diversion of
the mob, and the dreadful fear of little children, he finally carried
them to an entertainment at a summer-house, without the gate
that leads to St. Ligarius.

As they came near to the place, he espied Tickletoby afar off,
coming home from mumping, and told them in macaronic verse.

> Hic est de patria, natus, de gente belistra,
> Qui solet antiquo bribas portare bisacco.

A plague on his friarship, said the devils then; the lousy
beggar would not lend a poor cope to the fatherly father; let

us fright him. Well said, cried Villon; but let us hide ourselves till he comes by, and then charge him home briskly with your squibs and burning sticks. Tickletoby being come to the place, they all rushed on a sudden into the road to meet him, and in a frightful manner threw fire from all sides upon him and his filly foal, ringing and tingling their bells, and howling like so many real devils, Hho, hho, hho, hho, brrou, rrou, rrourrs, rrrourrs, hoo, hou, hho, hho, hhoi. Friar Stephen, don't we play the devils rarely? The filly was soon scared out of her seven senses, and began to start, to funk it, to squirt it, to trot it, to fart it, to bound it, to gallop it, to kick it, to spurn it, to calcitrate it, to wince it, to frisk it, to leap it, to curvet it, with double jerks, and bum-motions; insomuch that she threw down Tickletoby, though he held fast by the tree of the pack-saddle with might and main. Now his straps and stirrups were of cord; and on the right side, his sandals were so entangled and twisted, that he could not for the heart's blood of him get out his foot. Thus he was dragged about by the filly through the road, scratching his bare breech all the way; she still multiplying her kicks against him, and straying for fear over hedge and ditch; insomuch that she trepanned his thick skull so, that his cockle brains were dashed out near the Osanna or high-cross. Then his arms fell to pieces, one this way, and the other that way; and even so were his legs served at the same time. Then she made a bloody havoc with his puddings; and being got to the convent, brought back only his right foot and twisted sandal, leaving them to guess what had become of the rest.

Villon, seeing that things had succeeded as he intended, said to his devils, You will act rarely, gentlemen devils, you will act rarely; I dare engage you will top your parts. I defy the devils of Saumur, Douay, Montmorillon, Langez, St. Espain, Angers; nay, by gad, even those of Poictiers, for all their bragging and vapouring to match you.

Thus, friends, said Basché, I foresee, that hereafter you will act rarely this tragical farce, since the very first time you have so skilfully hampered, bethwacked, belammed, and bebumped the catchpole. From this day I double your wages. As for you, my dear, said he to his lady, make your gratifications as you please; you are my treasurer, you know. For my part, first and foremost, I drink to you all. Come on, box it about, it is good and cool. In the second place, you, Mr. Steward, take this silver basin, I give it you freely. Then you, my gentlemen of the horse, take these two silver gilt cups, and let not the pages be horse-whipped these three months. My dear, let them have my best white plumes of feathers, with the gold buckles to them. Sir Oudart, this silver flagon falls to your share: this other I give to the cooks. To the valets de chambre I give this silver basket; to the grooms, this silver gilt boat; to the porter, these two plates, to the hostlers, these ten porringers. Trudon, take you these silver spoons and this sugar box. You, footman, take this large salt. Serve me well, and I will remember you. For on the word of a gentleman, I had rather bear in war one hundred blows on my helmet in the service of my country, than be once cited by these knavish catchpoles, merely to humour this same gorbellied prior.

CHAPTER XIV

A further account of Catchpoles who were drubbed at Basché's house

FOUR days after, another, young, long-shanked, raw-boned catchpole, coming to serve Basché with a writ at the fat prior's request, was no sooner at the gate, but the porter smelt him out and rung the bell; at whose second pull, all the family understood the mystery. Loire was kneading his dough; his wife was sifting meal; Oudart was toping in his office; the gentlemen were playing at tennis; the Lord Basché at in and out with my lady; the waiting-men and gentlewomen at push-pin; the officers at lanterlue, and the pages at hot-cockles, giving one another smart bangs. They were all immediately informed that a catchpole was housed.

Upon this, Oudart put on his sacerdotal, and Loire and his wife their nuptial badges: Trudon piped it, and then taboured it like mad; all made haste to get ready, not forgetting the gauntlets. Basché went into the outward yard: there the catchpole meeting him fell on his marrow-bones, begged of him not to take it ill, if he served him with a writ at the suit of the fat prior; and in a pathetic speech, let him know that he was a public person, a servant to the monking tribe, apparitor to the abbatial mitre, ready to do as much for him, nay, for the least of his servants, whensoever he would employ and use him.

Nay, truly, said the lord, you shall not serve your writ till you have tasted some of my good quinquenays wine, and been a witness to a wedding which we are to have this very minute.

Let him drink and refresh himself, added he, turning towards
the levitical butler, and then bring him into the hall. After
which, Catchpole, well stuffed and moistened, came with Oudart
to the place where all the actors in the farce stood ready to begin.
The sight of their game set them a laughing, and the messenger of mischief grinned also for company's sake. Then the
mysterious words were muttered to and by the couple, their
hands joined, the bride bussed, and all besprinkled with holy
water. While they were bringing wine and kickshaws, thumps
began to trot about by dozens. The catchpole gave the levite
several blows. Oudart, who had his gauntlet hid under his
canonical shirt, draws it on like a mitten, and then, with his
clenched fist, souse he fell on the catchpole, and mauled him
like a devil: the junior gauntlets dropped on him likewise like
so many battering rams. Remember the wedding by this,
by that, by these blows, said they. In short they stroked him
so to the purpose, that he pissed blood out at mouth, nose, ears,
and eyes, and was bruised, thwackt, battered, bebumped, and
crippled at the back, neck, breast, arms, and so forth. Never
did the bachelors at Avignon, in carnival time, play more
melodiously at raphe, than was then played on the catchpole's
microcosm: at last down he fell.

They threw a great deal of wine on his snout, tied round the
sleeve of his doublet a fine yellow and green favour, and got
him upon his snotty beast, and God knows how he got to L'Isle
Bouchart; where I cannot truly tell you whether he was dressed
and looked after or no, both by his spouse and the able doctors
of the country; for the thing never came to my ears.

The next day they had a third part to the same tune, because it did not appear by the lean catchpole's bag, that he had
served his writ. So the fat prior sent a new catchpole at the
head of a brace of bums, for his *garde du corps*, to summon my
lord. The porter ringing the bell, the whole family was overjoyed, knowing that it was another rogue. Basché was at dinner
with his lady and the gentlemen; so he sent for the catchpole,
made him sit by him, and the bums by the women, and made
them eat till their bellies cracked with their breeches unbuttoned.
The fruit being served, the catchpole arose from table and before
the bums cited Basché. Basché kindly asked him for a copy of
the warrant, which the other had got ready: he then takes
witness, and a copy of the summons. To the catchpole and
his bums he ordered four ducats for civility money. In the
meantime all were withdrawn for the farce. So Trudon gave

the alarm with his tabour. Basché desired the catchpole to stay and see one of this servants married, and witness the contract of marriage, paying him his fee. The catchpole slap dash was ready, took out his ink-horn, got paper immediately, and his bums by him.

Then Loire came into the hall at one door, and his wife with the gentlewomen at another, in nuptial accoutrements. Oudart, in pontificalibus, takes them both by their hands, asketh them their will, giveth them the matrimonial blessing, and was very liberal of holy water. The contract written, signed, and registered, on one side was brought wine and comfits; on the other, white and orange-tawny-coloured favours were distributed: on another, gauntlets privately handed about.

CHAPTER XV

How the ancient custom at nuptials is renewed by the Catchpole

THE catchpole, having made shift to get down a swingeing sneaker of Breton wine, said to Basché, Pray, Sir, what do you mean? You do not give one another the memento of the wedding. By St. Joseph's wooden shoe, all good customs are forgot. We find the form, but the hare is scampered; and the nest, but the birds are flown. There are no true friends now-a-days. You see how, in several churches, the ancient laudable sustom of tippling, on account of the blessed saints O O, at Christmas, is come to nothing. The world is in its dotage, and doomsday is certainly coming all so fast. Now come on; the wedding, the wedding, the wedding; remember it by this. This he said, striking Basché and his lady; then her women and the levite. Then the tabour beat a point of war, and the gauntlets began to do their duty: insomuch that the catchpole had his crown cracked in no less than nine places. One of the bums had his right arm put out of joint, and the other his upper jawbone or mandibule dislocated; so that it hid half his chin, with a denudation of the uvula, and sad loss of the molar, masticatory, and canine teeth. Then the tabour beat a retreat; the gauntlets were carefully hid in a trice, and sweetmeats afresh distributed to renew the mirth of the company. So they all drank to one another, and especially to the catchpole and his bums. But Oudart cursed and damned the wedding to the pit of hell, complaining that one of the bums had utterly disincornifistibulated his nether

shoulder-blade. Nevertheless, he scorned to be thought a
flincher, and made shift to tope to him on the square.

The jawless bum shrugged up his shoulders, joined his hands,
and by signs begged his pardon; for speak he could not. The
sham bridegroom made his moan, that the crippled bum had
struck him such a horrid thump with his shoulder-of-mutton
fist on the nether elbow, that he was grown quite esperruquan-
chuzelubleouzerireliced down to his very heel, to the no small
loss of mistress bride.

But what harm had poor I done? cried Trudon, hiding his
left eye with his kerchief, and showing his tabour cracked on
one side: they were not satisfied with thus poaching, black and
blueing, and morrambouzevezengouzequoquemorgasacbaque-
vezinemaffreliding my poor eyes, but they have also broke my
harmless drum. Drums indeed are commonly beaten at
weddings,—and it is fit they should; but drummers are well
entertained, and never beaten. Now let Belzebub even take the
drum, to make his devilship a nightcap. Brother, said the
lame catchpole, never fret thyself; I will make thee a present
of a fine, large, old patent, which I have here in my bag, to patch
up thy drum and for Madame St. Ann's sake I pray thee forgive us. By Our Lady of Riviere, the blessed dame, I meant
no more harm than the child unborn. One of the equerries,
who hopping and halting like a mumping cripple, mimicked the
good limping Lord de la Roche Posay, directed his discourse
to the bum with the pouting jaw, and told him, What, Mr.
Manhound, was it not enough thus to have morcrosastebesast-
everestegrigeligoscopapopondrillated us all in our upper members
with your botched mittens, but you must also apply such mord-
eregripippiatabirofreluchamburelurecaquelurintimpaniments on
our shin-bones with the hard tops and extremities of your
cobbled shoes. Do you call this children's play? By the mass,
it is no jest. The bum, wringing his hands, seemed to beg his
pardon, muttering with his tongue, mon, mon, mon, vrelon,
von, von, like a dumb man. The bride crying laughed, and
laughing cried, because the catchpole was not satisfied with
drubbing her without choice or distinction of members, but had
also rudely roused and toused her; pulled off her topping,
and not having the fear of her husband before his eyes, treacherously trepignemanpenilloriifrizonoufresterfumbledtumbled
and squeezed her lower parts. The devil go with it, said Basché;
there was much need indeed that this same Master King (this
was the catchpole's name) should thus break my wife's back:

however, I forgive him now; these are little nuptial caresses. But this I plainly perceive, that he cited me like an angel, and drubbed me like a devil. He hath something in him of Friar Thumpwell. Come, for all this, I must drink to him, and to you likewise his trusty esquires. But, said his lady, why hath he been so very liberal of his manual kindness to me, without the least provocation? I assure you, I by no means like it: but this I dare say for him, that he hath the hardest knuckles that ever I felt on my shoulders. The steward held his left arm in a scarf, as if it had been rent and torn in twain: I think it was the devil, said he, that moved me to assist at these nuptials; shame on ill luck; I must needs be meddling with a pox, and now see what I have got by the bargain, both my arms are wretchedly engoulevezinemassed and bruised. Do you call this a wedding? By St. Bridget's tooth I had rather be at that of a Tom T——d-man. This is, on my word, even just such another feast as was that of the Lapithæ described by the philosopher of Samosata. One of the bums had lost his tongue. The two other, though they had more need to complain, made their excuse as well as they could, protesting that they had no ill design in this dumb-founding; begging that, for goodness sake, they would forgive them; and so, though they could hardly budge a foot, or wag along, away they crawled. About a mile from Basché's seat the catchpole found himself somewhat out of sorts. The bums got to L'Isle Bouchard, publicly saying, that since they were born, they had never seen an honester gentlemen than the Lord of Basché, or civiller people than his, and that they had never been at the like wedding (which I verily believe); but that it was their own faults if they had then tickled off, and tossed about from post to pillar, since themselves had begun the beating. So they lived I cannot exactly tell you how many days after this. But from that time to this it was held for a certain truth, that Basché's money was more pestilential, mortal, and per-nicious to the catchpoles and bums, than were formerly the *aurum Tholosanum* and the Sejan horse to those that possessed them. Ever since this, he lived quietly, and Basché's wedding grew into a common proverb.

CHAPTER XVI

How Friar John made trial of the nature of the Catchpoles

THIS story would seem pleasant enough, said Pantagruel, were we not to have always the fear of God before our eyes. It had been better, said Epistemon, if those gauntlets had fallen upon the fat prior. Since he took a pleasure in spending his money partly to vex Basché, partly to see those catchpoles banged, good lusty thumps would have done well on his shaven crown, considering the horrid concussions now-a-days among those puny judges. What harm had done those poor devils the catchpoles? This puts me in mind, said Pantagruel, of an ancient Roman named L. Neratius. He was of noble blood, and for some time was rich; but had this tyrannical inclination, that whenever he went out of doors, he caused his servants to fill their pockets with gold and silver, and meeting in the street your spruce gallants and better sort of beaux, without the least provocation, for his fancy, he used to strike them hard on the face with his fist; and immediately after that, to appease them, and hinder them from complaining to the magistrates, he would give them as much money as satisfied them according to the law of the twelve tables. Thus he used to spend his revenue, beating people for the price of his money. By St. Bennet's sacred boot, quoth Friar John, I will know the truth of it presently.

This said, he went on shore, put his hand in his fob, and took out twenty ducats; then said with a loud voice, in the hearing of a shoal of the nation of catchpoles, Who will earn twenty ducats, for being beaten like the devil? Io, Io, Io, said they all: you will cripple us for ever, sir, that is most certain; but the money is tempting. With this they were all thronging who should be first, to be thus preciously beaten. Friar John singled him out of the whole knot of these rogues in grain, a red-snouted catchpole, who upon his right thumb wore a thick broad silver hoop, wherein was set a good large toad-stone. He had no sooner picked him out from the rest, but I perceived that they all muttered and grumbled; and I heard a young thin-jawed catchpole, a notable scholar, a pretty fellow at his pen, and, according to public report, much cried up for his honesty at Doctors-Commons, making his complaint, and muttering, because this same crimson phiz carried away all the practice;

and that if there were but a score and a half of bastinadoes to be got, he would certainly run away with eight and twenty of them. But all this was looked upon to be nothing but mere envy.

Friar John so unmercifully thrashed, thumped, and belaboured Red-snout, back and belly, sides, legs, and arms, head, feet, and so forth, with the home and frequently repeated application of one of the best members of a faggot, that I took him to be a dead man: then he gave him the twenty ducats; which made the dog get on his legs, pleased like a little king or two. The rest were saying to Friar John, Sir, sir, brother devil, if it please you to do us the favour to beat some of us for less money, we are all at your devilship's command, bags, papers, pens, and all. Red-snout cried out against them, saying, with a loud voice, Body of me, you little prigs, will you offer to take the bread out of my mouth? will you take my bargain over my head; would you draw and inveigle from me my clients and customers? Take notice, I summon you before the official this day seven-night; I will law and claw you like any old devil of Vauverd, that I will——Then turning himself towards Friar John, with a smiling and joyful look, he said to him, Reverend father in the devil, if you have found me a good hide, and have a mind to divert yourself once more, by beating your humble servant, I will bate you half in half this time, rather than lose your custom: do not spare me, I beseech you: I am all, and more than all yours, good Mr. Devil; head, lungs, tripes, guts, and garbage; and that at a pennyworth, I'll assure you. Friar John never heeded his proffers, but even left them. The other catchpoles were making addresses to Panurge, Epistemon, Gymnast, and others, entreating them charitably to bestow upon their carcasses a small beating, for otherwise they were in danger of keeping a long fast: but none of them had a stomach to it. Some time after, seeking fresh water for the ship's company, we met a couple of old female catchpoles of the place, miserably howling and weeping in concert. Pantagruel had kept on board, and already had caused a retreat to be sounded. Thinking that they might be related to the catchpole that was bastinadoed, we asked them the occasion of their grief. They replied, that they had too much cause to weep; for that very hour from an exalted triple tree, two of the honestest gentlemen in Catchpole-land had been made to cut a caper on nothing. Cut a caper on nothing; said Gymnast; my pages use to cut capers on the ground: to cut a caper on nothing, should be hanging and choking, or I am out. Ay, ay, said Friar John, you speak of it like St. John de la Palisse.

We asked them why they treated these worthy persons with such a choking hempen sallad. They told us they had only borrowed, alias stolen, the tools of the mass, and hid them under the handle of the parish. This is a very allegorical way of speaking, said Epistemon.

CHAPTER XVII

How Pantagruel came to the islands of Tohu and Bohu; and of the strange death of Widenostrils, the swallower of Windmills

THAT day Pantagruel came to the two islands of Tohu and Bohu, where the devil a bit we could find any thing to fry with. For one Widenostrils, a huge giant, had swallowed every individual pan, skillet, kettle, frying-pan, dripping-pan, and brass and iron pot in the land, for want of windmills, which were his daily food. Whence it happened, that somewhat before day, about the hour of his digestion, the greedy churl was taken very ill, with a kind of a surfeit, or crudity of stomach, occasioned, as the physicians said, by the weakness of the concocting faculty of his stomach, naturally disposed to digest whole windmills at a gust, yet unable to consume perfectly the pans and skillets; though it had indeed pretty well digested the kettles and pots; as they said, they knew by the hypostases and eneoremes of four tubs of second-hand drink which he had evacuated at two different times that morning. They made use of divers remedies according to art, to give him ease: but all would not do; the distemper prevailed over the remedies, insomuch that the famous Widenostrils died that morning, of so strange a death, that, I think you ought no longer to wonder at that of the poet Æschylus. It had been foretold him by the soothsayers, that he would die on a certain day, by the ruin of something that should fall on him. That fatal day being come in its turn, he removed himself out of town, far from all houses, trees, rocks, or any other things that can fall, and endanger by their ruin; and strayed in a large field, trusting himself to the open sky; there, very secure, as he thought, unless, indeed, the sky should happen to fall, which he held to be impossible. Yet, they say, that the larks are much afraid of it; for if it should fall, they must all be taken.

The Celts that once lived near the Rhine—they are our noble

valiant French—in ancient times were also afraid of the sky's falling: for being asked by Alexander the Great, what they feared most in this world, hoping well they would say that they feared none but him, considering his great achievements; they made answer, that they feared nothing but the sky's falling: however, not refusing to enter into a confederacy with so brave a king; if you believe Strabo, *lib.* 7, and Arrian, *lib.* 1.

Plutarch also, in his book of the face that appears on the body of the moon, speaks of one Pharnaces, who very much feared the moon should fall on the earth, and pitied those that live under that planet, as the Æthiopians and Taprobanians, if so heavy a mass ever happened to fall on them; and would have feared the like of heaven and earth, had they not been duly propped up and borne by the atlantic pillars as the ancients believed, according to Aristotle's testimony, *lib.* 5, *Metaphys*. Notwithstanding all this, poor Æschylus was killed by the fall of the shell of a tortoise, which falling from betwixt the claws of an eagle high in the air, just on his head, dashed out his brains.

Neither ought you to wonder at the death of another poet, I mean old jolly Anacreon, who was choked with a grapestone. Nor at that of Fabius the Roman prætor, who was choked with a single goat's hair, as he was supping up a porringer of milk. Nor at the death of that bashful fool, who by holding in his wind, and for want of letting out a bumgunshot, died suddenly in the presence of the Emperor Claudius. Nor at that of the Italian, buried on the Via Flaminia at Rome, who, in his epitaph, complains that the bite of a she puss on his little finger was the cause of his death. Nor of that of Q. Lecanius Bassus, who died suddenly of so small a prick with a needle on his left thumb, that it could hardly be discerned. Nor of Quenelault, a Norman physician, who died suddenly at Montpellier, merely for having side-ways took a worm out of his hand with a penknife. Nor of Philomenes, whose servant having got him some new figs for the first course of his dinner, whilst he went to fetch wine, a straggling well-hung ass got into the house, and seeing the figs on the table, without further invitation soberly fell to. Philomenes coming into the room, and nicely observing with what gravity the ass eat its dinner, said to his man, who was come back, Since thou hast set figs here for this reverend guest of ours to eat, methinks it is but reason thou also give him some of this wine to drink. He had no sooner said this, but he was so excessively pleased, and fell into so exorbitant a fit of laughter, that the use of his spleen took that of his breath utterly away, and he immediately died. Nor of Spurius Saufeius, who died supping up a soft boiled egg as he came out of a bath. Nor of him who, as Boccacio tells us, died suddenly by picking his grinders with a sage-stalk. Nor of Phillipot Placut, who being brisk and hale, fell dead as he was paying an old debt; which causes, perhaps, many not to pay theirs, for fear of the like accident. Nor of the painter Zeuxis, who killed himself with laughing at the sight of the antic jobbernol of an old hag drawn by him. Nor, in short, of a thousand more of which authors write; as Varrius, Pliny, Valerius, J. Bapista Fulgosus, and Bacabery the elder. In short, Gaffer Widenostrils choked himself with eating a huge lump of fresh butter at the mouth of a hot oven, by the advice of physicians.

They likewise told us there, that the King of Cullan in Bohu had routed the grandees of King Mecloth, and made sad work with the fortresses of Belima.

After this, we sailed by the islands of Nargues and Zargues; also by the islands of Teleniabin and Geleniabin, very fine and fruitful in ingredients for clysters; and then by the islands of Enig and Evig, on whose account formerly the Landgrave of Hesse was swinged off with a vengeance.

CHAPTER XVIII

How Pantagruel met with a great storm at sea

THE next day we espied nine sail that came spooning before the wind: they were full of Dominicans, Jesuits, Capuchins, Hermits, Austins, Bernardins, Egnatins, Celestins, Theatins, Amadeans, Cordeliers, Carmelites, Minims, and the devil and all of other holy monks and friars, who were going to the Council of Chesil, to sift and garble some new articles of faith against the new heretics. Panurge was overjoyed to see them, being most certain of good luck for that day, and a long train of others. So having courteously saluted the blessed fathers, and recommended the salvation of his precious soul to their devout prayers and private ejaculations, he caused seventy-eight dozen of Westphalia hams, units of pots of caviare, tens of Bolonia sausages, hundreds of botargoes, and thousands of fine angels, for the souls of the dead, to be thrown on board their ships. Pantagruel seemed metagrabolized, dozing, out of sorts, and as melancholic as a cat. Friar John, who soon perceived it, was inquiring of him whence should come this unusual sadness? when the master, whose watch it was, observing the fluttering of the ancient above the poop, and seeing that it began to overcast, judged that we should have wind; therefore he bid the boatswain call all hands upon deck, officers, sailors, foremast-men, swabbers, and cabin-boys, and even the passengers; made them first settle their top-sails, take in their sprit-sail; then he cried, In with your top-sails, lower the foresail, tallow under the parrels, brade up close all them sails, strike your top-masts to the cap, make all sure with your sheepsfeet, lash your guns fast. All this was nimbly done. Immediately it blowed a storm; the sea began to roar, and swell mountain high; the rut of the sea was great, the waves breaking upon our ship's quarter; the north-west wind blustered and overblowed; boisterous gusts, dreadful clashing and deadly scuds of wind whistled through our yards, and made our shrouds rattle again. The thunder grumbled so horridly, that you would have thought heaven had been tumbling about our ears; at the same time it lightened, rained, hailed, the sky lost its transparent hue, grew dusky, thick, and gloomy, so that we had no other light than that of the flashes of lightning, and rending of the clouds: the hurricanes, flaws, and sudden whirlwinds began to make a flame about us, by the lightnings, fiery vapours, and other aerial ejaculations. Oh how our looks were full of amazement and trouble, while the saucy winds did rudely lift up above us the mountainous waves of the main! Believe me, it seemed to us a lively image of the chaos, where fire, air, sea, land, and all the elements were in a refractory confusion. Poor Panurge having, with the full contents of the inside of his doublet, plentifully fed the fish, greedy enough of such odious fare, sat on the deck all in a heap, with his nose and arse together, most sadly cast down, moping and half dead; invoked and called to his assistance all the blessed he and she saints he could muster up; swore and vowed to confess in time and place convenient, and then bawled out frightfully, Steward, *maître d'hôtel*, see hoe! my friend, my father, my uncle, prithee let us have a piece of powdered beef or pork; we shall drink but too much anon, for aught I see. Eat little and drink the more, will hereafter be my motto, I fear. Would to our dear Lord, and to our blessed, worthy, and sacred Lady, I were now, I say, this very minute of an hour, well on shore, on terra firma, hale and easy. O twice and thrice happy those that plant cabbages! O

Destinies, why did you not spin me for a cabbage-planter? O how few are there to whom Jupiter hath been so favourable, as to predestinate them to plant cabbages! They have always one foot on the ground, and the other not far from it. Dispute who will of felicity, and *summum bonum*, for my part, whosoever plants cabbages, is now, by my decree, proclaimed most happy; for as good a reason as the philosopher Pyrrho, being in the same danger, and seeing a hog near the shore, eating some scattered oats, declared it happy in two respects; first, because it had plenty of oats, and besides that, was on shore. Ha, for a divine and princely habitation, commend me to the cows' floor.

Murder! This wave will sweep us away, blessed Saviour! O my friends! a little vinegar. I sweat again with mere agony. Alas, the mizen sail is split, the gallery is washed away, the masts are sprung, the main-top-mast-head dives into the sea; the keel is up to the sun; our shrouds are almost all broke, and blown away. Alas! alas! where is our main course? *Al is verlooren, by Godt;* our top-mast is run adrift. Alas! who shall have this wreck? Friend, lend me here behind you one of these whales. Your lanthorn is fallen, my lads. Alas! do not let go the main tack nor the bowlin. I hear the block crack; is it broke? For the Lord's sake, let us have the hull, and let all the rigging be damned. Be, be, be, bous, bous, bous. Look to the needle of your compass, I beseech you, good Sir Astrophil, and tell us, if you can, whence comes this storm. My heart's sunk down below my midriff. By my troth, I am in a sad fright, bou, bou, bou, bou, bous, bous, I am lost for ever. I conskite myself for mere madness and fear. Bou, bou, bou, bou, Otto to to to to ti. Bou, bou, bou, ou, ou, ou, bou, bou, bous. I sink, I am drowned, I am gone, good people, I am drowned.

CHAPTER XIX

What countenances Panurge and Friar John kept during the storm

PANTAGRUEL, having first implored the help of the great and Almighty Deliverer, and prayed publicly with fervent devotion, by the pilot's advice held tightly the mast of the ship. Friar John had stripped himself to his waistcoat, to help the seamen. Epistemon, Ponocrates, and the rest did as much. Panurge alone sat on his breech upon deck, weeping and howling. Friar

John espied him going on the quarter-deck, and said to him,
Odzoons! Panurge the calf, Panurge the whiner, Panurge the
brayer, would it not become thee much better to lend us here
a helping hand, than to lie lowing like a cow, as thou dost,
sitting on thy stones like a bald-breeched baboon? Be, be,
be, bous, bous, bous, returned Panurge; Friar John, my friend,
my good father, I am drowning, my dear friend! I drown!
I am a dead man, my dear father in God, I am a dead man, my
friend: your cutting hanger cannot save me from this: alas!
alas! we are above *e la*. Above the pitch, out of tune, and off
the hinges. Be, be, be, bou, bous. Alas! we are now above
g sol re ut. I sink, I sink, ha, my father, my uncle, my all. The
water is got into my shoes by the collar; bous, bous, bous, paish,
hu, hu, hu, he, he, he, ha, ha, ha, I drown. Alas! alas! Hu, hu,
hu, hu, hu, hu, hu, be, be, bous, bous, bobous, bobous, ho,
ho, ho, ho, ho, alas! alas! Now I am like your tumblers, my
feet stand higher than my head. Would to heaven I were now
with those good holy fathers bound for the council, whom we
met this morning, so godly, so fat, so merry, so plump, and
comely. Holos, nolos, holas, holas, alas! This devilish wave,
(*mea culpa Deus*,) I mean this wave of God, will sink our vessel.
Alas, Friar John, my father, my friend, confession. Here I am
down on my knees; *confiteor*; your holy blessing. Come hither
and be damned, thou pitiful devil, and help us, said Friar,—
who fell a swearing and cursing like a tinker,—in the name of
thirty legions of black devils, come; will you come? Do not
let us swear, at this time, said Panurge; holy father, my friend,
do not swear, I beseech you; to-morrow as much as you please.
Holos, holos, alas, our ship leaks. I drown, alas, alas! I will
give eighteen hundred thousand crowns to any one that will
set me on shore, all bewrayed and bedaubed as I am now. If
ever there was a man in my country in the like pickle. *Confiteor*,
alas! a word or two of testament or codicil at least. A thousand
devils seize the cuckoldy cow-hearted mongrel, cried Friar John.
Ods belly, art thou talking here of making thy will, now we are
in danger, and it behoveth us to bestir our stumps lustily, or
never? Wilt thou come, ho devil? Midshipman, my friend;
O the rare lieutenant; here Gymnast, here on the poop. We are,
by the mass, all beshit now, our light is out. This is hastening
to the devil as fast as it can. Alas, bou, bou, bou, bou, bou,
alas, alas, alas, alas, said Panurge, was it here we were born
to perish? Oh! ho! good people I drown, I die. *Consummatum
est*. I am sped—*Magna, gna, gna*, said Friar John. Fie upon

him, how ugly the shitten howler looks. Boy, younker, see hoyh. Mind the pumps, or the devil choke thee. Hast thou hurt thyself? Zoons, here fasten it to one of these blocks. On this side, in the devil's name, hay—so my boy. Ah, Friar John, said Panurge, good ghostly father, dear friend, do not let us swear, you sin. Oh ho, oh ho, be be be bous, bous, bhous, I sink, I die, my friends. I die in charity with all the world. Farewell, *in manus*. Bohus bohous, bhousowauswaus. St. Michael of Aure! St. Nicholas! now, now or never, I here make you a solemn vow, and to our Saviour, that if you stand by me this time, I mean if you set me ashore out of this danger, I will built you a fine large little chapel or two, between Candé and Monsoreau, where neither cow nor calf shall feed. Oh ho, oh ho. Above eighteen pailfuls or two of it are got down my gullet; bous, bhous, bhous, bhous, how damned bitter and salt it is! By the virtue, said Friar John, of the blood, the flesh, the belly, the head, if I hear thee again howling, thou cuckoldy cur, I will maul thee worse than any sea wolf. Ods fish, why do not we take him up by the lugs and throw him overboard to the bottom of the sea? Here, sailor, ho honest fellow. Thus, thus, my friend, hold fast above. In truth here is a sad lightning and thundering; I think that all the devils are got loose; it is holiday with them; or else Madame Proserpine is in child's labour: all the devils dance a morrice.

CHAPTER XX

How the Pilots were forsaking their ships in the greatest stress of weather

OH, said Panurge, you sin, Friar John, my former crony! former, I say, for at this time I am no more, you are no more. It goes against my heart to tell it you: for I believe this swearing doth your spleen a great deal of good; as it is a great ease to a wood cleaver to cry hem at every blow; and as one who plays at nine pins is wonderfully helped, if, when he hath not thrown his bowl right, and is like to make a bad cast, some ingenious stander by leans and screws his body half way about, on that side which the bowl should have took to hit the pin. Nevertheless you offend, my sweet friend. But what do you think of eating some kind of cabirotadoes? Would not this secure us from this storm? I have read, that in a storm at sea no harm

ever befel the ministers of the gods Cabiri, so much celebrated
by Orpheus, Apollonius, Pherecides, Strabo, Pausanias, and
Herodotus. He dotes, he raves, the poor devil! A thousand,
a million, nay, a hundred million of devils seize the hornified
doddipole. Lend us a hand here, hoh, tiger, wouldst thou?
Here, on the starboard side. Ods me, thou buffalo's head
stuffed with relics, what ape's paternoster art thou muttering
and chattering here between thy teeth? That devil of a sea
calf is the cause of all this storm, and is the only man who doth
not lend a helping hand. By G—, if I come near thee, I'll
fetch thee out by the head and ears with a vengeance, and
chastise thee like any tempestative devil. Here mate, my lad,
hold fast, till I have made a double knot. O brave boy! Would
to heaven thou wert abbot of Talemouze, and that he that is
were guardian of Croullay. Hold, brother Ponocrates, you will
hurt yourself man. Epistemon, pray thee stand off out of the
hatchway. Methinks I saw the thunder fall there but just now.
Con the ship, so ho—Mind your steerage. Well said, thus,
thus, steady, keep her thus, get the long boat clear—steady.
Ods fish, the beak-head is staved to pieces. Grumble, devils,
fart, belch, shite, a turd on the wave. If this be weather, the
devil is a ram. Nay, by G—, a little more would have washed
me clear away into the current. I think all the legions of
devils hold here their provincial chapter, or are polling, can-
vassing, and wrangling for the election of a new rector. Starboard; well said. Take heed; have a care of your noddle, lad,
in the devil's name. So ho, starboard, starboard. Be, be, be,
bous, bous, bous, cried Panurge, bous, bous, be, be, be, bous,
bous, I am lost. I see neither heaven nor earth; of the four
elements we have here only fire and water left. Bou, bou,
bou, bous, bous, bous. Would it were the pleasure of the
worthy divine bounty, that I were at this present hour in the
close at Sevillé, or at Innocent's, the pastry-cook, over against
the painted wine vault at Chinon, though I were to strip to my
doublet, and bake the petti-pasties myself.

Honest man, could not you throw me ashore? you can do a
world of good things, they say. I give you all Salmigondinois,
and my large shore full of whilks, cockles, and periwinkles, if,
by your industry, I ever set foot on firm ground. Alas, alas,
I drown. Harkee, my friends, since we cannot get safe into
port, let us come to an anchor into some road, no matter whither.
Drop all your anchors; let us be out of danger, I beseech you.
Here honest tar, get you into the chains, and heave the lead,

if it please you. Let us know how many fathom water we are in. Sound, friend, in the Lord Harry's name. Let us know whether a man might here drink easily, without stooping. I am apt to believe one might. Helm a-lee, hoh, cried the pilot. Helm-a lee; a hand or two at the helm; about ships with her; helm a-lee; helm a-lee. Stand off from the leech of the sail. Hoh! belay, here make fast below; hoh, helm a-lee, lash sure the helm a-lee, and let her drive. Is it come to that? said Pantagruel: our good Saviour then help us. Let her lie under the sea, cried James Brahier, our chief mate, let her drive. To prayers, to prayers, let all think on their souls, and fall to prayers; nor hope to escape but by a miracle. Let us, said Panurge, make some good pious kind of vow: alas, alas, alas! bou, bou, be, be, be, bous, bous, bous, oho, oho, oho, oho, let us make a pilgrim: come, come, let every man club his penny towards it, come on. Here, here, on this side, said Friar John, in the devil's name. Let her drive, for the Lord's sake unhang the rudder: hoh, let her drive, let her drive, and let us drink, I say, of the best and most cheering; do you hear, steward, produce, exhibit; for, do you see this, and all the rest will as well go to the devil out of hand. A pox on that wind-broker Æolus, with his fluster-blusters. Sirrah, page, bring me here my drawer (for so he called his breviary); stay a little here, haul, friend, thus. Odzoons, here is a deal of hail and thunder to no purpose. Hold fast above, I pray you. When have we All-saints day? I believe it is the unholy holiday of all the devil's crew. Alas, said Panurge, Friar John damns himself here as black as buttermilk for the nonce. Oh what a good friend I lose in him. Alas, alas, this is another gats-bout than last year's. We are falling out of Scylla into Charybdis. Oho! I drown. *Confiteor*; one poor word or two by way of testament, Friar John, my ghostly father; good Mr. Abstractor, my crony, my Achates, Xenomanes, my all. Alas! I drown; two words of testament here upon this ladder.

CHAPTER XXI

A continuation of the storm, with a short discourse on the subject of making testaments at sea

To make one's last will, said Epistemon, at this time that we ought to bestir ourselves and help our seamen, on the penalty of being drowned, seems to me as idle and ridiculous a maggot

as that of some of Cæsar's men, who, at their coming into the
Gauls, were mightily busied in making wills and codicils; bemoaned their fortune, and the absence of their spouses and
friends at Rome; when it was absolutely necessary for them
to run to their arms, and use their utmost strength against
Ariovistus their enemy.

This also is to be as silly, as that jolt-headed loblolly of a
carter, who, having laid his waggon fast in a slough, down on
his marrow-bones, was calling on the strong-backed deity,
Hercules, might and main, to help him at a dead lift, but all the
while forgot to goad on his oxen, and lay his shoulder to the
wheels, as it behoved him: as if a Lord have mercy upon us,
alone, would have got his cart out of the mire.

What will it signify to make your will now? for either we
shall come off or drown for it. If we escape, it will not signify
a straw to us; for testaments are of no value or authority, but
by the death of the testators. If we are drowned, will it not
be drowned too? Pr'ythee who will transmit it to the executors?
Sone kind wave will throw it ashore, like Ulysses, replied
Panurge; and some king's daughter, going to fetch a walk in
the fresco, on the evening, will find it, and take care to have
it proved and fulfilled; nay, and have some stately cenotaph
erected to my memory, as Dido had to that of her good man
Sichæus; Æneas to Deiphobus, upon the Trojan shore, near
Rhœte; Andromache to Hector, in the city of Buthrotus;
Aristotle to Hermias and Eubulus; the Athenians to the poet
Euripides; the Romans to Drusus in Germany, and to Alexander Severus, their emperor, in the Gauls; Argentier to Callais-
chre; Xenocrates to Lysidices; Timares to his son Teleutagoras;
Eupolis and Aristodice to their son Theotimus; Onestus to
Timocles; Callimachus to Sopolis, the son of Dioclides; Catullus
to his brother; Statius to his father; Germain of Brie to Hervé,
the Breton tarpaulin. Art thou mad, said Friar John, to run
on at this rate? Help, here, in the name of five hundred
thousand millions of cart-loads of devils, help! may a shanker
gnaw thy moustachios, and the three rows of pock-royals and
cauliflowers cover thy bum and turd-barrel, instead of breeches
and cod-piece. Codsooks our ship is almost overset. Ods death,
how shall we clear her? it is well if she do not founder. What
a devilish sea there runs! She will neither try nor hull; the
sea will overtake her, so we shall never escape; the devil escape
me. Then Pantagruel was heard to make a sad exclamation,
saying, with a loud voice, Lord save us, we perish; yet not as

we would have it, but thy holy will be done. The Lord and the blessed Virgin be with us, said Panurge. Holos, alas, I drown; be be be bous, be bous, bous: *in manus*. Good heavens, send me some dolphin to carry me safe on shore, like a pretty little Arion. I shall make shift to sound the harp, if it be not unstrung. Let nineteen legions of black devils seize me, said Friar John, (the Lord be with us, whispered Panurge, between his chattering teeth.) If I come down to thee, I will show thee to some purpose, that the badge of thy humanity dangles at a calf's breech, thou ragged, horned, cuckoldy booby: mgna, mgnan, mgnan: come hither and help us, thou great weeping calf, or may thirty millions of devils leap on thee. Wilt thou come, sea-calf? Fie! how ugly the howling whelp looks. What, always the same ditty? Come on now, my bonny drawer. This he said, opening his breviary. Come forward, thou and I must be somewhat serious for a while; let me peruse thee stiffly. *Beatus vir qui non abiit.* Pshaw, I know all this by heart; let us see the legend of Mons. St. Nicholas.

Horrida tempestas montem turbavit acutum.

Tempeste was a mighty flogger of lads, at Mountaigu College. If pedants be damned for whipping poor little innocent wretches their scholars, he is, upon my honour, by this time fixed within Ixion's wheel, lashing the crop-eared, bob-tailed cur that gives it motion. If they are saved for having whipped innocent lads, he ought to be above the——

CHAPTER XXII

An end of the storm

SHORE, shore! cried Pantagruel. Land ho, my friends, I see land! Pluck up a good spirit, boys, it is within a kenning. So! we are not far from a port.—I see the sky clearing up to the northwards.—Look to the south-east! Courage, my hearts, said the pilot; now she will bear the hullock of a sail: the sea is much smoother; some hands aloft to the main top. Put the helm a-weather. Steady! steady! Haul your after mizen bowlings. Haul, haul, haul! Thus, thus, and no near. Mind your steerage; bring your main tack aboard. Clear your sheets; clear your bowlings; port, port. Helm a-lee. Now to the sheet on the starboard side, thou son of a whore. Thou art mightily pleased, honest fellow, quoth Friar John, with hearing make mention of thy mother. Luff, luff, cried the quarter-master that conned the ship, keep her full, luff the helm. Luff. It is, answered the steersman. Keep her thus. Get the bonnets fixed. Steady, steady.

That is well said, said Friar John; now, this is something like a tansey. Come, come, come children, be nimble. Good. Luff, luff, thus. Helm a-weather. That is well said and thought on. Methinks the storm is almost over. It was high time, faith: however, the Lord be thanked. Our devils begin to scamper. Out with all your sails. Hoist your sails. Hoist. That is spoke like a man, hoist, hoist. Here, a God's name, honest Ponocrates; thou art a lusty fornicator; the whoreson will get none but boys. Eusthenes, thou art a notable fellow. Run up to the fore-top sail. Thus, thus. Well said, i' faith; thus, thus. I dare not fear anything all this while, for it is holiday. Vea, vea, vea! huzza! This shout of the seaman is not amiss, and pleases me, for it is holiday. Keep her full thus. Good. Cheer up my merry mates, all, cried out Epistemon; I see already Castor on the right. Be, be, bous, bous, bous, said Panurge, I am much afraid it is the bitch Helen. It is truly Mixarchagenas, returned Epistemon, if thou likest better that denomination, which the Argives give him. Ho, ho! I see land too; let her bear in with the harbour: I see a good many people on the beach: I see a light on an obeliscolychny. Shorten your sails, said the pilot; fetch the sounding line; we must double that point of land, and mind the sands. We are clear of them, said the sailors. Soon after, Away she goes, quoth the pilot, and so doth the rest of our fleet; help came in good season.

By St. John, said Panurge, this is spoke somewhat like: O the sweet word! there is the soul of music in it. Mgna, mgna, mgna, said Friar John; if ever thou taste a drop of it, let the devil's dam taste me, thou ballocky devil. Here, honest soul, here is a full sneaker of the very best. Bring the flagons: dost hear, Gymnast? and that same large pasty jambic, or gammonic, even as you will have it. Take heed you pilot her in right.

Cheer up, cried out Pantagruel; cheer up my boys: let us be ourselves again. Do you see yonder, close by our ship, two barks, three sloops, five ships, eight pinks, four yawls, and six frigates, making towards us, sent by the good people of the neighbouring island to our relief? But who is this Ucalegon below, that cried, and makes such a sad moan?

Were it not that I hold the mast firmly with both my hands, and keep it straighter than two hundred tacklings—I would ——It is, said Friar John, that poor devil, Panurge, who is troubled with a calf's ague; he quakes for fear when his belly is full. If, said Pantagruel, he hath been afraid during this dreadful hurricane and dangerous storm, provided he hath done his part like a man, I do not value him a jot the less for it. For as, to fear in all encounters, is the mark of a heavy and cowardly heart; as Agamemnon did, who, for that reason, is ignominiously taxed by Achilles with having dog's eyes, and a stag's heart: so, not to fear when the case is evidently dreadful, is a sign of want or smallness of judgment. Now, if anything ought to be feared in this life, next to offending God, I will not say it is death. I will not meddle with the disputes of Socrates and the academics, that death of itself is neither bad nor to be feared; but, I will affirm, that this kind of shipwreck is to be feared, or nothing is. For, as Homer saith, it is a grievous, dreadful, and unnatural thing, to perish at sea. And, indeed, Æneas, in the storm that took his fleet near Sicily, was grieved that he had not died by the hand of the brave Diomedes; and said that those were three, nay four times happy, who perished in the conflagration at Troy. No man here hath lost his life, the Lord our Saviour be eternally praised for it: but in truth here is a ship sadly out of order. Well, we must take care to have the damage repaired. Take heed we do not run aground and bulge her.

CHAPTER XXIII

How Panurge played the good fellow when the storm was over

WHAT cheer, ho, fore and aft? quoth Panurge. Oh ho! all is well, the storm is over. I beseech ye, be so kind as to let me be the first that is sent on shore; for I would by all means a little untruss a point. Shall I help you still? Here, let me see, I will coil this rope; I have plenty of courage, and of fear as little as may be. Give it me yonder, honest tar. No, no, I have not a bit of fear. Indeed, that same decumane wave, that took us fore and aft, somewhat altered my pulse. Down with your sails; well said. How now, Friar John? you do nothing. Is it time for us to drink now? Who can tell but St. Martin's running footman may still be hatching us some further mischief? shall I come and help you again? Pork and peas choke me, if I do heartily repent, though too late, not having followed the doctrine of the good philosopher, who tells us that to walk by the sea, and to navigate by the shore, are very safe and pleasant things: just as it is to go on foot, when we hold our horse by the bridle. Ha! ha! ha! by G— all goes well. Shall I help you here too? Let me see, I will do this as it should be, or the devil is in it.

Epistemon, who had the inside of one of his hands all flayed and bloody, having held a tackling with might and main, hearing what Pantagruel had said, told him: You may believe me, lord, I had my share of fear as well as Panurge; yet I spared no pains in lending my helping hand. I considered, that since by fatal and unavoidable necessity, we must all die, it is the blessed will of God that we die this or that hour, and this or that kind of death: nevertheless we ought to implore, invoke, pray, beseech, and supplicate him: but we must not stop there; it behoveth us also to use our endeavours on our side, and, as the holy writ saith, to co-operate with him.

You know what C. Flaminius, the consul said, when by Hannibal's policy he was penned up near the lake of Peruse, alias Thrasymene. Friends, said he to his soldiers, you must not hope to get out of this place barely by vows or prayers to the gods; no, it is by fortitude and strength we must escape and cut ourselves a way with the edge of our swords through the midst of our enemies.

Sallust likewise makes M. Portius Cato say this: The help of the gods is not obtained by idle vows and womanish complaints; it is by vigilance, labour, and repeated endeavours, that all things succeed according to our wishes and designs. If a man, in time of need and danger, is negligent, heartless, and lazy, in vain he implores the gods; they are then justly angry and incensed against him. The devil take me, said Friar John (I'll go his halves, quoth Panurge), if the close of Sevillé had not been all gathered, vintaged, gleaned, and destroyed, if I had only sung *contra hostium insidias* (matter of breviary) like all the rest of the monkish devils, and had not bestirred myself to save the vineyard as I did, dispatching the truant picaroons of Lerné with the staff of the cross.

Let her sink or swim a God's name, said Panurge, all's one to Friar John; he doth nothing; his name is Friar John Do-little; for all he sees me here sweating and puffing to help with all my might this honest tar, first of the name.—Hark you me, dear soul, a word with you,—but pray be not angry. How thick do you judge the planks of our ship to be? Some two good inches and upwards, returned the pilot; don't fear. Odskilderkins, said Panurge, it seems then we are within two fingers' breadth of damnation.

Is this one of the nine comforts of matrimony? Ah, dear soul, you do well to measure the danger by the yard of fear. For my part, I have none on't; my name is William Dreadnought. As for my heart, I have more than enough on't; I mean none of your sheep's heart; but of wolf's heart; the courage of a bravo. By the pavilion of Mars, I fear nothing but danger.

CHAPTER XXIV

How Panurge was said to have been afraid without reason, during the storm

GOOD morrow, gentlemen said Panurge, good morrow to you all: you are in very good health, thanks to heaven and your selves; you are all heartily welcome, and in good time. Let us go on shore.—Here cockswain, get the ladder over the gunnel; man the sides: man the pinnace, and get her by the ship's side. Shall I lend you a hand here? I am stark mad for want of business, and would work like any two yokes of oxen. Truly this is a fine place, and these look like a very good people. Children, do you want me still in anything? do not spare the sweat of my body, for God's sake. Adam —that is man—was made to labour and work, as the birds were made to fly. Our Lord's will is, that we get our bread with the sweat of our brows, not idling and doing nothing, like this tatterdamallion of a monk here, this Friar Jack, who is fain to drink to hearten himself up, and dies for fear.—Rare weather. —I now find the answer of Anacharsis, the noble philosopher, very proper: being asked what ship he reckoned the safest? he replied, That which is in the harbour. He made yet a better repartee, said Pantagruel, when somebody inquiring which is greater, the number of the living or that of the dead? he asked them, amongst which of the two they reckoned those that are at sea? ingeniously implying, that they are continually in danger of death, dying live, and living die. Portius Cato also said, that there were but three things of which he would repent; if ever he had trusted his wife with his secret, if he had idled away a day, and if he had ever gone by sea to a place which he could visit by land. By this dignified frock of mine, said Friar John to Panurge, friend, thou hast been afraid during the storm, without cause or reason: for thou wert not born to be drowned, but rather to be hanged, and exalted in the air, or to be roasted in the midst of a jolly bonfire. My lord, would you have a good cloak for the rain; leave me off your wolf and badger-skin mantle: let Panurge but be flayed, and cover yourself with his hide. But do not come near the fire, nor near your blacksmith's forges, a God's name; for in a moment you will see it in ashes. Yet be as long as you please in the rain, snow, hail, nay by the devil's maker, throw yourself, or dive down to the very bottom of the water, I'll engage you'll not be wet at all. Have some winter boots made of it, they'll never take in a drop of water: make bladders of it to lay under boys, to teach them to swim, instead of corks, and they will learn without the least danger. His skin, then, said Pantagruel, should be like the herb called true maiden's hair, which never takes wet nor moistness, but still keeps dry, though you lay it at the bottom of the water as long as you please; and for that reason is called *Adiantos*.

Friend Panurge, said Friar John, I pray thee never be afraid of water: thy life for mine thou art threatened with a contrary element. Ay, ay, replied Panurge, but the devil's cooks dote sometimes, and are apt to make horrid blunders as well as others: often putting to boil in water, what was designed to be roasted on the fire: like the head cooks of our kitchen, who often lard partridges, queests, and stock-doves, with intent to roast them, one would think; but it happens sometimes, that they even turn the partridges into the pot, to be boiled with cabbages, the queests with leek pottage, and the stock-doves with turnips. But hark you me, good friends, I protest before this noble company, that as for the chapel which I vowed to Mons. St. Nicholas, between Candé and Monsoreau, I honestly mean that it shall be a chapel of rose-water, which shall be where neither cow nor calf shall be fed: for between you and I, I intend to throw it to the bottom of the water. Here is a rare rogue for you, said Eusthenes: here is a pure rogue, a rogue in grain, a rogue enough, a rogue and a half. He is resolved to make good the Lombardic proverb, *Passato il pericolo, egabato il santo*.

> The devil was sick, the devil a monk would be
> The devil was well, the devil a monk was he.

CHAPTER XXV

How, after the storm, Pantagruel went on shore in the Island of the Macreons

IMMEDIATELY after, he went ashore at the port of an island which they called the island of the Macreons. The good people of the place received us very honourably. An old Macrobius (so they called their eldest elderman) desired Pantagruel to come to the town-house to refresh himself, and eat something: but he would not budge a foot from the mole till all his men were landed. After he had seen them, he gave order that they should all change clothes, and that some of all the stores in the fleet should be brought on shore, that every ship's crew might live well: which was accordingly done, and God wot how well they all toped and caroused. The people of the place brought them provisions in abundance. The Pantagruelists returned them more: as the truth is their's were somewhat damaged by the late storm. When they had well-stuffed the insides of their doublets, Pantagruel desired every one to lend their help to repair the damage; which they readily did. It was easy enough to refit there; for all the inhabitants of the island were carpenters, and all such handicrafts as are seen in the arsenal at Venice. None but the largest island was inhabited, having three ports and ten parishes; the rest being overrun with wood, and desert, much like the forest of Arden. We entreated the old Macrobius to show us what was worth seeing in the island; which he did; and in the desert and dark forest we discovered several old ruined temples, obelisks, pyramids, monuments, and ancient tombs, with divers inscriptions and epitaphs; some of them in hieroglyphic characters; others in the Ionic dialect; some in the Arabic, Agarenian, Sclavonian, and other tongues; of which Epistemon took an exact account. In the interim, Panurge said to Friar John, Is this the island of the Macreons? Macreon signifies in Greek an old man, or one much stricken in years. What is that to me, said Friar John, how can I help it? I was not in the country when they christened it. Now I think on it, quoth Panurge, I believe the name of mackerel (that is a bawd in French) was derived from it: for procuring is the province of the old, as buttock-riggling is that of the young. Therefore I do not know but this may be the bawdy or Mackerel island, the original and prototype of the island of that name at Paris.   Let us go and dredge for cock-oysters.   Old Macrobius asked, in the Ionic tongue, How, and by what industry and labour, Pantagruel got to their port that day, there having been such blustering weather, and such a dreadful storm at sea.   Pantagruel told him that the Almighty Preserver of mankind had regarded the simplicity and sincere affection of his servants, who did not travel for gain or sordid profit; the sole design of their voyage being a studious desire to know, see, and visit the Oracle of Bacbuc, and take the word of the Bottle upon some difficulties offered by one of the company: nevertheless this had not been without great affliction, and evident danger of shipwreck.   After that, he asked him what he judged to be the cause of that terrible tempest, and if the adjacent seas were thus frequently subject to storms; as in the ocean are the Ratz of Sammaieu, Maumusson, and in the Mediterranean sea the gulph of Sataly, Montargentan, Piombino, Capo Melio in Laconia, the Straits of Gibraltar, Faro di Messina, and others.

CHAPTER XXVI

How the good Macrobius gave us an account of the Mansion and Decease of the Heroes

THE good Macrobius then answered,—Friendly strangers, this island is one of the Sporades; not of your Sporades that lie in the Carpathian sea, but one of the Sporades of the ocean: in former times rich, frequented, wealthy, populous, full of traffic, and in the dominions of the rulers of Britain, but now, by course of time, and in these latter ages of the world, poor and desolate, as you see.   In this dark forest, above seventy-eight thousand Persian leagues in compass, is the dwelling-place of the demons and heroes, that are grown old, and we believed that some one of them died yesterday; since the comet, which we saw for three days before together, shines no more: and now it is likely, that at his death there arose this horrible storm; for while they are alive all happiness attends both this and the adjacent islands, and a settled calm and serenity.   At the death of every one of them, we commonly hear in the forest, loud and mournful groans, and the whole land is infested with pestilence, earthquakes, inundations, and other calamities; the air with fogs and obscurity, and the sea with storms and hurricanes. What you tell us, seems to me likely enough, said Pantagruel. For, as a torch or candle, as long as it hath life enough and is lighted, shines round about, disperses its light, delights those that are near it, yields them its service and clearness, and never causes any pain or displeasure; but as soon as it is extinguished, its smoke and evaporation infect the air, offend the by-standers, and are noisome to all: so, as long as those noble and renowned souls inhabit their bodies, peace, profit, pleasure, and honour never leave the places where they abide; but as soon as they leave them, both the continent and adjacent islands are annoyed with great commotions; in the air fogs, darkness, thunder, hail; tremblings, pulsations, agitations of the earth; storms and hurricanes at sea; together with sad complaints amongst the people, broaching of religions, changes in governments, and ruins of commonwealths.

We had a sad instance of this lately, said Epistemon, at the death of that valiant and learned knight, William du Bellay; during whose life France enjoyed so much happiness, that all the rest of the world looked upon it with envy, sought friendship with it, and stood in awe of its power; but now, after his decease, it hath for a considerable time been the scorn of the rest of the world.

Thus, said Pantagruel, Anchises being dead at Drepani, in Sicily, Æneas was dreadfully tossed and endangered by a storm; and perhaps for the same reason, Herod, that tyrant and cruel King of Judea, finding himself near the passage of a horrid kind of death,—for he died of a phthiriasis, devoured by vermin and lice; as before him died L. Sylla, Pherecydes, the Syrian, the preceptor of Pythagoras, the Greek poet Alcmæon, and others, —and foreseeing that the Jews would make bonfires at his death, caused all the nobles and magistrates to be summoned to his seraglio, out of all the cities, towns, and castles of Judea, fraudulently pretending that he had some things of moment to impart to them. They made their personal appearance; whereupon he caused them all to be shut up in the hippodrome of the seraglio; then said to his sister Salome, and Alexander her husband: I am certain that the Jews will rejoice at my death; but if you will observe and perform what I tell you, my funeral shall be honourable, and there will be a general mourning. As soon as you see me dead, let my guards, to whom I have already given strict commission to that purpose, kill all the noblemen and magistrates that are secured in the hippodrome. By these means, all Jewry shall, in spite of themselves, be

obliged to mourn and lament, and foreigners will imagine it to
be for my death, as if some heroic soul had left her body. A
desperate tyrant wished as much when he said, When I die,
let earth and fire be mixed together; which was as good as to
say, let the whole world perish. Which saying the tyrant
Nero altered, saying, While I live, as Suetonius affirms it.
This detestable saying, of which Cicero, *lib. De Finib.* and
Seneca, *lib. 2, De Clementia*, make mention, is ascribed to the
Emperor Tiberius, by Dion Nicæus and Suidas.

CHAPTER XXVII

*Pantagruel's discourse of the decease of heroic souls; and of the
dreadful prodigies that happened before the death of the late
Lord de Langey*

I WOULD not, continued Pantagruel, have missed the storm that
hath thus disordered us, were I also to have missed the relation
of these things told us by this good Macrobius. Neither am I
unwilling to believe what he said of a comet that appears in
the sky some days before such a decease. For some of these
souls are so noble, so precious, and so heroic that heaven gives
us notice of their departing some days before it happens. And
as a prudent physician, seeing by some symptoms that his
patient draws towards his end, some days before, gives notice
of it to his wife, children, kindred, and friends, that, in that
little time he hath yet to live, they may admonish him to settle
all things in his family, to tutor and instruct his children as
much as he can, recommend his relict to his friends in her
widowhood, and declare what he knows to be necessary about
a provision for the orphans; that he may not be surprised by
death without making his will, and may take care of his soul
and family: in the same manner the heavens, as it were, joyful
for the approaching reception of those blessed souls, seem to
make bonfires by those comets and blazing meteors, which
they at the same time kindly design should prognosticate to
us here, that in a few days one of those venerable souls is to
leave her body, and this terrestrial globe. Not altogether
unlike this was what was formerly done at Athens, by the judges
of the Areopagus. For when they gave their verdict to cast
or clear the culprits that were tried before them, they used
certain notes according to the substance of the sentences; by

Θ, signifying sentence to death; by T, absolution; by A, ampliation or a demur, when the case was not sufficiently examined. Thus having publicly set up those letters, they eased the relations and friends of the prisoners, and such others as desired to know their doom, of their doubts. Likewise by these comets, as in ætherial characters, the heavens silently say to us, Make haste mortals, if you would know or learn of the blessed souls any thing concerning the public good, or your private interest; for their catastrophe is near, which being past, you will vainly wish for them afterwards.

The good-natured heavens still do more: and that mankind may be declared unworthy of the enjoyment of those renowned souls, they fright and astonish us with prodigies, monsters, and other foreboding signs, that thwart the order of nature.

Of this we had an instance several days before the decease of the heroic soul of the learned and valiant Chevalier de Langey, of whom you have already spoken. I remember it, said Epistemon; and my heart still trembles within me, when I think on the many dreadful prodigies that we saw five or six days before he died. For the Lords D'Assier, Chemant, one-eyed Mailly, St. Ayl, Villeneufve-la-Guart, Master Gabriel, physician of Savillan, Rabelais, Cohuau, Massuau, Majorici, Ballou, Cercu alias Bourgmaistre, Francis Proust, Ferron, Charles Girard, Francis Bourré, and many other friends and servants to the deceased, all dismayed, gazed on each other without uttering one word; yet not without foreseeing that France would in a short time be deprived of a knight so accomplished, and necessary for its glory and protection, and that heaven claimed him again as its due. By the tufted tip of my cowl, cried Friar John, I am even resolved to become a scholar before I die. I have a pretty good head-piece of my own, you must confess. Now pray give me leave to ask a civil question. Can these same heroes or demigods you talk of, die? May I never be damned, if I was not so much a lobcock as to believe they had been immortal, like so many fine angels. Heaven forgive me! but this most reverend father, Macrobius, tells us they die at last. Not all, returned Pantagruel.

The stoics held them all to be mortal, except one, who alone is immortal, impassable, invisible. Pindar plainly saith, that there is no more thread, that is to say, no more life, spun from the distaff and flax of the hard-hearted fates for the goddesses Hamadryades, than there is for those trees that are preserved by them, which are good, sturdy, downright oaks; whence they derived their original, according to the opinion of Callimachus, and Pausanias *in Phoci*. With whom concurs Martianus Capella. As for the demigods, fauns, satyrs, sylvans, hobgoblins, ægipanes, nymphs, heroes, and demons, several men have, from the total sum, which is the result of the divers ages calculated by Hesiod, reckoned their life to be 9720 years: that sum consisting of four special numbers orderly arising from one, the same added together, and multiplied by four every way, amounts to forty; these forties, being reduced into triangles by five times, make up the total of the aforesaid number. See Plutarch, in his book about the Cessation of Oracles.

This, said Friar John, is not matter of breviary; I may believe as little or as much of it as you and I please. I believe, said Pantagruel, that all intellectual souls are exempted from Atropos's scissors. They are all immortal, whether they be of angels, of demons, or human: yet I will tell you a story concerning this, that is very strange, but is written and affirmed by several learned historians.

CHAPTER XXVIII

How Pantagruel related a very sad story of the Death of the Heroes

EPITHERSES, the father of Æmilian the rhetorician, sailing from Greece to Italy, in a ship freighted with divers goods and passengers, at night the wind failed them near the Echinades, some islands that lie between the Morea and Tunis, and the vessel was driven near Paxos. When they got thither, some of the passengers being asleep, others awake, the rest eating and drinking, a voice was heard that called aloud, Thamous! which cry surprised them all. This same Thamous was their pilot, an Egyptian by birth, but known by name only to some few travellers. The voice was heard a second time, calling Thamous, in a frightful tone; and none making answer, but trembling, and remaining silent, the voice was heard a third time, more dreadful than before.

This caused Thamous to answer: Here am I; what dost thou call me for? What wilt thou have me do? Then the voice, louder than before, bid him publish, when he should come to Palodes, that the great god Pan was dead.

Epitherses related that all the mariners and passengers, having heard this, were extremely amazed and frighted; and that consulting among themselves, whether they had best conceal or divulge what the voice had enjoined; Thamous said his advice was, that if they happened to have a fair wind, they should proceed without mentioning a word of it, but if the chanced to be becalmed, he would publish what he had heard Now when they were near Palodes, they had no wind, neither were they in any current. Thamous then getting up on the top of the ship's forecastle and casting his eyes on the shore, said that he had been commanded to proclaim that the great god Pan was dead. The words were hardly out of his mouth, when deep groans, great lamentations, and doleful shrieks, not of one person, but of many together, were heard from the land.

The news of this—many being present—was soon spread at Rome; insomuch that Tiberius, who was then emperor, sent for this Thamous, and having heard him, gave credit to his words. And inquiring of the learned in his court, and at Rome, who was that Pan? he found by their relation that he was the son of Mercury and Penelope, as Herodotus and Cicero in his third book of the Nature of the Gods had written before.

For my part, I understand it of that great Saviour of the faithful, who was shamefully put to death at Jerusalem, by the envy and wickedness of the doctors, priests, and monks of the Mosaic law. And methinks, my interpretation is not improper; for he may lawfully be said in the Greek tongue to be *Pan*, since he is our *all*. For all that we are, all that we live, all that we have, all that we hope, is him, by him, from him, and in him. He is the good Pan, the great shepherd, who, as the loving shepherd Corydon affirms, hath not only a tender love and affection for his sheep, but also for their shepherds. At his death, complaints, sighs, fears, and lamentations were spread through the whole fabric of the universe, whether heavens, land, sea or hell.

The time also concurs with this interpretation of mine; for this most good, most mighty Pan, our only Saviour, died near Jerusalem, during the reign of Tiberius Cæsar.

Pantagruel, having ended this discourse, remained silent, and full of contemplation. A little while after, we saw the tears flow out of his eyes as big as ostrich's eggs. God take me presently, if I tell you one single syllable of a lie in the matter.

CHAPTER XXIX

How Pantagruel sailed by the Sneaking Island, where Shrovetide reigned

THE jovial fleet being refitted and repaired, new stores taken in, the Macreons over and above satisfied and pleased with the money spent there by Pantagruel, our men in better humour than they used to be, if possible, we merrily put to sea the next day, near sunset, with a delicious fresh gale.

Xenomanes showed us afar off the Sneaking Island, where reigned Shrovetide of whom Pantagruel had heard much talk formerly: for that reason he would gladly have seen him in person, had not Xenomanes advised him to the contrary: first, because this would have been much out of our way: and then for the lean cheer, *(manger maigre,)* which he told us was to be found at that prince's court, and indeed all over the island.

You can see nothing there for your money, said he, but a huge greedy guts, a tall woundy swallower of hot wardens and muscles; a long-shanked mole-catcher; an overgrown bottler of hay; a mossy-chinned demi-giant, with a double shaven crown, of lantern breed; a very great loitering noddy-peaked youngster, banner-bearer to the fish-eating tribe, dictator of mustard land, flogger of little children, calciner of ashes, father and foster-father to physicians; swarming with pardons, indulgences, and stations; a very honest man; a good catholic, and as brimful of devotion as ever he can hold.

He weeps the three-fourth parts of the day, and never assists at any weddings; but, give the devil his due, he is the most industrious larding-stick and skewer-maker in forty kingdoms.

About six years ago, as I passed through Sneaking-land, I brought home a large skewer from thence, and made a present of it to the butchers of Quande, who set a great value upon them, and that for a cause. Some time or other, if ever we live to come back to our own country, I will show you two of them fastened on the great church porch. His usual food is pickled coats of mail, salt helmets and headpieces, and salt sallads; which sometimes makes him piss pins and needles. As for his clothing, it is comical enough of conscience, both for make and colour; for he wears grey and cold, nothing before, and nought behind, with the sleeves of the same.

You will do me a kindness, said Pantagruel, if, as you have

described his clothes, food, actions, and pastimes, you will also give me an account of his shape and disposition in all its parts. Prithee do, dear cod, said Friar John, for I have found him in my breviary, and then follows the moveable holy-days. With all my heart, answered Xenomanes; we may chance to hear more of him as we touch at the Wild Island, the dominions of the squab Chitterlings, his enemies; against whom he is eternally at odds: and were it not for the help of the noble Carnival, their protector, and good neighbour, this meagre-looking Shrovetide would long before this have made sad work among them, and rooted them out of their habitation. Are these same Chitterlings, said Friar John, male or female, angels, or mortals, women or maids? They are, replied Xenomanes, females in sex, mortal in condition, some of them maids, others not. The devil have me, said Friar John, if I be not for them. What a shameful disorder in nature, is it not, to make war against women? Let us go back, and hack the villain to pieces.—What! meddle with Shrovetide? cried Panurge, in the name of Belzebub, I am not yet so weary of my life. No, I am not yet so mad as that comes to. *Quid juris?* Suppose we should find ourselves pent up between the Chitterlings and Shrovetide? between the anvil and the hammers? Shankers and buboes stand off! godzooks, let us make the best of our way. I bid you good night, sweet Mr. Shrovetide; I recommend to you the Chitterlings, and pray don't forget the puddings.

CHAPTER XXX

How Shrovetide is anatomized and described by Xenomanes

As for the inward parts of Shrovetide, said Xenomanes; his brain is (at least it was in my time) in bigness, colours, substance, and strength, much like the left cod of a he hand-worm.

The ventricles of his said brain like an auger.

The worm-like excrescence, like a christmas-box.

The membranes, like a monk's cowl.

The funnel, like a mason's chisel.

The fornix, like a casket.

The glandula pinealis, like a bag-pipe.

The rete mirabile, like a gutter.

The dug-like processes, like a patch.

The tympanums, like a whirly-gig.

The rocky bones, like a goose-wing.

The nape of the neck, like a paper lantern.

The nerves, like a pipkin.

The uvula, like a sackbut.

The palate, like a mitten.

The spittle, like a shuttle.

The almonds, like a telescope.

The bridge of his nose, like a wheel-barrow.

The head of the larynx, like a vintage-basket.

The stomach, like a belt.

The pylorus, like a pitchfork.

The wind-pipe, like an oyster-knife.

The throat, like a pincushion stuffed with oakum.

The lungs, like a prebend's fur-gown.

The heart, like a cope.

The mediastine, like an earthen cup.

The pleura, like a crow's bill.

The arteries, like a watch-coat.

The midriff, like a montero-cap.

The liver, like a double-tongued mattock.

The veins, like a sash-window.

The spleen, like a catcall.

The guts, like a trammel.

The gall, like a cooper's adze.

The entrails, like a gantlet.

The mesentery, like an abbot's mitre.

The hungry-gut, like a button.

The blind gut like a breast-plate.

The colon like a bridle.

The arse-gut like a monk's leathern bottle.

The kidneys, like a trowel.

The loins, like a padlock.

The ureters, like a pot-hook.

The emulgent veins, like two gilli-flowers.

The spermatic vessels, like a cully-mully-puff.

The parastata, like an ink-pot.

The bladder, like a stone-bow.

The neck, like a mill-clapper.

The mirach, or lower parts of the belly, like a high-crowned hat.

The siphach, or its inner rind, like a wooden cuff.

The muscles, like a pair of bellows.

The tendons, like a hawking-glove.

The ligaments, like a tinker's budget.

The bones, like three-cornered cheese-cakes.

The marrow, like a wallet.

The cartilages, like a field-tortoise, alias a mole.

The glandules in the mouth, like a pruning-knife.

The animal spirits, like swingeing fisty-cuffs.

The blood-fermenting, like a multi-plication of flirts on the nose.

The urine, like a fig-pecker.

The sperm, like a hundred tenpenny nails.

And his nurse told me, that being married to Mid-lent, he only begot a good number of local adverbs, and certain double fasts.

His memory he had like a scarf.

His common sense, like a buzzing of bees.

His imagination, like the chime of a set of bells.

His thoughts, like a flight of starlings.

His conscience, like the unnestling of a parcel of young herons.

His deliberations, like a set of organs.

His repentance, like the carriage of a double cannon.

His undertakings, like the ballast of a galleon.

His understanding, like a torn breviary.

His notions, like snails crawling out of strawberries.

His will, like three filberts in a porringer.

His desire, like six trusses of hay.

His judgment, like a shoeing horn.

His discretion, like the truckle of a pully.

His reason, like a cricket stool.

CHAPTER XXXI

Shrovetide's outward parts anatomized

SHROVETIDE, continued Xenomanes, is somewhat better proportioned in his outward parts, excepting the seven ribs which he had over and above the common shape of men.

His toes, were like a virginal on an organ.

His nails, like a gimlet.

His feet, like a guitar.

His heels, like a club.

The soles of his feet like a crucible.

His legs, like a hawk's lure.

His knees, like a joint-stool.

His thighs, like a steel cap.

His hips, like a wimble.

His belly as big as a tun, buttoned after the old fashion, with a girdle riding over the middle of his bosom.

His navel, like a cymbal.

His groin, like a minced pie.

His member, like a slipper.

His purse, like an oil cruet.

His genitals, like a joiner's plainer.

Their erecting muscles, like a racket.

The perineum, like a flageolet.

His arse-hole, like a crystal looking-glass.

His bum, like a harrow.

His loins, like a butter-pot.

The peritonæum, or caul, wherein his bowels were wrapped, like a billiard-table.

His back, like an overgrown rack-bent cross-bow.

The vertebræ, or joints of his back-bone, like a bagpipe.

His ribs, like a spinning-wheel.

His brisket, like a canopy.

His shoulder-blades, like a mortar.

His breast, like a game at nine-pins.

His paps, like a horn-pipe.

His arm-pits, like a chequer.

His shoulders like a hand-barrow.

His arms, like a riding-hood.

His fingers, like a brotherhood's andirons.

The fibulæ, or lesser bones of his legs, like a pair of stilts.

His shin-bones, like sickles.

His elbows, like a mouse-trap.

His hands, like a curry-comb.

His neck, like a talboy.

His throat, like a felt to distil hippocras.

The knob in his throat, like a barrel, where hanged two brazen wens, very fine and harmonious, in the shape of an hour-glass.

His beard, like a lantern.

His chin, like a mushroom

His ears, like a pair of gloves.

His nose, like a buskin.

His nostrils, like a forehead cloth.

His eye-brows, like a dripping-pan.

On his left brow was a mark of the shape and bigness of an urinal.

His eye-lids, like a fiddle.

His eyes, like a comb-box.

His optic nerves, like a tinder-box.

His forehead, like a false cup.

His temples, like the cock of a cistern.

His cheeks, like a pair of wooden shoes.

His jaws, like a caudle cup.

His teeth, like a hunter's staff. Of such colt's teeth as his, you will find one at Colonges les Royaux in Poictou, and two at la Brosse in Xaintonge, on the cellar door.

His tongue, like a jew's harp.

His mouth, like a horse-cloth.

His face embroidered like a mule's pack saddle.

His head contrived like a still.

His skull, like a pouch.

The suturæ, or seams of his skull, like the annulus piscatoris, or the fisher's signet.

His skin, like a gabardine.

His epidermis, or outward skin, like a bolting-cloth.

His hair, like a scrubbing-brush.

His fur, such as above said.

CHAPTER XXXII

*A continuation of Shrovetide's countenance, postures, and way
of behaving*

It is a wonderful thing, continued Xenomanes, to hear and see
the state of Shrovetide.

If he chanced to spit, it was whole baskets full of goldfinches.

If he blowed his nose, it was pickled grigs.

When he wept, it was ducks with onion sauce.

When he trembled, it was large venison pasties.

When he did sweat, it was old ling with butter sauce.

When he belched, it was bushels of oysters.

When he sneezed, it was whole tubs full of mustard.

When he coughed, it was boxes of marmalade.

When he sobbed, it was watercresses.

When he yawned, it was pots full of pickled pease.

When he sighed, it was dried neats' tongues.

When he whistled, it was a whole scuttle full of green apes.

When he snored, it was a whole pan full of fried beans.

When he frowned, it was soused hogs' feet.

When he spoke, it was coarse brown russet cloth; so little it was like crimson silk, with which Parisatis desired that the words of such as spoke to her son Cyrus, King of Persia, should be interwoven.

When he blowed, it was indulgence money-boxes.

When he winked, it was buttered buns.

When he grumbled, it was March cats.

When he nodded, it was iron-bound waggons.

When he made mouths, it was broken staves.

When he muttered, it was lawyers' revels.

When he hopped about, it was letters of licence and protections.

When he stepped back, it was sea cockle-shells.

When he slabbered, it was common ovens.

When he was hoarse, it was an entry of morrice-dancers.

When he broke wind, it was dun cows' leather spatterdashes.

When he funcked, it was washed-leather boots.

When he scratched himself, it was new proclamations.

When he sung, it was peas in cods.

When he evacuated, it was mushrooms and morilles.

When he puffed, it was cabbages with oil, alias caules amb'olif.

When he talked, it was the last year's snow.

When he dreamt, it was of a cock and a bull.

When he gave nothing, so much for the bearer.

If he thought to himself, it was whimsies and maggots.

If he dozed, it was leases of lands.

What is yet more strange, he used to work doing nothing,
and did nothing though he worked; caroused sleeping, and
slept carousing, with his eyes open, like the hares in our country,
for fear of being taken napping by the Chitterlings, his inveterate
enemies; biting he laughed, and laughing bit; eat nothing fasting,
and fasted eating nothing; mumbled upon suspicion, drank by
imagination, swam on the tops of high steeples, dried his clothes

in ponds and rivers, fished in the air, and there used to catch decumane lobsters; hunted at the bottom of the herring-pond, and caught there ibices, stamboucs, chamois, and other wild goats; used to put out the eyes of all the crows which he took sneakingly; feared nothing but his own shadow, and the cries of fat kids; used to gad abroad some days, like a truant school-boy; played with the ropes of bells on festival days of saints; made a mallet of his fist, and writ on hairy parchment prognostications and almanacks with his huge pin-case.

Is that the gentleman? said Friar John: he is my man: this is the very fellow I looked for; I will send him a challenge immediately. This is, said Pantagruel, a strange and monstrous sort of man, if I may call him a man. You put me in mind of the form and looks of Amodunt and Dissonance. How were they made, said Friar John? May I be peeled like a raw onion, if ever I heard a word of them. I'll tell you what I read of them in some ancient apologues, replied Pantagruel.

Physis—that is to say Nature—at her first burthen begat Beauty and Harmony, without carnal copulation, being of herself very fruitful and prolific. Antiphysis, who ever was the antagonist of Nature, immediately, out of a malicious spite against her for her beautiful and honourable productions, in opposition begot Amodunt and Dissonance, by copulation with Tellumon. Their heads were round like a football, and not gently flatted on both sides, like the common shape of men. Their ears stood pricked up like those of asses; their eyes, as hard as those of crabs, and without brows, stared out of their heads, fixed on bones like those of our heels; their feet were round, like tennis-balls; their arms and hands turned backwards towards the shoulders; and they walked on their heads, continually turning round like a ball, topsy-turvy, heels over head.

Yet—as you know that apes esteem their young the handsomest in the world—Antiphysis extolled her offspring, and strove to prove, that their shape was handsomer and neater than that of the children of Physis: saying, that thus to have spherical heads and feet, and walk in a circular manner, wheeling round, had something in it of the perfection of the divine power, which makes all beings eternally turn in that fashion; and that to have our feet uppermost, and the head below them, was to imitate the Creator of the universe; the hair being like the roots, and the legs like the branches of man: for trees are better planted by their roots, than they could be by their branches.

By this demonstration she implied, that her children were much more to be praised for being like a standing tree, than those of Physis, that made a figure of a tree upside down. As for the arms and hands, she pretended to prove that they were more justly turned towards the shoulders, because that part of the body ought not to be without defence, while the forepart is duly fenced with teeth, which a man cannot only use to chew, but also to defend himself against those things that offend him. Thus by the testimony and astipulation of the brute beasts, she drew all the witless herd and mob of fools into her opinion, and was admired by all brainless and nonsensical people.

Since that, she begot the hypocritical tribes of eaves-dropping dissemblers, superstitious pope-mongers, and priest-ridden bigots, the frantic Pistolets, the demoniacal Calvins, impostors of Geneva, the scrapers of benefices, apparitors with the devil in them, and other grinders and squeezers of livings, herb-stinking hermits, gulligutted dunces of the cowl, church vermin, false zealots, devourers of the substance of men, and many more other deformed and ill-favoured monsters, made in spite of nature.

CHAPTER XXXIII

How Pantagruel discovered a monstrous physeter, or whirlpool, near the Wild Island

ABOUT sunset, coming near the Wild Island, Pantagruel spied afar off a huge monstrous physeter,—a sort of whale, which some call a whirlpool,—that came right upon us, neighing, snorting, raised above the waves higher than our main-tops, and spouting water all the way into the air, before itself, like a large river falling from a mountain: Pantagruel showed it to the pilot, and to Xenomanes.

By the pilot's advice, the trumpets of the *Thalamege* were sounded, to warn all the fleet to stand close, and look to themselves. This alarm being given, all the ships, galleons, frigates, brigantines, — according to their naval discipline, — placed themselves in the order and figure of a Greek upsilon, (Ψ) the letter of Pythagoras, as cranes do in their flight; and like an acute angle, in whose cone and basis the *Thalamege* placed herself ready to fight smartly. Friar John, with the grenadiers, got on the forecastle.

Poor Panurge began to cry and howl worse than ever: Babillebabou, said he, shrugging up his shoulders, quivering all over with fear, there will be the devil upon dun. This is a worse business than that the other day. Let us fly, let us fly; old Nick take me if it is not Leviathan, described by the noble prophet Moses, in the life of patient Job. It will swallow us all, ships and men, shag, rag, and bobtail, like a dose of pills. Alas, it will make no more of us, and we shall hold no more room in its hellish jaws, than a sugar-plum in an ass's throat. Look, look, it is upon us; let us wheel off, whip it away, and get ashore. I believe it is the very individual sea monster that was formerly designed to devour Andromeda: we are all undone. Oh! for some valiant Perseus here now to kill the dog.

I'll do its business presently said Pantagruel; fear nothing. Odds-belly, said Panurge, remove the cause of my fear then. When the devil would you have a man be afraid, but when there is so much cause? If your destiny be such, as Friar John was saying a while ago, replied Pantagruel, you ought to be afraid of Pyroeis, Eous, Æthon, and Phlegon, the sun's coach horses, that breathe fire at the nostrils; and not of physeters, that spout nothing but water at the snout and mouth. Their water will not endanger your life; and that element will rather save and preserve than hurt or endanger you.

Ay, ay, trust to that, and hang me, quoth Panurge: yours is a very pretty fancy. Odd's fish: did I not give you a sufficient account of the element's transmutation, and the blunders that are made of roast for boiled, and boiled for roast? Alas, here it is; I'll go hide myself below. We are dead men, every mother's son of us; I see upon our main-top that merciless hag Atropos, with her scissors new ground, ready to cut our threads all at one snip. Oh! how dreadful and abominable thou art; thou hast drowned a good many beside us, who never made their brags of it. Did it but spout good, brisk, dainty, delicious white wine, instead of this damned bitter salt water, one might better bear with it, and there would be some cause to be patient, like that English lord, who being doomed to die, and had leav to choose what kind of death he would, chose to be drowned in a butt of malmsey. Here it is.—Oh, oh! devil! Sathanas! Leviathan! I cannot abide to look upon thee, thou art so abominably ugly.—Go to the bar, go take the pettifoggers.

CHAPTER XXXIV

How the monstrous physeter was slain by Pantagruel

THE physeter, coming between the ships and the galleons, threw water by whole tuns upon them, as if it had been the cataracts of the Nile in Ethiopia. On the other side, arrows, darts, gleaves, javelins, spears, harping-irons, and partizans, flew upon it like hail. Friar John did not spare himself in it. Panurge was half dead for fear. The artillery roared and thundered like mad, and seemed to gall it in good earnest, but did but little good: for the great iron and brass cannon-shot, entering its skin, seemed to melt like tiles in the sun.

Pantagruel then, considering the weight and exigency of the matter, stretched out his arms, and showed what he could do. You tell us, and it is recorded, that Commodus, the Roman emperor, could shoot with a bow so dexterously, that at a good distance he would let fly an arrow through a child's fingers, and never touch them. You also tell us of an Indian archer, who lived when Alexander the Great conquered India, and was so skilful in drawing the bow, that at a considerable distance he would shoot his arrows through a ring, though they were three cubits long, and their iron so large and weighty, that with them he used to pierce steel cutlasses, thick shields, steel breast-plates, and generally what he did hit, how firm, resisting, hard, and strong soever it were. You also tell us wonders of the industry of the ancient Franks, who were preferred to all others in point of archery; and when they hunted either black or dun beasts, used to rub the head of their arrows with helle-bore, because the flesh of the venison, struck with such an arrow, was more tender, dainty, wholesome, and delicious—paring off, nevertheless, the part that was touched round about. You also talk of the Parthians, who used to shoot backwards, more dexterously than other nations forwards; and also celebrate the skill of the Scythians in that art, who sent once to Darius, King of Persia, an ambassador, that made him a present of a bird, a frog, a mouse, and five arrows, without speaking one word; and being asked what those presents meant, and if he had commission to say anything, answered, that he had not: which puzzled and gravelled Darius very much, till Gobrias, one of the seven captains that had killed the magi, explained it, saying to Darius: By these gifts and offerings the Scythians silently tell you, that except the Persians, like birds, fly up to heaven, or like mice, hide themselves near the centre of the earth, or, like frogs, dive to the very bottom of ponds and lakes, they shall be destroyed by the power and arrows of the Scythians.

The noble Pantagruel was, without comparison, more admirable yet in the art of shooting and darting: for with his dreadful piles and darts, nearly resembling the huge beams that support the bridges of Nantes, Saumur, Bergerac, and at Paris the millers' and the changers' bridges, in length, size, weight, and iron-work, he at a mile's distance, would open an oyster, and never touch the edges; he would snuff a candle, without putting it out; would shoot a mag-pie in the eye; take off a boot's under-sole, or, a riding-hood's lining, without soiling them a bit; turn over every leaf of Friar John's breviary, one after another, and not tear one.

With such darts, of which there was good store in the ship, at the first blow he ran the physeter in at the forehead so furiously, that he pierced both its jaws and tongue: so that from that time to this it no more opened its guttural trap-door, nor drew and spouted water. At the second blow he put out its right eye, and at the third its left: and we had all the pleasure to see the physeter bearing those three horns in its forehead, somewhat leaning forwards in an equilateral triangle.

Meanwhile it turned about to and fro, staggering and straying like one stunned, blinded, and taking his leave of the world. Pantagruel, not satisfied with this, let fly another dart, which took the monster under the tail likewise sloping; then with three other on the chine, in a perpendicular line, divided its flank from the tail to the snout at an equal distance: then he larded it with fifty on one side, and after that, to make even work, he darted as many on its other side: so that the body of the physeter seemed like the hulk of a galleon with three masts, joined by a competent dimension of its beams, as if they had been the ribs and chain-wales of the keel; which was a pleasant sight. The physeter then giving up the ghost, turned itself upon its back, as all dead fishes do; and being thus overturned, with the beams and darts upside down in the sea, it seemed a scolopendra or centipede, as that serpent is described by the ancient sage Nicander.

CHAPTER XXXV

*How Pantagruel went on shore in the Wild Island, the ancient
abode of the Chitterlings*

THE boat's crew of the ship *Lantern* towed the physeter ashore
on the neighbouring shore, which happened to be the Wild
Island, to make an anatomical dissection of its body, and save
the fat of its kidneys, which, they said, was very useful and
necessary for the cure of a certain distemper, which they called
want of money. As for Pantagruel, he took no manner of
notice of the monster; for he had seen many such, nay, bigger,
in the Gallic ocean. Yet he condescended to land in the Wild
Island, to dry and refresh some of his men, (whom the physeter
had wetted and bedaubed,) at a small desert sea-port, towards
the south, seated near a fine pleasant grove, out of which flowed
a delicious brook of fresh, clear, and purling water. Here they
pitched their tents, and set up their kitchens; nor did they
spare fuel.

Every one having shifted, as they thought fit, Friar John
rang the bell, and the cloth was immediately laid, and supper
brought in. Pantagruel eating cheerfully with his men, much
about the second course, perceived certain little sly Chitterlings
clambering up a high tree near the pantry, as still as so many
mice. Which made him ask Xenomanes, what kind of creatures
these were; taking them for squirrels, weazels, martins, or
ermines. They are Chitterlings, replied Xenomanes. This is
the Wild Island, of which I spoke to you this morning: there
hath been an irreconcilable war, this long time, between them
and Shrovetide, their malicious and ancient enemy. I believe
that the noise of the guns, which we fired at the physeter, hath
alarmed them, and made them fear their enemy hath come with
his forces to surprise them, or lay the island waste; as he hath
often attempted to do, though he still came off but bluely; by
reason of the care and vigilance of the Chitterlings, who, (as
Dido said to Æneas's companions, that would have landed at
Carthage without her leave or knowledge,) were forced to watch
and stand upon their guard, considering the malice of their
enemy, and the neighbourhood of his territories.

Pray, dear friend, said Pantagruel, if you find that by some
honest means we may bring this war to an end, and reconcile
them together, give me notice of it; I will use my endeavours

in it, with all my heart, and spare nothing on my side to moderate and accommodate the points in dispute between both parties.

That is impossible at this time, answered Xenomanes. About four years ago, passing incognito by this country, I endeavoured to make a peace, or at least a long truce among them; and I certainly had brought them to be good friends and neighbours, if both one and the other parties would have yielded to one single article. Shrovetide would not include in the treaty of peace, the wild puddings, nor the highland sausages, their ancient gossips and confederates. The Chitterlings demanded, that the fort of Cacques might be under their government, as is the Castle of Sullouoir, and that a parcel of I don't know what stinking villains, murderers, robbers, that held it then, should be expelled. But they could not agree in this, and the terms that were offered seemed too hard to either party. So the treaty broke off, and nothing was done. Nevertheless, they became less severe, and gentler enemies than they were before; but since the denunciation of the national Council of Chesil, whereby they —the Chitterlings—were roughly handled, hampered, and cited; whereby also Shrovetide was declared filthy, beshitten, and bewrayed, in case he made any league, or agreement with them; they are grown wonderfully inveterate, incensed, and obstinate against one another, and there is no way to remedy it. You might sooner reconcile cats and rats or hounds and hares together.

CHAPTER XXXVI

How the wild Chitterlings laid an ambuscade for Pantagruel

WHILE Xenomanes was saying this, Friar John spied twenty or thirty young slender-shaped Chitterlings, posting as fast as they could towards their town, citadel, castle, and fort of Chimney, and said to Pantagruel, I smell a rat: there will be here the devil upon two sticks, or I am much out. These worshipful Chitterlings may chance to mistake you for Shrovetide, though you are not a bit like him. Let us once in our lives leave our junketing for a while, and put ourselves in a posture to give them a bellyful of fighting, if they would be at that sport. There can be no false Latin in this, said Xenomanes: Chitterlings are still Chitterlings, always double-hearted and, treacherous.

Pantagruel then arose from table, to visit and scour the

thicket, and returned presently; having discovered, on the left, an ambuscade of squab Chitterlings; and on the right, about half a league from thence, a large body of huge giant-like armed Chitterlings, ranged in battalia along a little hill, and marching furiously towards us at the sound of bagpipes, sheep's paunches, and bladders, the merry fifes and drums, trumpets, and clarions, hoping to catch us as Moss caught his mare. By the conjecture of seventy-eight standards, which we told, we guessed their number to be two and forty thousand, at a modest computation.

Their order, proud gait, and resolute looks, made us judge that they were none of your raw, paltry links, but old warlike Chitterlings and Sausages. From the foremost ranks to the colours they were all armed cap-à-pié with small arms, as we reckoned them at a distance: yet, very sharp, and casehardened. Their right and left wings were lined with a great number of forest puddings, heavy pattipans, and horse sausages, all of them tall and proper islanders, banditti, and wild.

Pantagruel was very much daunted, and not without cause; though Epistemon told him that it might be the use and custom of the Chitterlingonians to welcome and receive thus in arms their foreign friends, as the noble kings of France are received and saluted at their first coming into the chief cities of the kingdom, after their advancement to the crown. Perhaps, said he, it may be the usual guard of the queen of the place; who, having notice given her, by the junior Chitterlings of the forlorn hope whom you saw on the tree, of the arrival of your fine and pompous fleet, hath judged that it was, without doubt, some rich and potent prince, and is come to visit you in person.

Pantagruel, little trusting to this, called a council, to have their advice at large in this doubtful case. He briefly showed them how this way of reception, with arms, had often, under colour of compliment and friendship, been fatal. Thus, said he, the Emperor Antonius Caracalla, at one time, destroyed the citizens of Alexandria, and at another time, cut off the attendants of Artabanus, King of Persia, under colour of marrying his daughter: which, by the way, did not pass unpunished: for, a while after, this cost him his life.

Thus Jacob's children destroyed the Sichemites, to revenge the rape of their sister Dinah. By such another hypocritical trick, Gallienus the Roman emperor, put to death the military men in Constantinople. Thus, under colour of friendship, Antonius enticed Artavasdes, King of Armenia; then, having caused him to be bound in heavy chains, and shackled, at last put him to death.

We find a thousand such instances in history; and King Charles VI is justly commended for his prudence to this day, in that, coming back victorious over the Ghenters and other Flemings, to his good city of Paris, and when he came to Bourget, a league from thence, hearing that the citizens with their mallets—whence they got the name of Maillotins—were marched out of town in battalia, twenty thousand strong, he would not go into the town, till they had laid down their arms, and retired to their respective homes; though they protested to him, that they had taken arms with no other design than to receive him with the greater demonstration of honour and respect.

CHAPTER XXXVII

How Pantagruel sent for Colonel Maul-Chitterling, and Colonel Cut-Pudding; with a discourse well worth your hearing, about the names of places and persons

THE resolution of the council was, that, let things be how they would, it behoved the Pantagruelists to stand upon their guard. Therefore Carpalim and Gymnast were ordered by Pantagruel to go for the soldiers that were on board the *Cup* galley, under the command of Colonel Maul-chitterling, and those on board the *Vine-tub* frigate, under the command of Colonel Cut-pudding the younger. I will ease Gymnast of that trouble, said Panurge, who wanted to be upon the run: you may have occasion for him here. By this worthy frock of mine, quoth Friar John, thou hast a mind to slip thy neck out of the collar, and absent thyself from the fight, thou white-livered son of a dunghill! upon my virginity thou wilt never come back. Well, there can be no great loss in thee; for thou wouldst do nothing here but howl, bray, weep, and dishearten the good soldiers. I will certainly come back, said Panurge, Friar John, my ghostly father, and speedily too: do but take care that these plaguy Chitterlings do not board our ships. All the while you will be a fighting, I will pray heartily for your victory, after the example of the valiant captain and guide of the people of Israel, Moses. Having said this, he wheeled off.

Then said Epistemon to Pantagruel, The denomination of these two colonels of yours, Maul-chitterling and Cut-pudding, promiseth us assurance, success, and victory, if those Chitterlings should chance to set upon us. You take it rightly, said Pantagruel, and it pleaseth me to see you foresee and prognosticate our victory by the name of our colonels.

This way of foretelling by names is not new; it was in old times celebrated, and religiously observed by the Pythagoreans. Several great princes and emperors have formerly made use of it. Octavianus Augustus, second emperor of the Romans, meeting on a day a country fellow named Eutychus,—that is, fortunate,—driving an ass named Nicon—that is in Greek, victorious,—moved by the signification of the ass's and assdriver's names, remained assured of all prosperity and victory.

The Emperor Vespasian, being once all alone at prayers, in the temple of Serapis, at the sight and unexpected coming of a certain servant of his, named Basilides,—that is, royal,—whom he had left sick a great way behind, took hopes and assurance of obtaining the empire of the Romans. Regilian was chosen emperor, by the soldiers, for no other reason, but the signification of his name. See the Cratylus of the divine Plato. (By my thirst I will read him, said Rhizotomus; I hear you so often quote him.) See how the Pythagoreans, by reason of the names and numbers, conclude that Patroclus was to fall by the hand of Hector; Hector by Achilles; Achilles by Paris; Paris by Philoctetes. I am quite lost in my understanding, when I reflect upon the admirable invention of Pythagoras, who by the number, either even or odd, of the syllables of every name, would tell you of what side a man was lame, hunchbacked, blind, gouty, troubled with the palsy, pleurisy, or any other distemper incident to human kind; allotting even numbers to the left, and odd ones to the right side of the body.

Indeed, said Epistemon, I saw this way of syllabising tried at Xaintes, at a general procession, in the presence of that good, virtuous, learned, and just president, Brian Vallée, Lord of Douhait. When there went by a man or woman that was either lame, blind of one eye, or hump-backed, he had an account brought him of his or her name; and if the syllables of the name were of an odd number, immediately, without seeing the persons, he declared them to be deformed, blind, lame, or crooked of the right side; and of the left, if they were even in number; and such indeed we ever found them.

By this syllabical invention, said Pantagruel, the learned have affirmed, that Achilles kneeling, was wounded by the arrow of Paris in the right heel; for his name is of odd syllables;

(here we ought to observe that the ancients used to kneel the right foot:) and that Venus was also wounded before Troy in the left hand; for her name in Greek is Ἀφροδίτη, of four syllables; Vulcan lamed of his left foot for the same reason; Philip, King of Macedon, and Hannibal, blind of the right eye; not to speak of sciaticas, broken bellies, and hemicranias, which may be distinguished by this Pythagorean reason.

But returning to names: do but consider how Alexander the Great, son of King Philip, of whom we spoke just now, compassed his undertaking, merely by the interpretation of a name. He had besieged the strong city of Tyre, and for several weeks battered it with all his power: but all in vain. His engines and attempts were still baffled by the Tyrians, which made him finally resolve to raise the seige, to his great grief; foreseeing the great stain which such a shameful retreat would be to his reputation. In this anxiety and agitation of mind he fell asleep, and dreamed that a satyr was come into his tent, capering, skipping, and tripping it up and down, with his goatish hoofs, and that he strove to lay hold on him. But the satyr still slipt from him, till at last, having penned him up into a corner, he took him. With this he awoke, and telling his dream to the philosophers and sages of his court, they let him know that it was a promise of victory from the gods, and that he should soon be master of Tyre; the word *satyros*, divided in two, being *sa Tyros*, and signifying Tyre is thine; and in truth, at the next onset, he took the town by storm, and, by a complete victory, reduced that stubborn people to subjection.

On the other hand, see how, by the signification of one word, Pompey fell into despair. Being overcome by Cæsar at the battle of Pharsalia, he had no other way left to escape but by flight; which, attempting by sea, he arrived near the island of Cyprus, and perceived on the shore, near the city of Paphos a beautiful and stately palace: now asking the pilot what was the name of it, he told him, that it was called Κακοβασιλέα, that is, evil king; which struck such a dread and terror in him, that he fell into despair, as being assured of losing shortly his life; insomuch that his complaints, sighs, and groans were heard by the mariners and other passengers. And indeed, a while after, a certain strange peasant, called Achillas, cut off his head.

To all these examples might be added what happened to L. Paulus Emilius, when the senate elected him imperator, that is, chief of the army which they sent against Perses, King of Macedon. That evening returning home to prepare for his expedition, and kissing a little daughter of his called Trasia, she seemed somewhat sad to him. What is the matter, said he, my chicken? Why is my Trasia thus sad and melancholy? Daddy, replied the child, Persa is dead. This was the name of a little bitch, which she loved mightily. Hearing this, Paulus took assurance of a victory over Perses.

If time would permit us to discourse of the sacred Hebrew writ, we might find a hundred noted passages, evidently showing how religiously they observed proper names and their significations.

He had hardly ended this discourse, when the two colonels arrived with their soldiers, all well armed and resolute. Pantagruel made them a short speech, entreating them to behave themselves bravely, in case they were attacked; for he could not yet believe that the Chitterlings were so treacherous: but he bad them by no means to give the first offence; giving them carnival for the watch-word.

CHAPTER XXXVIII

How Chitterlings are not to be slighted by men

You shake your empty noddles now, jolly topers, and do not believe what I tell you here, any more than if it were some tale of a tub. Well, well, I cannot help it. Believe it if you will; if you will not, let it alone. For my part, I very well know what I say. It was in the Wild Island, in our voyage to the Holy Bottle; I tell you the time and place; what would you have more? I would have you call to mind the strength of the ancient giants, that undertook to lay the high mountain Pelion, on the top of Ossa, and set among those the shady Olympus, to dash out the gods' brains, unnestle them, and scour their heavenly lodgings. Theirs was no small strength, you may well think, and yet they were nothing but Chitterlings from the waist downwards, or, at least, serpents, not to tell a lie for the matter.

The serpent that tempted Eve, too, was of the Chitterling kind, and yet it is recorded of him, that he was more subtle than any beast of the field. Even so are Chitterlings. Nay, to this very hour they hold in some universities, that this same tempter was the Chitterling called Ithyphallus, into which was transformed bawdy Priapus, arch-seducer of females in paradise, that is, a garden, in Greek.

Pray now tell me, who can tell but that the Swiss, now so bold and warlike, were formerly Chitterlings? For my part I would not take my oath to the contrary. The Himantopodes, a nation very famous in Ethiopia, according to Pliny's description, are Chitterlings, and nothing else. If all this will not satisfy your worships, or remove your incredulity, I would have you forthwith (I mean drinking first, that nothing be done rashly) visit Lusignan, Parthenay, Vouant, Mervant, and Ponzauges in Poictou. There you will find a cloud of witnesses, not of your affidavit men of the right stamp, but credible, time out of mind, that will take their corporal oath, on Rigomé's knuckle-bone, that Melusina, their founder, or foundress, which you please, was woman from the head to the prick-purse, and thence downwards was a serpentine Chitterling, or if you will have it otherwise, a Chitterlingdized serpent. She nevertheless had a genteel and noble gait, imitated to this very day by your hop-merchants of Britanny, in their paspié and country dances.

What do you think was the cause of Erichthonius's being the first inventor of coaches, litters, and chariots? Nothing but because Vulcan had begot him with Chitterlingdized legs; which to hide, he chose to ride in a litter, rather than on horseback; for Chitterlings were not yet in esteem at that time.

The Scythian nymph, Ora, was likewise half woman and half Chitterling; and yet seemed so beautiful to Jupiter, that nothing could serve him but he must give her a touch of his godship's kindness; and accordingly he had a brave boy by her, called Colaxes; and therefore I would have you leave off shaking your empty noddles at this, as if it were a story, and firmly believe that nothing is truer than the gospel.

CHAPTER XXXIX

How Friar John joined with the cooks to fight the Chitterlings

FRIAR JOHN, seeing these furious Chitterlings thus boldly march up, said to Pantagruel, Here will be a rare battle of hobby-horses, a pretty kind of puppet-show fight, for aught I see. Oh! what mighty honour and wonderful glory will attend our victory! I would have you only be a bare spectator of this fight, and for any thing else, leave me and my men to deal with them. What men? said Pantagruel. Matter of breviary, replied Friar John. How came Potiphar, who was head cook of Pharaoh's kitchens, he that bought Joseph, and whom the said Joseph might have made a cuckold, if he had not been a Joseph; how came he, I say, to be made general of all the horse in the kingdom of Egypt? Why was Nabuzardan, King Nebuchadnezzar's head cook, chosen, to the exclusion of all other captains, to besiege and destroy Jerusalem. I hear you, replied Pantagruel. By St. Christopher's whiskers, said Friar John, I dare lay a wager that it was because they had formerly engaged Chitterlings, or men as little valued; whom to rout, conquer, and destroy, cooks are, without comparison, more fit, than cuirassiers and gens d'armes armed at all points, or all the horse and foot in the world.

You put me in mind, said Pantagruel, of what is written amongst the facetious and merry sayings of Cicero. During the more than civil wars between Cæsar and Pompey, though he was much courted by the first, he naturally leaned more to the side of the latter. Now one day, hearing that the Pompeyians, in a certain rencontre, had lost a great many men, he took a fancy to visit their camp. There he perceived little strength, less courage, but much disorder. From that time, foreseeing that things would go ill with them, as it since happened, he began to banter now one and then another, and be very free of his cutting jests: so some of Pompey's captains, playing the good fellows, to show their assurance, told him, Do you see how many eagles we have yet? (They were then the device of the Romans in war.) They might be of use to you, replied Cicero, if you had to do with magpies.

Thus seeing we are to fight Chitterlings, pursued Pantagruel, you infer thence that it is a culinary war, and have a mind to join with the cooks. Well, do as you please, I will stay here in the meantime, and wait for the event of the rumpus.

Friar John went that very moment among the sutlers, into the cooks' tents, and told them in a pleasing manner; I must see you crowned with honour and triumph this day, my lads; to your arms are reserved such achievements as never yet were performed within the memory of man. Odd's belly, do they make nothing of the valiant cooks? let us go fight yonder fornicating Chitterlings! I will be your captain. But first let us drink, boys,—come on—let us be of good cheer. Noble captain, returned the kitchen tribe, this was spoken like yourself; bravely offered: huzza! we are all at your excellency's command, and will live and die by you. Live, live, said Friar John, a God's name: but die by no means. That is the Chitterlings' lot; they shall have their bellyful of it: come on then, let us put ourselves in order; Nabuzardan's the word.

CHAPTER XL

How Friar John fitted up the sow ; and of the valiant cooks that went into it

THEN, by Friar John's order, the engineers and their workmen fitted up the great sow that was in the ship *Leathern-Bottle*. It was a wonderful machine, so contrived, that, by means of large engines that were round about in rows, it threw forked iron bars, and four-square steel-bolts; and in its hold two hundred men at least could easily fight, and be sheltered. It was made after the model of the sow of Riole, by the means of which Bergerac was re-taken from the English, in the reign of Charles the Sixth.

Here are the names of the noble and valiant cooks who went into the sow, as the Greeks did into the Trojan horse.

Sour-sauce.	Crisp-pig.	Carbonadoe.
Sweet-meat.	Greasy-slouch.	Sop-in-pan.
Greedy-gut.	Fat-gut.	Pick-fowl.
Liquorice-chops.	Bray-mortar.	Mustard-pot.
Soused-pork.	Lick-sauce.	Hog's-haslet.
Slap-sauce.	Hog's-foot	Chopt-phiz.
Cock-broth.	Hodge-podge.	Gallimaufrey.
Slipslop.		

All these noble cooks, in their coat of arms, did bear, in a field gules, a larding-pin vert, charged with a chevron argent.

Lard, hog's-lard.	Pinch-lard.	Snatch-lard.
Nibble-lard.	Top-lard.	Gnaw-lard.
Filch-lard.	Pick-lard.	Scrape-lard.
Fat-lard.	Save-lard.	Chew-lard.

Gaillardon (by syncope) born near Rambouillet. The culinary doctor's name was Gaillardlardon, in the same manner as you use to say idololatrous for idololatrous.

Stiff-lard.	Catch-lard.	Waste-lard.
Dainty-lard.	Cut-lard.	Ogle-lard.
Watch-lard.	Mince-lard.	Weigh-lard.
Sweet-lard.	Fresh-lard.	Gulch-lard.
Eat-lard.	Rusty-lard.	Eye-lard.
Snap-lard.		

Names unknown among the Marranes and Jews.

Ballocky.	Monsieur-Ragout.	Mustard-sauce.
Pick-sallad.	Snail-dresser.	Claret-sauce.
Broil-rasher.	Soup-monger.	Swill-broth.
Cony-skin.	Brewis-belly.	Thirsty.
Dainty-chops.	Chine-picker.	Kitchen-stuff.
Pie-wright.	Crack-pipkin.	Verjuice.
Pudding-pan.	Scrape-pot.	Salt-gullet.
Save-dripping.	Porridge-pot.	Suck-gravy.
Water-cress.	Lick-dish.	Macaroon.
Scrape-turnip.	Toss-pot.	Skewer-maker.
Trivet.		

Smell-smock; he was afterwards taken from the kitchen, and removed to chamber-practice, for the service of the noble Cardinal Hunt-venison.

Rot-roast.	Flesh-smith.	Sirloin.
Dish-clout.	Cram-gut.	Spit-mutton.
Save-suet.	Tuzzy-mussy.	Fritter-fryer.
Fire-fumbler.	Jacket-liner.	Hog's-gullet.
Pillicock.	Guzzle-drink.	Saffron-sauce.
Long-tool.	Fox-tail.	Strutting-tom.
Prick-pride.	Fly-flap.	Slashed-snout.
Prick-madam.	Old-Grizzle.	Smutty-face.
Pricket.	Ruff-belly.	

Mondam, that first invented madam's sauce, and for that discovery, was thus called in the Scotch-French dialect.

Loblolly.	Goodman Goosecap.	Snap-gobbet.
Slabber-chops.	Munch-turnip.	Scurvy-phiz.
Scampot.	Sloven.	Trencher-man.
Gully-guts.	Swallow-pitcher.	Pudding-bag.
Rinse-pot.	Wafer-monger.	Pig-sticker.

Robert: he invented Robert's sauce, so good and necessary for roasted conies, ducks, fresh pork, poached eggs, salt fish, and a thousand other such dishes.

Cold-eel.	Frying-pan.	Big-snout.
Thornback.	Man of dough.	Lick-finger.
Gurnard.	Sauce-doctor.	Tit-bit.
Grumbling-gut.	Waste-butter.	Sauce-box.
Alms-scrip.	Shitbreech.	All fours.
Taste-all.	Thick-brawn.	Whimwham.
Scrap-merchant.	Tom T—d.	Baste-roast.
Belly-timberman.	Mouldy-crust.	Gaping-Hoyden.
Hashee.	Hasty.	Calf's pluck.
Frig-palate.	Red-herring.	Leather breeches.
Powdering-tub.	Cheesecake.	

All these noble cooks went into the sow, merry, cheery, hale, brisk, old dogs at mischief, and ready to fight stoutly. Friar John, ever and anon waving his huge scimitar, brought up the rear, and double-locked the doors on the inside.

CHAPTER XLI

How Pantagruel broke the Chitterlings at the knees

THE Chitterlings advanced so near, that Pantagruel perceived
that they stretched their arms, and already began to charge
their lances; which caused him to send Gymnast to know what
they meant, and why they thus, without the least provocation,
came to fall upon their old trusty friends, who had neither said
nor done the least ill thing to them.   Gymnast being advanced
near their front, bowed very low, and said to them, as loud as
ever he could: We are friends, we are friends; all, all of us your
friends, yours, and at your command; we are for Carnival,
your old confederate.   Some have since told me, that he mistook,
and said cavernal instead of carnival.

Whatever it was, the word was no sooner out of his mouth,
but a huge little squab Sausage, starting out of the front of
their main body, would have griped him by the collar.   By the
helmet of Mars, said Gymnast, I will swallow thee; but thou
shalt only come in in chips and slices; for, big as thou art, thou
couldest never come in whole.   This spoke, he lugs out his
trusty sword, Kiss-mine-arse, (so he called it,) with both his
fists, and cut the sausage in twain.   Bless me, how fat the foul
thief was! it puts me in mind of the huge bull of Berne, that was
slain at Marignan, when the drunken Swiss were so mauled
there.   Believe me, it had little less than four inches lard on
its paunch.

The Sausage's job being done, a crowd of others flew upon
Gymnast, and had most scurvily dragged him down, when
Pantagruel with his men came up to his relief.   Then began
the martial fray, higgledy piggledy.   Maul-chitterling did maul
Chitterlings; Cut-pudding did cut puddings; Pantagruel did
break the Chitterlings at the knees; Friar John play'd at least
in sight within his sow, viewing and observing all things; when
the pattipans, that lay in ambuscade, most furiously sallied
out upon Pantagruel.

Friar John, who lay snug all this while, by that time perceiving the route and hurly-burly, set open the doors of his
sow, and sallied out with his merry Greeks, some of them
armed with iron-spits, others with handirons, racks, fire-shovels,
frying-pans, kettles, gridirons, oven forks, tongs, dripping pans,
brooms, iron pots, mortars, pestles, all in battle array, like so

many house-breakers, hallooing and roaring out altogether
most frightfully, Nabuzardan, Nabuzardan, Nabuzardan. Thus
shouting and hooting, they fought like dragons, and charged
through the pattipans and sausages. The Chitterlings perceiving this fresh reinforcement, and that the others would be
too hard for them, betook themselves to their heels, scampering
off with full speed, as if the devil had come for them. Friar
John, with an iron crow, knocked them down as fast as hops:
his men too were not sparing on their side. O! what a woeful
sight it was! the field was all over strewed with heaps of dead
or wounded Chitterlings; and history relates, that had not
heaven had a hand in it, the Chitterling tribe had been totally
routed out of the world, by the culinary champions. But there
happened a wonderful thing, you may believe as little or as
much of it as you please.

From the north flew towards us a huge, fat, thick, grizzly
swine, with long and large wings, like those of a windmill; its
plumes red crimson, like those of a phenicoptere (which in
Languedoc they call flaman;) its eyes were red, and flaming
like a carbuncle; its ears green like a Prasin emerald; its teeth
like a topaz; its tail long and black like jet; its feet white,
diaphanous, and transparent like a diamond, somewhat broad,
and of the splay kind, like those of geese, and as Queen Dick's
used to be at Thoulouse, in the days of yore. About its neck
it wore a gold collar, round which were some Ionian characters,
whereof I could pick out but two words, 'ΥΣ 'ΑΘΗΝΑΝ: hog
teaching Minerva.

The sky was clear before; but at that monster's appearance,
it changed so mightily for the worse, that we were all amazed
at it. As soon as the Chitterlings perceived the flying hog,
down they all threw their weapons, and fell on their knees,
lifting up their hands, joined together without speaking one
word, in a posture of adoration. Friar John and his party
kept on mincing, felling, braining, mangling, and spitting the
Chitterlings like mad: but Pantagruel sounded a retreat, and
all hostility ceased.

The monster having several times hovered backwards and
forwards between the two armies, with a tail-shot voided above
twenty-seven butts of mustard on the ground; then flew away
through the air, crying all the while, Carnival, Carnival, Carnival.

CHAPTER XLII

How Pantagruel held a treaty with Niphleseth, Queen of the Chitterlings

THE monster being out of sight, and the two armies remaining silent, Pantagruel demanded a parley with the Lady Niphleseth, Queen of the Chitterlings, who was in her chariot, by the standards; and it was easily granted. The queen alighted, courteously received Pantagruel, and was glad to see him. Pantagruel complained to her of this breach of peace: but she civilly made her excuse, telling him that a false information had caused all this mischief; her spies having brought her word, that Shrovetide their mortal foe, was landed, and spent his time in examining the urine of physeters.

She, therefore, entreated him to pardon them their offence; telling him that sir-reverence was sooner found in Chitterlings than gall; and offering, for herself and all her successors, to hold of him, and his, the whole island and country; to obey him in all his commands, be friends to his friends, and foes to his foes; and also to send every year, as an acknowledgment of their homage, a tribute of seventy-eight thousand Chitterlings, to serve him at his first course at table, six months in the year; which was punctually performed. For the next day she sent the aforesaid quantity of royal Chitterlings to the good Gargantua, under the conduct of young Niphleseth, infanta of the island.

The good Gargantua made a present of them to the great King of Paris. But by change of air, and for want of mustard, (the natural balsam and restorer of Chitterlings,) most of them died. By the great king's particular grant, they were buried in heaps in a part of Paris, to this day called, *La Rue pavée d'Andouilles*; the street paved with Chitterlings. At the request of the ladies at his court, young Niphleseth was preserved, honourably used, and since that married to her heart's content; and was the mother of many fine children, for which heaven be praised.

Pantagruel civilly thanked the queen, forgave all offences, refused the offer she had made of her country, and gave her a pretty little knife. After that he asked her several nice questions concerning the apparition of that flying hog. She answered, that it was the idea of Carnival, their tutelary god in time of war, first founder, and original of all the Chitterling race; for which reason he resembled a hog; for Chitterlings drew their extraction from hogs.

Pantagruel asking for what purpose, and curative indication, he had voided so much mustard on the earth, the queen replied, that mustard was their sang-real, and celestial balsam, of which, laying but a little in the wounds of the fallen Chitterlings, in a very short time the wounded were healed, and the dead restored to life. Pantagruel held no further discourse with the queen, but retired on shipboard. The like did all the boon companions, with their implements of destruction, and their huge sow.

CHAPTER XLIII

How Pantagruel went into the Island of Ruach

Two days after, we arrived at the Island of Ruach; and I swear to you, by the celestial hen and chickens, that I found the way of living of the people so strange and wonderful, that I cannot, for the heart's blood of me, half tell it you. They live on nothing but wind, eat nothing but wind, and drink nothing but wind. They have no other houses but weathercocks. They sow no other seeds but the three sorts of wind-flowers, rue, and herbs that make one break wind to the purpose: these scour them off charmingly. The common sort of people, to feed themselves, make use of feather, paper, or linen fans, according to their abilities. As for the rich, they live by the means of windmills.

When they would have some noble treat, the tables are spread under one or two windmills. There they feast as merry as beggars, and during the meal, their whole talk is commonly of the goodness, excellency, salubrity, and rarity of winds; as you, jolly topers, in your cups, philosophize and argue upon wines. The one praises the south-east, the other the south-west, this the west and by south, and this the east and by north; another the west, and another the east; and so of the rest. As for lovers and amorous sparks, no gale for them like a smock-gale. For the sick they use bellows, as we use clysters among us.

Oh! (said to me a little diminutive swollen bubble) that I had now but a bladder-full of that same Languedoc wind which they call Cierce. The famous physician, Scurron, passing one day by this country, was telling us, that it is so strong, that it will make nothing of overturning a loaded waggon. Oh! what good would it not do my œdipodic leg. The biggest are not the best; but, said Panurge, rather would I had here a large butt of that same good Languedoc wine, that grows at Mirevaux, Canteperdrix, and Frontignan.

I saw a good likely sort of a man there, much resembling Ventrose, tearing and fuming in a grievous fret, with a tall burly groom, and a pimping little page of his, laying them on, like the devil, with a buskin. Not knowing the cause of his anger, at first I thought that all this was by the doctor's advice, as being a thing very healthy to the master to be in a passion, and to his man to be banged for it. But at last I heard him taxing his man with stealing from him like a rogue as he was, the better half of a large leathern bag of an excellent southerly wind, which he had carefully laid up, like a hidden reserve, against the cold weather.

They neither exonerate, dung, piss, nor spit in that island; but, to make amends, they belch, fizzle, funk, and give tail shots in abundance. They are troubled with all manner of distempers: and, indeed, all distempers are engendered, and proceed from ventosities, as Hippocrates demonstrates, *lib. De Flatibus*. But the most epidemical among them is the wind-cholic. The remedies which they use are large clysters, whereby they void store of windiness. They all die of dropsies and tympanies; the men farting, and the women fizzling: so that their soul takes her leave at the back-door.

Some time after, walking in the island, we met three hairbrained airy fellows, who seemed mightily puffed up, and went to take their pastime, and view the plovers, who live on the same diet as themselves, and abound in the island. I observed that as your true topers, when they travel, carry flasks, leathern bottles, and small runlets along with them, so each of them had at his girdle a pretty little pair of bellows. If they happened to want wind, by the help of those pretty bellows they immediately drew some, fresh and cool, by attraction and reciprocal expulsion: for, as you well know, wind essentially defined, is nothing but fluctuating and agitated air.

Awhile after, we were commanded, in the king's name, not to receive, for three hours, any man or woman of the country, on board our ships; some having stolen from him a rousing fart, of the very individual wind which old goodman Æolus, the snorer, gave Ulysses, to conduct his ship, whenever it should happen to be becalmed. Which fart the king kept religiously, like another sang-real, and performed a world of wonderful cures with it, in many dangerous diseases, letting loose, and distributing to the patient, only as much of it as might frame a virginal fart; which is, if you must know, what our sanctimonials, alias nuns, in their dialect, call ringing backwards.

CHAPTER XLIV

How small rain lays a high wind

PANTAGRUEL commended their government and way of living, and said to their hypenemian mayor, If you approve Epicurus's opinion, placing the *summum bonum* in pleasure, (I mean pleasure that is easy and free from toil,) I esteem you happy; for your food being wind, costs you little or nothing, since you need but blow. True, sir, returned the mayor, but, alas! nothing is perfect here below: for too often, when we are at table, feeding on some good blessed wind of God, as on celestial manna, merry as so many friars, down drops on a sudden some small rain, which lays our wind, and so robs us of it. Thus many a meal is lost for want of meat.

Just so, quoth Panurge, Jenin Toss-pot, of Quinquenais, evacuating some wine of his own burning [urine] on his wife's posteriors, laid the ill-fumed wind that blowed out of their centre, as out of some magisterial æolipile. Here is a kind of a whim on that subject, which I made formerly:

> One evening when Toss-pot had been at his butts,
> And Joan, his fat spouse, crammed with turnips her guts,
> Together they pigg'd, nor did drink so besot him,
> But he did what was done when his daddy begot him.
> Now, when to recruit, he'd fain have been snoring,
> Joan's back-door was filthily puffing and roaring:
> So for spite he bepiss'd her, and quickly did find.
> That a small rain lays a very high wind.

We are also plagued yearly with a very great calamity, cried the mayor, for a giant, called Widenostrils, who lives in the Island of Tohu, comes hither every spring to purge, by the advice of his physicians, and swallows us, like so many pills, a great number of windmills, and of bellows also, at which his mouth waters exceedingly.

Now this is a sad mortification to us here, who are fain to

fast over three or four whole Lents every year for this, besides
certain petty Lents, ember weeks, and other orison and starving
tides.   And have you no remedy for this? asked Pantagruel.
By the advice of our Mezarims, replied the mayor, about the
time that he uses to give us a visit, we garrison our windmills
with good store of cocks and hens.   The first time that the
greedy thief swallowed them, they had like to have done his
business at once: for they crowed and cackled in his maw, and
fluttered up and down athwart and along in his stomach, which
threw the glutton into a lipothymy cardiac passion, and dreadful
and dangerous convulsions, as if some serpent, creeping in at
his mouth, had been frisking in his stomach.

Here is a comparative *as*, altogether incongruous and impertinent, cried Friar John, interrupting them; for I have formerly
heard, that if a serpent chance to get into a man's stomach, it
will not do him the least hurt, but will immediately get out, if
you do but hang the patient by the heels, and lay a pan full of
warm milk near his mouth.   You were told this, said Pantagruel, and so were those who gave you this account; but none
ever saw or read of such a cure.   On the contrary, Hippocrates,
in his fifth book of *Epidem.*, writes, that such a case happening
in his time, the patient presently died of a spasm and convulsion.

Besides the cocks and hens, said the mayor, continuing his
story, all the foxes in the country whipped into Widenostrils'
mouth, posting after the poultry; which made such a stir with
Reynard at their heels, that he grievously fell into fits each
minute of an hour.

At last, by the advice of a Baden enchanter, at the time of
the paroxysm, he used to flay a fox, by way of antidote and
counter-poison.   Since that he took better advice, and eases
himself with taking a clyster made with a decoction of wheat
and barley corns, and of livers of goslings; to the first of which
the poultry run, and the foxes to the latter.   Besides, he swallows
some of your badgers or fox-dogs, by the way of pills and
boluses.   This is our misfortune.

Cease to fear, good people, cried Pantagruel, this huge Widenostrils, this same swallower of Windmills, is no more, I will
assure you: he died, being stifled and choked with a lump of
fresh butter at the mouth of a hot oven, by the advice of his
physicians.

CHAPTER XLV

How Pantagruel went ashore in the Island of Pope-Figland

THE next morning we arrived at the Island of Pope-figs; formerly
a rich and free people, called the Gaillardets; but now, alas!
miserably poor, and under the yoke of the Papimen. The
occasion of it was this.

On a certain yearly high holiday, the burgomaster, syndics,
and topping rabbies of the Gaillardets, chanced to go into the
neighbouring island Papimany to see the festival, and pass
away the time. Now one of them having espied the pope's
picture, (with the sight of which, according to a laudable custom,
the people were blessed on high-offering holidays,) made mouths
at it, and cried, A fig for it! as a sign of manifest contempt and
derision. To be revenged of this affront, the Papimen, some
days after, without giving the others the least warning, took
arms, and surprised, destroyed, and ruined the whole island of
the Gaillardets; putting the men to the sword, and sparing
none but the women and children; and those too only on condition to do what the inhabitants of Milan were condemned to,
by the Emperor Frederick Barbarossa.

These had rebelled against him in his absence, and ignominiously turned the empress out of the city, mounting her a
horseback on a mule called Thacor, with her breech foremost
towards the old jaded mule's head, and her face turned towards
the crupper. Now Frederick being returned, mastered them,
and caused so careful a search to be made, that he found out
and got the famous mule Thacor. Then the hangman, by his
order, clapped a fig into the mule's jimcrack, in the presence of
the enslaved cits that were brought into the middle of the
great market-place, and proclaimed, in the emperor's name,
with trumpets, that whosoever of them would save his own
life, should publicly pull the fig out with his teeth, and after
that, put it in again in the very individual cranny whence he
had drawn it, without using his hands, and that whoever
refused to do this, should presently swing for it, and die in his
shoes. Some sturdy fools, standing upon their punctillio, chose
honourably to be hanged, rather than submit to so shameful
and abominable a disgrace; and others, less nice in point of
ceremony, took heart of grace, and even resolved to have at
the fig, and a fig for it, rather than make a worse figure with a

hempen collar, and die in the air, at so short warning: accordingly when they had neatly picked out the fig with their teeth, from old Thacor's snatch-blatch, they plainly showed it the head's-man, saying, *Ecco lo fico*, behold the fig.

By the same ignominy the rest of these poor distressed Gaillardets saved their bacon, becoming tributaries and slaves, and the name of Pope-figs was given them, because they said, A fig for the pope's image. Since this, the poor wretches never prospered, but every year the devil was at their doors, and they were plagued with hail, storms, famine, and all manner of woes, as an everlasting punishment for the sin of their ancestors and relations. Perceiving the misery and calamity of that generation, we did not care to go further up into the country; contenting ourselves with going into a little chapel near the haven, to take some holy water. It was dilapidated and ruined, wanting also a cover—like Saint Peter at Rome. When we were in, as we dipped our fingers in the sanctified cistern, we spied in the middle of that holy pickle, a fellow muffled up with stoles, all under water, like a diving duck, except the tip of his snout to draw his breath. About him stood three priests, true shavelings, clean shorn, and polled, who were muttering strange words to the devils out of a conjuring book.

Pantagruel was not a little amazed at this, and, inquiring what kind of sport these were at, was told, that, for three years last past, the plague had so dreadfully raged in the island, that the better half of it had been utterly depopulated, and the lands lay fallow and unoccupied. Now, the mortality being over, this same fellow, who had crept into the holy tub, having a large piece of ground, chanced to be sowing it with white winter wheat, at the very minute of an hour that a kind of a silly sucking devil, who could not yet write or read, or hail and thunder, unless it were on parsley or coleworts, had got leave of his master Lucifer to go into this Island of Pope-figs, where the devils were very familiar with the men and women, and often went to take their pastime.

This same devil being got thither, directed his discourse to the husbandman, and asked him what he was doing. The poor man told him, that he was sowing the ground with corn, to help him to subsist the next year. Ay, but the ground is none of thine, Mr. Plough-jobber, cried the devil, but mine; for since the time that you mocked the pope, all this land has been proscribed, adjudged, and abandoned to us. However, to sow corn is not my province: therefore I will give thee leave to sow the field, that is to say, provided we share the profit. I will, replied the farmer. I mean, said the devil, that of what the land shall bear, two lots shall be made, one of what shall grow above ground, the other of what shall be covered with earth: the right of choosing belongs to me; for I am a devil of noble and ancient race; thou art a base clown. I therefore chose what shall lie under ground, take thou what shall be above. When dost thou reckon to reap, hah? About the middle of July, quoth the farmer. Well, said the devil, I'll not fail thee then: in the meantime, slave as thou oughtest. Work, clown, work: I am going to tempt to the pleasing sin of whoring, the nuns of Dryfart, the sham saints of the cowl, and the gluttonish crew: I am more than sure of these. They need but meet, and the job is done: true fire and tinder, touch and take: down falls nun and up gets friar.

CHAPTER XLVI

How a junior devil was fooled by a husbandman of Pope-Figland

In the middle of July, the devil came to the place aforesaid, with all his crew at his heels, a whole choir of the younger fry of hell; and having met the farmer, said to him, Well, clod-pate, how hast thou done, since I went? Thou and I must share the concern. Ay, master devil, quoth the clown, it is but reason we should. Then he and his men began to cut and reap the corn: and, on the other side, the devil's imps fell to work, grubbing up and pulling out the stubble by the root.

The countryman had his corn thrashed, winnowed it, put it into sacks, and went with it to market. The same did the devil's servants, and sat them down there by the man to sell their straw. The countryman sold off his corn at a good rate, and with the money filled an old kind of a demi-buskin, which was fastened to his girdle. But the devil a sou the devils took: far from taking handsel, they were flouted and jeered by the country louts.

Market being over, quoth the devil to the farmer, Well, clown, thou hast choused me once, it is thy fault; chouse me twice, it will be mine. Nay, good sir devil, replied the farmer, how can I be said to have choused you, since it was your worship that chose first? The truth is, that, by this trick, you thought to cheat me, hoping that nothing would spring out of the earth for my share, and that you should find whole under ground the corn which I had sowed, and with it tempt the poor and needy, the close hypocrite, or the covetous griper; thus making them fall into your snares. But troth, you must even go to school yet: you are no conjuror, for aught I see: for the corn that was sown is dead and rotten, its corruption having caused the generation of that which you saw me sell: so you chose the worst, and therefore are cursed in the gospel. Well, talk no more of it, quoth the devil: what canst thou sow our field with for next year? If a man would make the best of it, answered the ploughman, it were fit he sow it with radishes. Now, cried the devil, thou talkest like an honest fellow, bumpkin: well, sow me good store of radishes, I will see and keep them safe from storms, and will not hail a bit on them. But harkye me, this time I bespeak for my share what shall be above ground; what is under shall be thine. Drudge on, looby, drudge on. I am going to tempt heretics; their souls are dainty victuals, when broiled in rashers, and well powdered. My Lord Lucifer has the griping in the guts; they will make a dainty warm dish for his honour's maw.

When the season of radishes was come, our devil failed not to meet in the field, with a train of rascally underlings, all waiting devils, and finding there the farmer and his men, he began to cut and gather the leaves of the radishes. After him the farmer with his spade dug up the radishes, and clapped them up into pouches. This done, the farmer, and their gangs, hied them to market, and there the farmer presently made good money of his radishes: but the poor devil took nothing; nay, what was worse, he was made a common laughing stock by the gaping hoydons. I see thou hast played me a scurvy trick, thou villanous fellow, cried the angry devil: at last I am fully resolved even to make an end of the business betwixt thee and myself, about the ground, and these shall be the terms: we will clapperclaw each other, and whoever of us two shall first cry, Hold, shall quit his share of the field, which shall wholly belong to the conqueror. I fix the time for this trial of skill, on this day seven-night: assure thyself that I will claw thee off like a devil. I was going to tempt your fornicators, bailiffs, perplexers of causes, scriveners, forgers of deeds, two-handed councillors, prevaricating solicitors, and other such vermin; but they were so civil as to send me word by an interpreter, that they are all mine already. Besides our master Lucifer is so cloyed with their souls, that he often sends them back to the smutty scullions, and slovenly devils of his kitchen, and they scarce go down with them, unless now and then, when they are high-seasoned.

Some say there is no breakfast like a student's, no dinner like a lawyer's, no afternoon's nunchion like a vinedresser's, no supper like a tradesman's, no second supper like a serving wench's, and none of these meals equal to a frockified hobgoblin's. All this is true enough. Accordingly, at my Lord Lucifer's first course, hobgoblins, alias imps in cowls, are a standing dish. He willingly used to breakfast on students; but, alas, I do not know by what ill luck they have of late years joined the Holy Bible to their studies: so the devil a one we can get down among us; and I verily believe that unless the hypocrites of the tribe of Levi help us in it, taking from the enlightened book-mongers their St. Paul, either by threats, revilings, force, violence, fire, and faggot, we shall not be able to hook in any more of them, to nibble at below. He dines commonly on councillors, mischief-mongers, multipliers of law suits, such as wrest and pervert right and law, and grind and fleece the poor: he never fears to want any of these. But who can endure to be wedded to a dish?

He said, the other day, at a full chapter, that he had a great mind to eat the soul of one of the fraternity of the cowl, that had forgot to speak for himself, in his sermon; and he promised double pay, and a large pension, to any one that should bring him such a tit-bit piping hot. We all went a hunting after such a rarity, but came home without the prey: for they all admonish the good women to remember their convent. As for afternoon nunchions, he has left them off, since he was so woefully griped with the cholic; his fosterers, sutlers, charcoal-men, and boiling cooks having been sadly mauled and peppered off in the northern countries.

His high devilship sups very well on tradesmen, usurers, apothecaries, cheats, coiners, and adulterers of wares. Now and then, when he is on the merry pin, his second supper is of serving wenches; who, after they have, by stealth, soaked their faces with their master's good liquor, fill up the vessel with it at second hand, or with other stinking water.

Well, drudge on, boor, drudge on; I am going to tempt the students of Trebisonde, to leave father and mother, forego for ever the established and common rule of living, disclaim and free themselves from obeying their lawful sovereign's edicts, live in absolute liberty, proudly despise every one, laugh at all mankind, and taking the fine jovial little cap of poetic licence, become so many pretty hobgoblins.

CHAPTER XLVII

How the Devil was deceived by an old woman of Pope-Figland

THE country lob trudged home very much concerned and
thoughtful, you may swear; insomuch that his good woman,
seeing him thus look moping, weened that something had been
stolen from him at market: but when she had heard the cause
of his affliction, and seen his budget well lined with coin, she
bade him be of good cheer, assuring him that he would be never
the worse for the scratching bout in question; wishing him only
to leave her to manage that business, and not trouble his head
about it; for she had already contrived how to bring him off
cleverly. Let the worst come to the worst, said the husbandman, it will be but a scratch; for I'll yield at the first stroke,
and quit the field. Quit a fart, replied the wife; he shall have
none of the field: rely upon me, and be quiet; let me alone
to deal with him, You say he is a pimping little devil, that is
enough; I will soon make him give up the field, I will warrant
you. Indeed, had he been a great devil, it had been somewhat.

The day that we landed in the island happened to be that
which the devil had fixed for the combat. Now the countryman, having, like a good Catholic, very fairly confessed himself
and received, betimes in the morning, by the advice of the vicar,
had hid himself, all but the snout, in the holy water pot, in the
posture in which we found him; and just as they were telling us
this story, news came that the old woman had fooled the devil,
and gained the field. You may not be sorry, perhaps, to hear
how this happened.

The devil, you must know, came to the poor man's door,
and rapping there, cried, So ho! ho the house! ho, clodpate!
where art thou? Come out with a vengeance; come out with
a wannion; come out and be damned: now for clawing. Then
briskly and resolutely entering the house, and not finding the
countryman there, he spied his wife lying on the ground
piteously weeping and howling. What is the matter? asked
the devil. Where is he? what does he? Oh! that I knew where
he is, replied threescore and five, the wicked rogue, the butcherly
dog, the murderer! He has spoiled me; I am undone; I die of
what he has done to me. How, cried the devil, what is it?
I will tickle him off for you by and by. Alas, cried the old
dissembler, he told me, the butcher, the tyrant, the tearer of

devils, told me, that he had made a match to scratch with you this day, and to try his claws, he did but just touch me with his little finger, here betwixt the legs, and has spoiled me for ever. Oh! I am a dead woman; I shall never be myself again: do but see! Nay, and besides, he talked of going to the smith's, to have his pounces sharpened and pointed. Alas! you are undone, Mr. Devil; good sir, scamper quickly, I am sure he won't stay; save yourself, I beseech you. While she said this, she uncovered herself up to the chin, after the manner in which the Persian women met their children who fled from the fight, and plainly showed her what do ye call it. The frighten'd devil, seeing the enormous solution of the continuity in all its dimensions, blessed himself, and cried out, Mahon, Demiourgon, Megæra, Alecto, Persephone; 'slife, catch me here when he comes! I am gone: 'sdeath, what a gash! I resign him the field.

Having heard the catastrophe of the story, we retired a shipboard, not being willing to stay there any longer. Pantagruel gave to the poor's box of the fabric of the church, eighteen thousand good royals, in commiseration of the poverty of the people, and the calamity of the place.

CHAPTER XLVIII

How Pantagruel went ashore at the Island of Papiman

HAVING left the desolate Island of the Pope-figs, we sailed, for the space of a day, very fairly and merrily, and made the blessed Island Papimany. As soon as we had dropt anchor in the road, before we had well moored our ship with ground-tackle, four persons, in different garbs, rowed towards us in a skiff. One of them was dressed like a monk in his frock, draggle-tailed, and booted: the other like a falconer, with a lure, and a long-winged hawk on his fist: the third like a solicitor, with a large bag, full of informations, subpœnas, breviates, bills, writs, cases, and other implements of pettifogging. The fourth looked like one of your vine barbers about Orleans, with a jantee pair of canvass trousers, a dosser, and a pruning knife at his girdle.

As soon as the boat had clapped them on board, they all with one voice asked, Have you seen him, good passengers, have you seen him?—Who? asked Pantagruel. You know, answered they. Who is it? asked Friar John. 'Sblood and 'ounds, I'll thrash him thick and threefold. This he said, thinking that they inquired after some robber, murderer, or church-breaker. Oh wonderful, cried the four, do not you foreign people know the one? Sirs, replied Epistemon, we do not understand those terms: but if you will be pleased to let us know who you mean, we will tell you the truth of the matter, without any more ado. We mean, said they, He that is. Did you ever see him? He that is, returned Pantagruel, according to our theological doctrine, is God, who said to Moses, I am that I am. We never saw him, nor can he be beheld by mortal eyes. We mean nothing less than that supreme God, who rules in heaven, replied they; we mean the god on earth. Did you ever see him? Upon my honour, replied Carpalim, they mean the pope. Ay, ay, answered Panurge: yea verily, gentlemen, I have seen three of them, whose sight has not much bettered me. How! cried they, our sacred decretals inform us, that there never is more than one living. I mean successively, one after the other, returned Panurge: otherwise I never saw more than one at a time.

O thrice and four times happy people! cried they, you are welcome, and more than double welcome! They then kneeled down before us and would have kissed our feet, but we would not suffer it, telling them that, should the pope come thither in his own person, it is all they could do to him. No, certainly, answered they, for we have already resolved upon the matter. We would kiss his bare arse, without boggling at it, and eke his two pounders: for he has a pair of them, the holy father, that he has; we find it so by our five decretals, otherwise he could not be pope. So that, according to our subtile decretalin philosophy, this is a necessary consequence: he is pope; therefore, he has genitories (genitals) and should genitories no more be found in the world, the world could no more have a pope.

While they were talking thus, Pantagruel inquired of one of the coxswain's crew, who those persons were? He answered, that they were the four estates of the realm; and added, that we should be made as welcome as princes, since we had seen the pope. Panurge having been acquainted with this by Pantagruel, said to him in his ear, I swear and vow, sir, it is even so; he that has patience may compass any thing. Our seeing the pope hath done us no good; now, in the devil's name, it will do us a great deal. We then went ashore, and the whole country, men, women, and children, came to meet us as in a solemn procession. Our four estates cried out to them with a loud voice, They have seen him! they have seen him! they have seen him! That proclamation being made, all the mob kneeled before us, lifting up their hands towards heaven, and crying, O happy men! O most happy! and this acclamation lasted about a quarter of an hour.

Then came the school-master of the place, with all his ushers, and school-boys, whom he magisterially flogged, as they used to whip children in our country formerly, when some criminal was hanged, that they might remember it. This displeased Pantagruel, who said to them, Gentlemen, if you do not leave off whipping these poor children, I am gone. The people were amazed, hearing his stentorian voice; and I saw a little hump with long fingers, say to the hypodidascal, What! in the name of wonder do all those that see the pope grow as tall as yon huge fellow that threatens us! Ah! how I shall think time long till I have seen him too, that I may grow and look as big. In short, the acclamations were so great, that Homenas (so they called their bishop) hastened thither, on an unbridled mule, with green trappings, attended by his apposts (as they said) and his supposts, or officers, bearing crosses, banners, standards, canopies, torches, holy water-pots, etc. He too wanted to kiss our feet, (as the good Christian Valfinier did to Pope Clement,) saying, that one of their hypothetes, that is, one of the scavengers, scourers, and commentators of their holy decretals, had written that, in the same manner as the Messiah, so long and so much expected by the Jews, at last appeared among them; so, on some happy day of God, the pope would come into that island; and that, while they waited for that blessed time, if any who had seen him at Rome, or elsewhere, chanced to come among them, they should be sure to make much of them, feast them plentifully, and treat them with a great deal of reverence. However, we civilly desired to be excused.

CHAPTER XLIX

How Homenas, Bishop of Papimany, showed us the Uranopet decretals

HOMENAS then said to us: It is enjoined us by our holy decretals to visit churches first, and taverns after. Therefore, not to decline that fine institution, let us go to church; we will afterwards go and feast ourselves. Man of God, quoth Friar John, do you go before, we will follow you: you spoke in the matter properly, and like a good Christian; it is long since we saw any such. For my part this rejoices my mind very much, and I verily believe that I shall have the better stomach after it. Well it is a happy thing to meet with good men! Being come near the gate of the church, we spied a huge thick book, gilt, and covered all over with precious stones, as rubies, emeralds, diamonds, and pearls, more, or at least as valuable as those which Augustus consecrated to Jupiter Capitolinus. This book hung in the air, being fastened with two thick chains of gold to the zoophore of the porch. We looked on it, and admired it. As for Pantagruel, he handled it, and dandled it, and turned it as he pleased, for he could reach it without straining; and he protested, that whenever he touched it, he was seized with a pleasant tickling at his finger's end, new life and activity in his arms, and a violent temptation in his mind to beat one or two serjeants, or such officers, provided they were not of the shaveling kind. Homenas then said to us, The law was formerly given to the Jews by Moses, written by God himself. At Delphos, before the portal of Apollo's temple, this sentence, ΓΝΩΘΙ ΣΕ ΑΥΤΟΝ was found written with a divine hand. And some time after it, Ε Ι was also seen and as divinely written and transmitted from heaven. Cybele's image was brought out of heaven, into a field called Pessinunt, in Phrygia; so was that of Diana to Tauris, if you will believe Euripides; the oriflamb, or holy standard, was transmitted out of heaven to the noble and most Christian kings of France, to fight against the unbelievers. In the reign of Numa Pompilius, second King of the Romans, the famous copper buckler called Ancile, was seen to descend from heaven. At Acropolis, near Athens, Minerva's statue formerly fell from the imperial heaven. In like manner the sacred decretals, which you see, were written with the hand of an angel, of the cherubim kind. You outlandish people will hardly believe this, I fear, Little enough of conscience, said Panurge. — And then, continued Homenas, they were miraculously transmitted to us here from the very heaven of heavens; in the same manner as the river Nile is called Diipetes by Homer, the father of all philosophy, (the holy decretals always excepted.) Now, because you have seen the pope, their evangelist and everlasting protector, we will give you leave to see and kiss them on the inside, if you think meet. But then you must fast three days before, and canonically confess; nicely and strictly mustering up, and inventorising your sins great and small, so thick that one single circumstance of them may not escape you; as our holy decretals, which you see direct. This will take up some time. Man of God, answered Panurge, we have seen and descried decrees, and eke decretals enough of conscience; some on paper, others on parchment, fine and gay like any painted paper lantern, some on vellum, some in manuscript, and others in print: so you need not take half these pains to show these. We will take the good-will for the deed, and thank you as much as if we had. Ay, marry, said Homenas, but you never saw those that are angelically written. Those in your country are only transcripts from ours; as we find it written by one of our old decretaline scholiasts. For me, do not spare me; I do not value the labour; so I may serve you: do but tell me whether you will be confessed, and fast only three short little days of God? As for confessing, answered Panurge, there can be no great harm in it; but this same fasting, master of mine, will hardly down with us at this time, for we have so very much overfasted ourselves at sea, that the spiders have spun their cobwebs over our grinders. Do but look on this good Friar John des Entomeures, (Homenas then courteously demy-clipped him about the neck) some moss is growing in his throat, for want of bestirring and exercising his chaps. He speaks the truth, vouched Friar John; I have so much fasted that I am almost grown hump-shouldered. Come, then, let us go into the church, said Homenas; and pray forgive us if for the present, we do not sing you a fine high mass. The hour of mid-day is past, and after it our sacred decretals forbid us to sing mass, I mean your high and lawful mass. But I will say a low and dry one, for you. I had rather have one moistened with some good Anjou wine, cried Panurge; fall to, fall to your low mass, and dispatch. Odd's-boddikins, quoth Friar John, it frets me to the guts that I must have an empty stomach at this time of day. For, had I eaten a good breakfast and fed like a monk, if he should chance to sing us the *Requiem æternam dona eis, Domine*, I had then brought thither bread and wine for the *traits passez*, (those that are gone before.) Well, patience; pull away, and save tide: short and sweet, I pray you, and this for a cause.

CHAPTER L

How Homenas showed us the Arch-type, or representation of a pope

MASS being mumbled over, Homenas took a huge bundle of keys out of a trunk near the head altar, and put thirty-two of them into so many key-holes; put back so many springs; then with fourteen more mastered so many padlocks, and at last opened an iron window strongly barred above the said altar. This being done, in token of great mystery, he covered himself with wet sackcloth, and drawing a curtain of crimson satin, showed us an image daubed over, coarsely enough, to my thinking: then he touched it with a pretty long stick, and made us all kiss the part of the stick that had touched the image. After this he said unto us, What think you of this image? It is the likeness of a pope, answered Pantagruel: I know it by the triple crown, his furred amice, his rochet, and his slipper. You are in the right, said Homenas; it is the idea of that same good god on earth, whose coming we devoutly await, and whom we hope one day to see in this country. O happy, wished for, and much expected day! and happy, most happy you, whose propitious stars have so favoured you, as to let you see the living and real face of this good god on earth! by the single sight of whose picture we obtain full remission of all the sins which we remember that we have committed, as also a third part, and eighteen quarantaines of the sins which we have forgot: and indeed we only see it on high annual holidays.

This caused Pantagruel to say, that it was a work like those which Dædalus used to make, since, though it were deformed and ill drawn, nevertheless some divine energy, in point of pardons, lay hid and concealed in it. Thus, said Friar John, at Sevillé, the rascally beggars being one evening on a solemn holiday at supper in the spital, one bragged of having got six blancs, or two-pence half-penny; another eight liards, or two-pence; a third, seven caroluses, or six-pence; but an old mumper made his vaunts of having got three testons, or five shillings. Ah, but, cried his comrades, thou hast a leg of God; as if, continued Friar John, some divine virtue could lie hid in a stenching ulcerated rotten shank. Pray, said Pantagruel, when you are for telling us some such nauseous tale, be so kind as not to forget to provide a bason, Friar John: I'll assure you, I had much ado to forbear bringing up my breakfast. Fie! I wonder a man

of your coat is not ashamed to use thus the sacred name of
God, in speaking of things so filthy and abominable! fie, I say.
If among your monking tribes such an abuse of words is allowed,
I beseech you leave it there, and do not let it come out of the
cloisters. Physicians, said Epistemon, thus attribute a kind
of divinity to some diseases: Nero also extolled mushrooms, and,
in a Greek proverb, termed them divine food, because with
them he had poisoned Claudius his predecessor. But methinks,
gentlemen, this same picture is not over like our late pope's.
For I have seen them, not with their pallium, amice, or rochet
on, but with helmets on their heads, more like the top of a
Persian turban; and while the Christian commonwealth was in
peace, they alone were most furiously and cruelly making war.
This must have been then, returned Homenas, against the
rebellious, heretical Protestants; reprobates, who are disobe-
dient to the holiness of this good god on earth. It is not only
lawful for him to do so, but it is enjoined him by the sacred decretals; and if any dare transgress one single iota against their
commands, whether they be emperors, kings, dukes, princes,
or commonwealths, he is immediately to pursue them with
fire and sword, strip them of all their goods, take their kingdoms
from them, proscribe them, anathematize them, and destroy not
only their bodies, those of their children, relations, and others,
but damn also their souls to the very bottom of the most hot
and burning cauldron in hell. Here, in the devil's name, said
Panurge, the people are no heretics; such as was our Raminagrobis, and as they are in Germany and England. You are
Christians of the best edition, all picked and culled, for aught
I see. Ay, marry are we, returned Homenas, and for that
reason we shall all be saved. Now let us go and bless ourselves
with holy-water, and then to dinner.

CHAPTER LI

Table-talk in praise of the decretals

Now, topers, pray observe that while Homenas was saying his
dry mass, three collectors, or licensed beggars of the church,
each of them with a large bason, went round among the people
with a loud voice; Pray remember the blessed men who have
seen his face. As we came out of the temple, they brought
their basons brim full of papimany chink to Homenas, who

told us that it was plentifully to feast with; and that, of this contribution and voluntary tax, one part should be laid out in good drinking, another in good eating, and the remainder in both: according to an admirable exposition hidden in a corner of their holy decretals; which was performed to a T, and that at a noted tavern not much unlike that of Will's at Amiens. Believe me, we tickled it off there with copious cramming, and numerous swilling.

I made two notable observations at that dinner: the one, that there was not one dish served up, whether of cabrittas, capons, hogs, (of which latter there is great plenty in Papimany,) pigeons, conies, leverets, turkeys, or others, without abundance of magistral stuffing: the other, that every course, and the fruit also, were served up by unmarried females of the place, tight lasses, I will assure you, waggish, fair, good-conditioned, and comely, spruce, and fit for business. They were all clad in fine long white albs, with two girdles; their hair interwoven with narrow tape and purple riband, stuck with roses, gilly-flowers, marjoram, daffidown-dillies, thyme, and other sweet flowers.

At every cadence, they invited us to drink and bang it about, dropping us neat and genteel courtesies: nor was the sight of them unwelcome to all the company; and as for Friar John, he leered on them sideways, like a cur that steals a capon. When the first course was taken off, the females melodiously sung us an epode in the praise of the sacrosant decretals; and then the second course being served up, Homenas, joyful and cheery, said to one of the she butlers, Light here, Clerica. Immediately one of the girls brought him a tall-boy brim-full of extravagant wine. He took fast hold of it, and fetching a deep sigh, said to Pantagruel, My lord, and you my good friends, here's to ye, with all my heart: you are all very welcome. When he had tipped that off, and given the tall-boy to the pretty creature, he lifted up his voice and said, O most holy decretals, how good is good wine found through your means! This is the best jest we have had yet, observed Panurge. But it would still be better, said Pantagruel, if they could turn bad wine into good.

O seraphic Sextum! continued Homenas, how necessary are you not to the salvation of poor mortals! O cherubic Clementinæ! how perfectly the perfect institution of a true Christian is contained and described in you! O angelical Extravagantés! how many poor souls that wander up and down in mortal bodies, through this vale of misery, would perish, were it not for you! When, ah! when shall this special gift of grace be bestowed on mankind, as to lay aside all other studies and concerns, to use you, to peruse you, to understand you, to know you by heart, to practise you, to incorporate you, to turn you into blood, and incentre you into the deepest ventricles of their brains, the inmost marrow of their bones, and most intricate labyrinth of their arteries? Then, ah, then! and no sooner than then, nor otherwise than thus, shall the world be happy! While the old man was thus running on, Epistemon rose and softly said to Panurge, For want of a close stool, I must even leave you for a moment or two: this stuff has unbunged the orifice of my mustard-barrel: but I'll not tarry long.

Then, ah then! continued Homenas, no hail, frost, ice, snow, overflowing, or *vis major*: then plenty of all earthly goods here below. Then uninterrupted and eternal peace through the universe, an end of all wars, plunderings, drudgeries, robbing, assassinates, unless it be to destroy these cursed rebels the heretics. Oh, then, rejoicing, cheerfulness, jollity, solace, sports, and delicious pleasures, over the face of the earth. Oh! what great learning, inestimable erudition, and god-like precepts, are knit, linked, rivetted, and mortised in the divine chapters of these eternal decretals!

Oh! how wonderfully, if you read but one demy canon, short paragraph, or single observation of these sacrosanct decretals, how wonderfully, I say, do you not perceive to kindle in your hearts a furnace of divine love, charity towards your neighbour, (provided he be no heretic,) bold contempt of all casual and sublunary things, firm content in all your affections, and ecstatic elevation of soul even to the third heaven.

CHAPTER LII

A continuation of the miracles caused by the decretals

SPOKE like an organ, quoth Panurge; but for my part, I believe as little of it as I can. For, one day by chance I happened to read a chapter of them at Poictiers, at the most decretalipotent Scotch doctor's, and old Nick turn me into bumfodder, if this did not make me so hide-bound and costive, that for four or five days I hardly scumbered one poor butt of sir-reverence;

and that, too, was full as dry and hard, I protest, as Catullus
tells us were those of his neighbour Furius:

> Nec toto decies cacas in anno,
> Atque id durius est fabâ, et lapillis:
> Quod tu si manibus teras, fricesque,
> Non unquam digitum inquinare possis.

Oh, ho, cried Homenas, by our lady, it may be you were then
in a state of mortal sin, my friend.   Well turned, cried Panurge,
this was a new strain egad.

One day, said Friar John, at Sevillé I had applied to my
posteriors, by way of hind-towel, a leaf of an old Clementinæ
which our rent-gatherer, John Guimard, had thrown out into
the green of our cloister; now the devil broil me like a black
pudding, if I was not so abominably plagued with chaps, chawns,
and piles at the fundament, that the orifice of my poor nockandroe was in a most woeful pickle for I do not know how long.
By our lady, cried Homenas, it was a plain punishment of God,
for the sin that you had committed in bewraying that sacred
book, which you ought rather to have kissed and adored; I say
with an adoration of latria, or of hyperdulia at least: the
Panormitan never told a lie in the matter.

Saith Ponocrates: At Montpelier, John Choüart having
bought of the monks of St. Olary a delicate set of decretals,
written on fine large parchment of Lamballe, to beat gold between the leaves, not so much as a piece that was beaten in
them came to good, but all were dilacerated and spoiled.   Mark
this, cried Homenas; it was a divine punishment and vengeance.

At Mans, said Eudemon, Francis Cornu, apothecary, had
turned an old set of Extravagantés into waste paper: may
I never stir, if whatever was lapped up in them was not immediately corrupted, rotten, and spoiled; incense, pepper, cloves,
cinnamon, saffron, wax, cassia, rhubarb, tamarinds, all drugs
and spices, were all lost without exception.   Mark, mark,
quoth Homenas, an effect of divine justice!   This comes of
putting the sacred Scriptures to such profane uses.

At Paris, said Carpalim, snip Groignet the tailor had turned
an old Clementinæ into patterns and measures, and all the
clothes that were cut on them were utterly spoiled and lost;
gowns, hoods, cloaks, cassocks, jerkins, jackets, waistcoats,
capes, doublets, petticoats, corps de robes, farthingales, and so
forth.   Snip, thinking to cut a hood, would cut you out a codpiece; instead of a cassock, he would make you a high-crowned
hat; for a waistcoat, he would shape you out a rochet; on the

pattern of a doublet, he would make you a thing like a frying-pan; then his journeymen having stitched it up, did jag it and pink it at the bottom, and so it looked like a pan to fry chesnuts. Instead of a cape, he made a buskin; for a farthingale, he shaped a montero cap; and thinking to make a cloak, he would cut out a pair of our big out-strouting Swiss breeches, with panes like the outside of a tabour. Insomuch that Snip was condemned to make good the stuffs to all his customers; and to this day poor cabbage's hair grows through his hood, and his arse through his pocket-holes. Mark, an effect of heavenly wrath and vengeance! cried Homenas.

At Cahusac, said Gymnast, a match being made by the lords of Estissac and Viscount Lausun to shoot at a mark, Perotou had taken to pieces a set of decretals, and set one of the leaves for the white to shoot at: now I sell, nay I give and bequeath for ever and aye, the mould of my doublet to fifteen hundred hampers full of black devils, if ever any archer in the country (though they are singular marksmen in Guienne) could hit the white. Not the least bit of the holy scribble was contaminated or touched: nay, and Sansornin the elder, who held stakes, swore to us, *figues dioures*, hard figs, (his greatest oath,) that he had openly, visibly, and manifestly seen the bolt of Carquelin moving right to the round circle in the middle of the white; and that just on the point, when it was going to hit and enter, it had gone aside above seven foot and four inches wide of it towards the bakehouse.

Miracle! cried Homenas, miracle! miracle! Clerica, come wench, light, light here. Here's to you all, gentlemen; I vow you seem to me very sound Christians. While he said this, the maidens began to snicker at his elbow, grinning, giggling, and twittering among themselves. Friar John began to paw, neigh, and whinny at the snout's end, as one ready to leap, or at least to play the ass, and get up and ride tantivy to the devil, like a beggar on horseback.

Methinks, said Pantagruel, a man might have been more out of danger near the white of which Gymnast spoke, than was formerly Diogenes near another. How is that? asked Homenas; what was it? Was he one of our decretalists? Rarely fallen in again egad, said Epistemon, returning from stool; I see he will hook his decretals in, though by the head and shoulders.

Diogenes, said Pantagruel, one day, for pastime, went to see some archers that shot at butts, one of whom was so unskilful, that, when it was his turn to shoot, all the bystanders went aside, lest he should mistake them for the mark. Diogenes had seen him shoot extremely wide of it: so when the other was taking aim a second time, and the people removed at a great distance to the right and left of the white, he placed himself close by the mark; holding that place to be the safest, and that so bad an archer would certainly rather hit any other.

One of the Lord d'Estissac's pages at last found out the charm, pursued Gymnast, and by his advice Peroton put in another white made up of some papers of Pouillac's lawsuit, and then every one shot cleverly.

At Landerousse, said Rhizotomus, at John Delif's wedding were very great doings, as it was then the custom of the country. After supper, several farces, interludes, and comical scenes were acted: they had also several morris-dancers with bells and tabours; and divers sorts of masks and mummers were let in. My school-fellows and I, to grace the festival to the best of our power, (for fine white and purple liveries had been given to all of us in the morning) contrived a merry mask with store of cockle-shells, shells of snails, periwinkles, and such other. Then for want of cuckoo pintle, or priest-pintle, lousebur, clote, and paper, we made ourselves false faces with the leaves of an old Sextum, that had been thrown by, and lay there for any one that would take it up: cutting out holes for the eyes, nose, and mouth. Now, did you ever hear the like since you were born? when we had played out little boyish antic tricks, and came to take off our sham faces, we appeared more hideous and ugly than the little devils that acted the "Passion" at Douay: for our faces were uttely spoiled at the places which had been touched by those leaves: one had there the small-pox; another, God's token, or the plague-spot; a third, the crinckums; a fourth, the measles; a fifth, botches, pushes, and carbuncles; in short, he came off the least hurt, who only lost his teeth by the bargain. Miracle! bawled out Homenas, miracle!

Hold, hold, cried Rhizotomus, it is not yet time to clap. My sister Kate, and my sister Ren, had put the crepines of their hoods, their ruffles, snuffekins, and neck-ruffs new washed, starched, and ironed, into that very book of decretals; for, you must know, it was covered with thick boards, and had strong clasps. Now by the virtue of God— Hold, interrupted Homenas, what God do you mean? There is but one, answered Rhizotomus. In heaven, I grant, replied Homenas; but we have another here on earth, do you see. Ay, marry have we, said Rhizotomus; but on my soul I protest I had quite forgot it. Well then, by the virtue of god the pope, their pinners, neck-ruffs, bibs, coifs, and other linen, turned as black as a charcoal-man's sack. Miracle! cried Homenas. Here, Clerica, light me here; and pr'ythee, girl, observe these rare stories. How comes it to pass then, asked Friar John, that people say,

> Ever since decrees had tails,
> And gens d'armes lugged heavy mails,
> Since each monk would have a horse,
> All went here from bad to worse.

I understand you, answered Homenas: this is one of the quirks and little satires of the newfangled heretics.

CHAPTER LIII

How by the virtue of the decretals, gold is subtilely drawn out of France to Rome

I WOULD, said Epistemon, it had cost me a pint of the best tripe that ever can enter into gut, so we had but compared withthe original the dreadful chapters, *Execrabilis, De multa, Si plures, De annatis per totum, Nisi essent, Cum ad monasterium, Quod delectio, Mandatum*; and certain others, that draw every year out of France to Rome, four hundred thousand ducats and more.

Do you make nothing of this? asked Homenas. Though, methinks, after all, it is but little, if we consider that France, the most Christian, is the only nurse the see of Rome has. However, find me in the whole world a book, whether of philosophy, physic, law, mathematics, or other human learning, nay, even, by my God, of the Holy Scripture itself, will draw as much money thence? None, none, pshaw, tush, blurt, pish; none can. You may look till your eyes drop out of your head, nay, till doomsday in the afternoon, before you can find another of that energy; I will pass my word for that.

Yet these devilish heretics refuse to learn and know it. Burn them, tear them, nip them with hot pincers, drown them, hang them, spit them at the bunghole, pelt them, paut them, bruise them, beat them, cripple them, dismember them, cut them, gut them, bowel them, paunch them, thrash them, slash them, gash them, chop them, slice them, slit them, carve them, saw them.

bethwack them, pare them, hack them, hew them, mince them, flea them, boil them, broil them, roast them, toast them, bake them, fry them, crucify them, crush them, squeeze them, grind them, batter them, burst them, quarter them, unlimb them, behump them, bethump them, belump them, belabour them, pepper them, spitchcock them, and carbonade them on gridirons, these wicked heretics! decretalifuges, decretalicides, worse than homicides, worse than patricides, decretalictiones of the devil of hell.

As for you other good people, I must earnestly pray and beseech you to believe no other thing, to think on, say, undertake, or do no other thing, than what's contained in our sacred decretals, and their corollaries, this fine Sextum, these fine Clementinæ, these fine Extravagantés. O deific books! So shall you enjoy glory, honour, exaltation, wealth, dignities, and preferments in this world; be revered, and dreaded by all, preferred, elected, and chosen, above all men.

For, there is not under the cope of heaven a condition of men, out of which you will find persons fitter to do and handle all things, than those who by divine prescience, eternal predestination, have applied themselves to the study of the holy decretals.

Would you choose a worthy emperor, a good captain, a fit general in time of war, one that can well foresee all inconveniences, avoid all dangers, briskly and bravely bring his men on to a breach or attack, still be on sure grounds, always overcome without loss of his men, and know how to make a good use of his victory? Take me a decretist.—No, no, I mean a decretalist. Ho, the foul blunder, whispered Epistemon.

Would you, in time of peace, find a man capable of wisely governing the state of a commonwealth, of a kingdom, of an empire, of a monarchy; sufficient to maintain the clergy, nobility, senate, and commons in wealth, friendship, unity, obedience, virtue, and honesty? Take a decretalist.

Would you find a man, who, by his exemplary life, eloquence, and pious admonitions, may in a short time, without effusion of human blood, conquer the Holy Land, and bring over to the holy church the misbelieving Turks, Jews, Tartars, Muscovites, Mamelukes, and Sarrabonites? Take me a decretalist.

What makes, in many countries, the people rebellious and depraved, pages saucy and mischievous, students sottish and duncical? Nothing but that their governors, and tutors were not decretalists.

But what, on your conscience, was it, do you think, that established, confirmed, and authorised those fine religious orders, with whom you see the Christian world every where adorned, graced, and illustrated, as the firmament is with its glorious stars? The holy decretals.

What was it that founded, underpropped, and fixed, and now maintains, nourishes, and feeds the devout monks, and friars in convents, monasteries, and abbeys; so that did they not daily and nightly pray without ceasing, the world would be in evident danger of returning to its primitive chaos? The sacred decretals.

What makes and daily increases the famous and celebrated patrimony of St. Peter in plenty of all temporal, corporeal, and spiritual blessings? The holy decretals.

What made the holy apostolic see and pope of Rome, in all times, and at this present, so dreadful in the universe, that all kings, emperors, potentates, and lords, willing, nilling, must depend upon him, hold of him, be crowned, confirmed, and authorised by him, come thither to strike sail, buckle, and fall down before his holy slipper, whose picture you have seen? The mighty decretals of God.

I will discover you a great secret. The universities of your world have commonly a book either open or shut in their arms, and devices: what book do you think it is? Truly, I do not know, answered Pantagruel; I never read it. It is the decretals, said Homenas, without which the privileges of all universities would soon be lost. You must own, that I have taught you this; ha, ha, ha, ha, ha!

Here Homenas began to belch, to fart, to funk, to laugh, to slaver, and to sweat; and then he gave his huge greasy four-cornered cap to one of the lasses, who clapt it on her pretty head with a great deal of joy, after she had lovingly bussed it, as a sure token that she should be first married. *Vivat*, cried Epistemon, *fifat, bibat, pipat.*

O apocalyptic secret! continued Homenas; light, light, Clerica, light here with double lanterns. Now for the fruit, virgins.

I was saying then, that giving yourselves thus wholly to the study of the holy decretals, you will gain wealth and honour in this world: I add, that in the next you will infallibly be saved in the blessed kingdom of heaven, whose keys are given to our good god and decretaliarch. O my good god, whom I adore and never saw, by thy special grace open unto us, at the point of death at least, this most sacred treasure of our holy mother church, whose protector, preserver, butler, chief larder, administrator, and disposer thou art; and take care, I beseech thee, O lord, that the precious works of supererogation, the goodly pardons, do not fail us in time of need: so that the devils may not find an opportunity to gripe our precious souls, and the dreadful jaws of hell may not swallow us. If we must pass through purgatory, thy will be done. It is in thy power to draw us out of it when thou pleasest. Here Homenas began to shed huge hot briny tears, to beat his breast, and kiss his thumbs in the shape of a cross.

CHAPTER LIV

How Homenas gave Pantagruel some bon-Christian pears

EPISTEMON, Friar John, and Panurge, seeing this doleful catastrophe, began, under the cover of their napkins, to cry, meeow, meeow, meeow; feigning to wipe their eyes all the while as if they had wept. The wenches were doubly diligent, and brought brimmers of Clementine wine to every one, besides store of sweetmeats; and thus the feasting was revived.

Before we arose from table, Homenas gave us a great quantity of fair large pears; saying, Here, my good friends, these are singular good pears; you will find none such any where else, I dare warrant. Every soil bears not every thing, you know; India alone boasts black ebony; the best incense is produced in Sabæa; the sphragitid earth at Lemnos: so this island is the only place where such fine pears grow. You may, if you please, make nurseries with their kernels in your country.

I like their taste extremely, said Pantagruel. If they were sliced, and put into a pan on the fire with wine and sugar, I fancy they would be very wholesome meat for the sick, as well as for the healthy. Pray what do you call them? No otherwise than you have heard, replied Homenas. We are a plain downright sort of people, as God would have it, and call figs, figs; plums, plums; and pears, pears. Truly, said Pantagruel, if I live to go home,—which I hope will be speedily, God willing,—I'll set off and graff some in my garden in Touraine, by the banks of the Loire, and will call them bon-Christian or good-Christian pears: for I never saw better Christians than are these good Papimans. I would like him two to one better yet, said Friar John, would he but give us two or three cart-loads of yon buxom lasses. Why, what would you do with them? cried Homenas. Quoth Friar John, No harm, only bleed the kind-hearted souls straight between the two great toes, with certain clever lancets of the right stamp: by which operation good Christian children would be inoculated upon them, and the breed be multiplied in our country, in which there are not many over good, the more's the pity.

Nay verily, replied Homenas, we cannot do this; for you would make them tread their shoes awry, crack their pipkins, and spoil their shapes: you love mutton, I see, you will run at sheep; I know you by that same nose and hair of yours, though I never saw your face before. Alas! alas! how kind you are! And would you indeed damn your precious soul? Our decretals forbid this. Ah, I wish you had them at your finger-end. Patience, said Friar John; but, *si tu vis dare, præsta, quæsumus.* Matter of breviary. As for that, I defy all the world, and I fear no man that wears a head and a hood, though he were a chrystallin, I mean a decretalin doctor.

Dinner being over, we took our leave of the right reverend Homenas, and of all the good people, humbly giving thanks; and, to make them amends for their kind entertainment, promised them that, at our coming to Rome, we would make our applications so effectually to the pope, that he would speedily be sure to come to visit them in person. After this we went on board.

Pantagruel, by an act of generosity, and as an acknowledgment of the sight of the pope's picture, gave Homenas nine pieces of double frized cloth of gold, to be set before the grates of the window. He also caused the church box, for its repairs and fabric, to be quite filled with double crowns of gold; and ordered nine hundred and fourteen angels to be delivered to each of the lasses, who had waited at table, to buy them husbands when they could get them.

CHAPTER LV

How Pantagruel, being at sea, heard various unfrozen words

WHEN we were at sea, junketting, tippling, discoursing, and telling stories, Pantagruel rose and stood up to look out: then asked us, Do you hear nothing, gentlemen? Methink I hear some people talking in the air, yet I can see nobody. Hark! According to his command we listened, and with full ears sucked in the air, as some of you suck oysters, to find if we could hear some sound scattered through the sky; and to lose none of it, like the Emperor Antoninus, some of us laid their hands hollow next to their ears; but all this would not do, nor could we hear any voice. Yet Pantagruel continued to assure us he heard various voices in the air, some of men, and some of women.

At last we began to fancy that we also heard something, or at least that our ears tingled; and the more we listened, the plainer we discerned the voices, so as to distinguish articulate sounds. This mightily frightened us, and not without cause; since we could see nothing, yet heard such various sounds and voices of men, women, children, horses, etc., insomuch that Panurge cried out, Cods belly, there is no fooling with the devil; we are all beshit, let us fly. There is some ambuscade hereabouts. Friar John, art thou here, my love? I pray thee, stay by me, old boy. Hast thou got thy swingeing tool? See that it do not stick in thy scabbard; thou never scourest it half as it should be. We are undone. Hark! They are guns, gad judge me: let us fly, I do not say with hands and feet, as Brutus said at the Battle of Pharsalia; I say, with sails and oars: let us whip it away: I never find myself to have a bit of courage at sea; in cellars, and elsewhere, I have more than enough. Let us fly and save our bacon. I do not say this for any fear that I have; for I dread nothing but danger, that I do not; I always say it, that should not. The free archer of Baignolet said as much. Let us hazard nothing therefore, I say, lest we come off bluely. Tack about, helm a lee, thou son of a bachelor. Would I were now well in Quinquenois, though I were never to marry. Haste away, let us make all the sail we can; they will be too hard for us; we are not able to cope with them; they are ten to our one; I will warrant you; nay, and they are on their dung-hill, while we do not know the country. They will be the death of us. We will lose no honour by flying: Demosthenes saith, that the man that runs away, may fight another day. At least, let us retreat to the leeward. Helm a lee; bring the main tack aboard, hawl the bowlins, hoist the topgallants; we are all dead men; get off, in the devil's name, get off.

Pantagruel, hearing the sad outcry which Panurge made, said, Who talks of flying? Let us first see who they are; perhaps they may be friends: I can discover nobody yet, though I can see a hundred miles round me. But let us consider a little: I have read that a philosopher, named Petron, was of opinion, that there were several worlds, that touched each other in an equilateral triangle; in whose centre, he said, was the dwelling of truth: and that the words, ideas, copies, and images of all things past, and to come, resided there; round which was the age; and that with success of time part of them used to fall on mankind, like rheums and mildews; just as the dew fell on Gideon's fleece, till the age was fulfilled.

I also remember, continued he, that Aristotle affirms Homer's words to be flying, moving, and consequently animated. Besides, Antiphanes said, that Plato's philosophy was like words, which, being spoken in some country during a hard winter are immediately congealed, frozen up, and not heard: for what Plato taught young lads, could hardly be understood by them when they were grown old. Now continued he, we should philosophize and search whether this be not the place where those words are thawed.

You would wonder very much, should this be the head and lyre of Orpheus. When the Thracian women had torn him to pieces, they threw his head and lyre into the river Hebrus; down which they floated to the Euxine sea, as far as the island of Lesbos; the head continually uttering a doleful song, as it were, lamenting the death of Orpheus, and the lyre, with the wind's impulse, moving its strings, and harmoniously accompanying the voice. Let us see if we cannot discover them hereabouts.

CHAPTER LVI

How among the frozen words Pantagruel found some odd ones

THE skipper made answer: Be not afraid, my lord, we are on confines of the Frozen Sea, on which, about the beginning of last winter, happened a great and bloody fight between the

Arimaspians and the Nephelibates. Then the words and cries of men and women, the hacking, slashing, and hewing of battle-axes, the shocking, knocking, and jolting of armours and harnesses, the neighing of horses, and all other martial din and noise, froze in the air; and now, the rigour of the winter being over, by the succeeding serenity and warmth of the weather, they melt and are heard.

By jingo, quoth Panurge, the man talks somewhat like; I believe him: but could not we see some of them? I think I have read, that, on the edge of the mountain on which Moses received the Judaic law, the people saw the voices sensibly.—Here, here, said Pantagruel, here are some that are not yet thawed. He then threw us on the deck whole handfuls of frozen words, which seemed to us like your rough sugar plums, of many colours, like those used in heraldry; some words gules, (this means also jests and merry sayings,) some vert, some azure, some black, some or, (this means fair words;) and when we had somewhat warmed them between our hands, they melted like snow, and we really heard them, but could not understand them, for it was a barbarous gibberish. One of them, only, that was pretty big, having been warmed between Friar John's hands, gave a sound much like that of chesnuts when they are thrown into the fire, without being first cut, which made us all start. This was the report of a field piece in its time, cried Friar John.

Panurge prayed Pantagruel to give him some more; but Pantagruel told him, that to give words was the part of a lover. Sell me some then, I pray you, cried Panurge. That is the part of a lawyer, returned Pantagruel. I would sooner sell you silence, though at a dearer rate; as Demosthenes formerly sold it by the means of his *argentangina*, or silver quinsey.

However, he threw three or four handfuls of them on the deck; among which I perceived some very sharp words, and some bloody words, which, the pilot said, used sometimes to go back, and recoil to the place whence they came, but it was with a slit weasand: we also saw some terrible words, and some others not very pleasant to the eye.

When they had been all melted together, we heard a strange noise, hin, hin, hin, hin, his, tick, tock, taack, bredelin-brededack, frr, frr, frr, bou, bou, bou, bou, bou, bou, track, track, trr, trr, trr, trrr, trrrrr; on, on, on, on, on, ououououon, gog, magog, and I do not know what other barbarous words; which, the pilot said, were the noise made by the charging squadrons, the shock and neighing of horses.

Then we heard some large ones go off like drums and fifes, and others like clarions and trumpets. Believe me we had very good sport with them. I would fain have saved some merry odd words, and have preserved them in oil, as ice and snow are kept, and between clean straw. But Pantagruel would not let me, saying, that it is a folly to hoard up what we are never like to want, or have always at hand; odd, quaint, merry, and fat words of gules, never being scarce among all good and jovial Pantagruelists.

Panurge somewhat vexed Friar John, and put him in the pouts; for he took him at his word, while he dreamed of nothing less. This caused the friar to threaten him with such a piece of revenge as was put upon G. Jousseaume, who having taken the merry Patelin at his word, when he had overbid himself in some cloth, was afterwards fairly taken by the horns like a bullock, by his jovial chapman, whom he took at his word like a man. Panurge, well knowing that threatened folks live long, bobbed, and made mouths at him, in token of derision, then cried, Would I had here the word of the Holy Bottle, without being thus obliged to go further in pilgrimage to her.

CHAPTER LVII

How Pantagruel went ashore at the dwelling of Gaster, the first master of arts in the world

THAT day Pantagruel went ashore in an island, which, for situation and governor, may be said not to have its fellow. When you just come into it, you find it rugged, craggy, and barren, unpleasant to the eye, painful to the feet, and almost as inaccessible as the mountain of Dauphiné, which is somewhat like a toad-stool, and was never climbed, as any can remember, by any but Doyac, who had the charge of King Charles the Eighth's train of artillery.

This same Doyac, with strange tools and engines, gained that mountain's top, and there he found an old ram. It puzzled many a wise head to guess how it got thither. Some said that some eagle, or great horn-coot, having carried it thither while it was yet a lambkin, it had got away, and saved itself among the bushes.

As for us, having with much toil and sweat overcome the difficult ways at the entrance, we found the top of the mountain so fertile, healthful, and pleasant, that I thought I was then in the true garden of Eden, or earthly paradise, about whose situation our good theologues are in such a quandary, and keep such a pother.

As for Pantagruel, he said, that there was the seat of Areté —that is as much as to say, virtue—described by Hesiod. This, however, with submission to better judgments. The ruler of this place was one Master Gaster, the first master of arts in the world. For, if you believe that fire is the great master of arts, as Tully writes, you very much wrong him and yourself: alas, Tully never believed this. On the other side, if you fancy Mercury to be the first inventor of arts, as our ancient Druids believed of old, you are mightily beside the mark. The satirist's sentence, that affirms master Gaster to be the master of all arts, is true. With him peacefully resided old goody Penia, alias Poverty, the mother of the ninety-nine Muses, on whom Porus, the lord of Plenty, formerly begot Love, that noble child, the mediator of heaven and earth, as Plato affirms *in Symposio*.

We were all obliged to pay our homage, and swear allegiance to that mighty sovereign; for he is imperious, severe, blunt, hard, uneasy, inflexible: you cannot make him believe, represent to him, or persuade him anything.

He does not hear: and, as the Egyptians said that Harpocrates, the god of silence, named Sigalion in Greek, was *astomé*, that is, without a mouth; so Gaster was created without ears, even like the image of Jupiter in Candia.

He only speaks by signs: but those signs are more readily obeyed by every one, than the statutes of senates, or commands of monarchs: neither will he admit the least let or delay in his summons. You say, that when a lion roars, all the beasts at a considerable distance round about, as far as his roar can be heard, are seized with a shivering. This is written, it is true; I have seen it. I assure you, that at master Gaster's command, the very heavens tremble, and all the earth shakes: his command is called, Do this or die. Needs must when the devil drives; there's no gainsaying of it.

The pilot was telling us how, on a certain time, after the manner of the members that mutinied against the belly, as Æsop describes it, the whole kingdom of the Somates went off into a direct faction against Gaster, resolving to throw off his yoke: but they soon found their mistake, and most humbly submitted; for otherwise they had all been famished.

What company soever he is in, none dispute with him for precedence or superiority; he still goes first, though kings, emperors, or even the pope, were there. So he held the first place at the council of Basle; though some will tell you that the council was tumultuous, by the contention and ambition of many for priority.

Every one is busied, and labours to serve him; and, indeed, to make amends for this, he does this good to mankind, as to invent for them all arts, machines, trades, engines, and crafts: he even instructs brutes in arts which are against their nature, making poets of ravens, jackdaws, chattering jays, parrots, and starlings, and poetesses of magpies, teaching them to utter human language, speak and sing; and all for the gut. He reclaims and tames eagles, gerfalcons, falcons gentle, sakers, lanners, goshawks, sparrow-hawks, merlins, hagards, passengers, wild rapacious birds; so that setting them free in the air, whenever he thinks fit, as high and as long as he pleases, he keeps them suspended, straying, flying, hovering, and courting him above the clouds: then on a sudden he makes them stoop, and come down amain from heaven next to the ground; and all for the gut.

Elephants, lions, rhinoceroses, bears, horses, mares, and dogs, he teaches to dance, prance, vault, fight, swim, hide themselves, fetch and carry what he pleases; and all for the gut.

Salt and fresh-water fish, whales, and the monsters of the main, he brings them up from the bottom of the deep; wolves he forces out of the woods, bears out of the rocks, foxes out of their holes, and serpents out of the ground; and all for the gut.

In short, he is so unruly, that in his rage he devours all men and beasts: as was seen among the Vascons, when Q. Metellus besieged them in the Sertorian wars; among the Saguntines besieged by Hannibal; among the Jews besieged by the Romans, and six hundred more; and all for the gut. When his regent Penia takes a progress, wherever she moves, all senates are shut up, all statutes repealed, all orders and proclamations vain; she knows, obeys, and has no law. All shun her, in every place choosing rather to expose themselves to shipwreck at sea, and venture through fire, rocks, caves, and precipices, than be seized by that most dreadful tormentor.

CHAPTER LVIII

How, at the court of the Master of Ingenuity, Pantagruel detested the Engastrimythes and the Gastrolaters

At the court of that great master of ingenuity, Pantagruel observed two sorts of troublesome and too officious apparitors, whom he very much detested. The first were called Engastrimythes; the others, Gastrolaters.

The first pretended to be descended of the ancient race of Eurycles; and for this brought the authority of Aristophanes, in his comedy called *The Wasps*: whence of old they were called Euryclians, as Plato writes, and Plutarch in his book of the Cessation of Oracles. In the holy decrees, 26, qu. 3, they are styled Ventriloqui: and the same name is given them in Ionian by Hippocrates, in his fifth book of *Epid.*, as men who speak from the belly. Sophocles calls them Sternomantes. These were soothsayers, enchanters, cheats, who gulled the mob, and seemed not to speak and give answers from the mouth, but from the belly.

Such a one, about the year of our Lord 1513, was Jacoba Rodogina, an Italian woman of mean extract: from whose belly, we, as well as an infinite number of others at Ferrara, and elsewhere, have often heard the voice of the evil spirit speak; low, feeble, and small, indeed; but yet very distinct, articulate, and intelligible, when she was sent for, out of curiosity, by the lords and princes of the Cisalpine Gaul. To remove all manner of doubt, and be assured that this was not a trick, they used to have her stripped stark naked, and caused her mouth and nose to be stopped. This evil spirit would be called Curledpate, or Cincinnatulo, seeming pleased when any called him by that name; at which, he was always ready to answer. If any spoke to him of things past or present, he gave pertinent answers, sometimes to the amazement of the hearers: but if of things to come, then the devil was gravelled, and used to lie as fast as a dog can trot. Nay, sometimes he seemed to own his ignorance; instead of an answer, letting out a rousing fart, or muttering some words with barbarous and uncouth inflexions, and not to be understood.

As for the Gastrolaters, they stuck close to one another in knots and gangs. Some of them merry, wanton, and soft as so many milksops; others louring, grim, dogged, demure, and crabbed; all idle, mortal foes to business, spending half their time in sleeping, and the rest in doing nothing, a rent-charge and dead unnecessary weight on the earth, as Hesiod saith; afraid, as we judged, of offending or lessening their paunch. Others were masked, disguised, and so oddly dressed, that it would have done you good to have seen them.

There's a saying, and several ancient sages write, that the skill of nature appears wonderful in the pleasure which she seems to have taken in the configuration of sea-shells, so great is their variety in figures, colours, streaks, and inimitable shapes. I protest the variety we perceived in the dresses of the gastrolatrous coquillons was not less. They all owned Gaster for their supreme god, adored him as a god, offered him sacrifices as to their omnipotent deity, owned no other god, served, loved, and honoured him above all things.

You would have thought that the holy apostle spoke of those, when he said, *Phil.* chap. 3, "Many walk, of whom I have told you often, and now tell you even weeping, that they are enemies of the cross of Christ: whose end is destruction, whose God is their belly." Pantagruel compared them to the cyclops Polyphemus, whom Euripides brings in speaking thus: I only sacrifice to myself (not to the gods) and to this belly of mine the greatest of all gods.

CHAPTER LIX

Of the ridiculous statue Manduce; and how, and what the Gastrolaters sacrifice to their ventripotent god

WHILE we fed our eyes with the sight of the phyzzes and actions of these lounging gulli-gutted Gastrolaters, we on a sudden heard the sound of a musical instrument called a bell; at which all of them placed themselves in rank and file, as for some mighty battle, every one according to his office, degree, and seniority.

In this order, they moved towards master Gaster, after a plump, young, lusty, gorbellied fellow, who, on a long staff, fairly gilt, carried a wooden statue, grossly carved, and as scurvily daubed over with paint; such a one as Plautus, Juvenal, and Pomp. Festus describe it. At Lyons, during the Carnival, it is called Maschecroute, or Gnaw-crust; they call this Manduce.

It was a monstrous, ridiculous, hideous figure, fit to fright

little children: its eyes were bigger than its belly, and its head
larger than all the rest of its body: well mouth-cloven however,
having a goodly pair of wide, broad jaws, lined with two rows
of teeth, upper tier and under tier, which, by the magic of a
small twine hid in the hollow part of the golden staff, were made
to clash, clatter, and rattle dreadfully one against another; as
they do at Metz, with St. Clement's dragon.

Coming near the Gastrolaters, I saw they were followed by
a great number of fat waiters and tenders, laden with baskets,
dossers, hampers, dishes, wallets, pots, and kettles. Then
under the conduct of Manduce, and singing I do not know what
dithyrambics, crepalocomes, and epenons, opening their baskets
and pots, they offered their god,

White hippocras, with dry toasts.	Fricassees, nine sorts.	Cold loins of veal, with spice.
White bread.	Monastical brewis.	Zinziberine.
Brown bread.	Gravy soup.	Beatille pies.
Carbonadoes, six sorts.	Hotch-pots.	Brewis.
Brawn.	Soft bread.	Marrow-bones, toast, and cabbage.
Sweet-breads.	Household bread.	Hashes.
	Capirotades.	

Eternal drink intermixed. Brisk delicate white wine led
the van; claret and champaign followed, cool, nay, as cold as
the very ice, I say; filled and offered in large silver cups. Then
they offered,

Chitterlings garnished with mustard.	Scotch collops.	Hogs' haslets.
Hams.	Puddings.	Brawn heads.
Hung beef.	Carvelats.	Powdered venison with turnips.
Sausages.	Bolognia sausages.	Pickled olives.
Neats' tongues.	Chines and peas.	

All this associated with sempiternal liquor. Then they
housed within his muzzle,

Legs of mutton with shalots.	Plovers.	Fried pasty-crust.
Olias.	Dwarf-herons.	Forced capons.
Lumber pies with hot sauce.	Teals.	Parmesan cheese.
Ribs of pork with onion sauce.	Duckers.	Red and pale hippocras.
Roast capons, basted with their own dripping.	Bitterns.	Gold-peaches.
	Shovelers.	Artichokes.
	Curlews.	Dry and wet sweetmeats, seventy-eight sorts.
Caponets.	Wood-hens.	
Caviare and toast.	Coots, with leeks.	
Fawns, deer.	Fat-kids.	Boiled hens, and fat capons marinated.
Hears, leverets.	Shoulders of mutton with capers.	Pullets with eggs.
Partridges and young partridges.	Sirloins of beef.	Chickens
	Breasts of veal.	Rabbits, and sucking rabbits.
	Pheasants and pheasant poots.	

Quails, and young quails.
Pigeons, squabs, and squeakers.
Herons, and young herons.
Fieldfares.
Olives.
Thrushes.
Young sea-ravens.
Geese, goslings.
Queests.
Widgeons.
Souced hog's feet.
Mavises.
Grouse.
Turtles.
Doe-conies.
Peacocks.
Storks.
Woodcocks.
Snipes.
Ortolans.
Turkey cocks, hen tur-

keys, and turkey poots.
Stock-doves, and wood-culvers.
Pigs, with wine sauce.
Blackbirds, ousels, and rayles.
Moor-hens.
Bustards, and bustard poots.
Fig-peckers.
Young Guinea hens.
Flamingoes.
Cygnets.
A reinforcement of vinegar intermixed.
Venison pasties.
Lark-pies.
Dormice-pies.
Cabretto pasties.
Roe-buck pies.
Pigeon pies.
Kid pasties.
Capon-pies.

Bacon pies.
Hedgehogs.
Snites.
Then large puffs.
Thistle-finches.
Whores' farts.
Fritters.
Cakes, sixteen sorts.
Crisp wafers.
Quince tarts.
Curds and cream.
Whipped cream.
Preserved myrabolans.
Jellies.
Welsh barrapyclids.
Macaroons.
Tarts, twenty sorts.
Lemon - cream, rasp-berry cream, etc.
Comfits, one hundred colours.
Cream wafers.
Cream-cheese.

Vinegar brought up the rear to wash the mouth, and for fear of the squinsy: also toasts to scour the grinders.

CHAPTER LX

What the Gastrolaters sacrificed to their god on interlarded fish-days

PANTAGRUEL did not like this pack of rascally scoundrels, with their manifold kitchen sacrifices, and would have been gone, had not Epistemon prevailed with him to stay and see the end of the farce. He then asked the skipper, what the idle lobcocks used to sacrifice to their gorbellied god on interlarded fish-days? For his first course, said the skipper, they give him:

Caviare.
Botargoes.
Fresh butter.
Pease soup.
Spinage.
Fresh herrings, full roed.
Salads, a hundred varieties, of cresses,

sodden, hop-tops, bishop's - cods, cellery, chives, rampions, jew's-ears (a sort of mushrooms that sprout out of old elders) asparagus, wood-bine, and a world of others.

Red herrings.
Pilchards.
Anchovies.
Fry of tunny.
Cauliflowers.
Beans.
Salt salmon.
Pickled griggs.
Oysters in the shell.

Then he must drink, or the devil would gripe him at the throat: this, therefore, they take care to prevent, and nothing is wanting. Which being done, they give him lampreys with hippocras sauce:

Gurnards.
Salmon-trouts.
Barbels, great and small.
Roaches.
Cockerells.
Minnows.
Thornbacks.
Sleeves.
Sturgeons.
Sheath-fish.
Mackerels.
Maids.
Plaice.
Fried oysters.
Cockles.
Prawns.
Smelts.
Rock-fish.
Gracious lords.
Sword-fish.
Skate-fish.
Lamprels.
Jegs.
Pickerells.
Golden carps.
Burbates.
Salmons.
Salmon-peels.
Dolphins.
Barn trouts.

Millers'-thumbs.
Precks.
Bret fish.
Flounders.
Sea-nettles.
Mullets.
Gudgeons.
Dabs and sandings.
Haddocks.
Carps.
Pikes.
Bottitoes.
Rochets.
Sea-bears.
Sharplings.
Tunnies.
Silver-eels.
Chevins.
Cray-fish.
Pallours.
Shrimps.
Congers.
Porpoises.
Bases.
Shads.
Murenes, a sort of lampreys.
Craylings.
Smys.
Turbots.

Trout, not above a foot long.
Salmon.
Meagers.
Sea breams.
Halibuts.
Soles.
Dog's tongue, or kind fool.
Mussels.
Lobsters.
Great prawns.
Dace.
Bleaks.
Tenches.
Ombres.
Fresh cods.
Dried melwels.
Darefish.
Fausens, and grigs.
Eelpouts.
Tortoises.
Serpents, i.e. wood-eels.
Dorees.
Moor-game.
Perches.
Loaches.
Crab-fish.
Snails and whelks.
Frogs.

If, when he had crammed all this down his guttural trap-door, he did not immediately make the fish swim again in his paunch, death would pack him off in a trice. Special care is taken to antidote his godship with vine-tree syrup. Then is sacrificed to him, haberdines, poor-jack, minglemangled mismashed, etc.

Eggs fried, beaten, buttered, poached, hardened, boiled, broiled, stewed,
sliced, roasted in the embers, tossed in the chimney, etc.
Stock-fish.
Green-fish.
Sea-batts.
Cods' sounds.
Sea-pikes.

Which to concoct and digest the more easily, vinegar is multiplied. For the latter part of their sacrifices they offer,

Rice milk, and hasty pudding.
Buttered, wheat, and flummery.
Water-gruel, and milk porridge.
Frumenty and bonny clamber.

Stewed prunes, and baked bullace.
Pistachios, or fistic nuts.
Figs.
Almond-butter.
Skirret-root
White-pot.

Raisins.
Dates.
Chestnuts and walnuts.
Filberts.
Parsnips.
Artichokes.

Perpetuity of soaking with the whole.

It was none of their fault, I will assure you, if this same god of theirs was not publicly, preciously, and plentifully served in the sacrifices, better yet than Heliogabalus's idol; nay, more than Bel and the Dragon in Babylon, under King Belshazzar. Yet Gaster had the manners to own that he was no god, but a poor, vile, wretched creature. And as King Antigonus, first of the name, when one Hermodotus, (as poets will flatter, especially princes,) in some of his fustian dubbed him a god, and made the sun adopt him for his son, said to him; My lasanophore (or in plain English my groom of the close-stool), can give thee the lie; so master Gaster very civilly used to send back his bigoted worshippers to his close-stool, to see, smell, taste, philosophise, and examine what kind of divinity they could pick out of his sir-reverence.

CHAPTER LXI

How Gaster invented means to get and preserve corn

THOSE gastrolatrous hobgoblins being withdrawn, Pantagruel carefully minded the famous master of arts, Gaster. You know that, by the institution of nature, bread has been assigned him for provision and food; and that, as an addition to this blessing, he should never want the means to get bread.

Accordingly, from the beginning he invented the smith's art, and husbandry to manure the ground, that it might yield him corn; he invented arms, and the art of war, to defend corn; physic and astronomy, with other parts of mathematics, which might be useful to keep corn a great number of years in safety from the injuries of the air, beasts, robbers, and purloiners: he invented water, wind, and handmills, and a thousand other engines to grind corn, and to turn it into meal; leaven to make the dough ferment, and the use of salt to give it a savour; for he knew that nothing bred more diseases than heavy, unleavened, unsavoury bread.

He found a way to get fire to bake it; hour-glasses, dials, and clocks to mark the time of its baking; and as some countries wanted corn, he contrived means to convey it out of one country into another.

He had the wit to pimp for asses and mares, animals of different species, that they might copulate for the generation of a third, which we call mules, more strong and fit for hard service than the other two. He invented carts and waggons, to draw him along with greater ease: and as seas and rivers hindered his progress, he devised boats, gallies, and ships (to the astonishment of the elements) to waft him over to barbarous, unknown, and far distant nations, thence to bring, or thither to carry corn.

Besides, seeing that, when he had tilled the ground, some years the corn perished in it for want of rain in due season, in others rotted, or was drowned by its excess, sometimes spoiled by hail, shook out by the wind, or beaten down by storms, and so his stock was destroyed on the ground; we are told that ever since the days of yore, he has found out a way to conjure the rain down from heaven only with cutting certain grass, common enough in the field, yet known to very few, some of which was then shown us. I took it to be the same as the plant, one of whose boughs being dipped by Jove's priest in the Agrian fountain, on the Lycian mountain in Arcadia, in time of drought, raised vapours which gathered into clouds, and then dissolved into rain, that kindly moistened the whole country.

Our master of arts was also said to have found a way to keep the rain up in the air, and make it to fall into the sea; also to annihilate the hail, suppress the winds, and remove storms as the Methanensians of Trœzene used to do. And as in the fields thieves and plunderers sometimes stole, and took by force the corn and bread which others had toiled to get, he invented the art of building towns, forts, and castles, to hoard and secure that staff of life. On the other hand, finding none in the fields, and hearing that it was stored up and secured in towns, forts, and castles, and watched with more care than ever were the golden pippins of the Hesperides, he turned engineer, and found ways to beat, storm, and demolish forts and castles, with machines and warlike thunderbolts, battering-rams, ballistas, and catapults, whose shapes were shown us, not over-well understood by our engineers, architects, and other disciples of Vitruvius; as master Philibert de l'Orme, King Megistus's principal architect, has owned to us.

And seeing that sometimes all these tools of destruction were baffled by the cunning subtilty or the subtle cunning (which you please) of fortifiers, he lately invented cannons, field-pieces, culverins, mortar-pieces, basilisks, murdering instruments that dart iron, leaden, and brazen balls, some of them outweighing huge anvils. This by the means of a most dreadful powder, whose hellish compound and effect has even amazed nature, and made her own herself out-done by art; the Oxydracian thunders, hails, and storms, by which the people of that name immediately destroyed their enemies in the field, being but mere popguns to these. For, one of our great guns, when used is more dreadful, more terrible, more diabolical, and maims, tears, breaks, slays, mows down, and sweeps away more men, and causes a greater consternation and destruction, than a hundred thunderbolts.

CHAPTER LXII

How Gaster invented an art to avoid being hurt or touched by cannon balls

GASTER having secured himself with his corn within strongholds, has sometimes been attacked by enemies; his fortresses, by that thrice three-fold cursed instrument, levelled and destroyed: his dearly beloved corn and bread snatched out of his mouth, and sacked by a tyrannic force; therefore he then sought means to preserve his walls, bastions, rampiers, and sconces from cannon-shot, and to hinder the bullets from hitting him, stopping them in their flight, or at least from doing him or the besieged walls any damage. He showed us a trial of this, which has been since used by Fronton, and is now common among the pastimes and harmless recreations of the Thelemites. I will tell you how he went to work, and pray for the future be a little more ready to believe what Plutarch affirms to have tried. Suppose a herd of goats were all scampering as if the devil drove them, do but put a bit of eringo into the mouth of the hindmost nanny, and they will all stop stock still, in the time you can tell three.

Thus Gaster, having caused a brass falcon to be charged with a sufficient quantity of gunpowder, well purged from its sulphur, and curiously made up with fine camphor; he then had a suitable ball put into the piece, with twenty-four little pellets like hail-shot, some round, some pearl fashion: then taking his aim, and levelling it at a page of his, as if he would have hit him on the breast; about sixty strides off the piece, half-way between it and the page in a right line, he hanged on a gibbet by a rope a very large siderite, or iron-like stone, otherwise called her-culean, formerly found on Ida in Phrygia by one Magnes, as Nicander writes, and commonly called load-stone; then he gave fire to the prime on the piece's touch-hole, which in an instant

consuming the powder, the ball and hail-shot were with incredible violence and swiftness hurried out of the gun at its
muzzle, that the air might penetrate to its chamber, where
otherwise would have been a vacuum; which nature abhors so
much, that this universal machine, heaven, air, land, and sea
would sooner return to the primitive chaos, than admit the
least void any where. Now the ball and small shot, which
threatened the page with no less than quick destruction, lost
their impetuosity, and remained suspended and hovering round
the stone: nor did any of them, notwithstanding the fury with
which they rushed, reach the page.

Master Gaster could do more than all this yet, if you will
believe me: for he invented a way how to cause bullets to fly
backwards, and recoil on those that sent them, with as great
a force, and in the very numerical parallel for which the guns
were planted. And indeed, why should he have thought this
difficult, seeing the herb ethiopis opens all locks whatsoever;
and an echinus or remora, a silly weakly fish, in spite of all the
winds that blow from the thirty-two points of the compass,
will in the midst of a hurricane make you the biggest first-rate
remain stock still, as if she were becalmed, or the blustering
tribe had blown their last: nay, and with the flesh of that fish,
preserved with salt, you may fish gold out of the deepest well
that was ever sounded with a plummet; for it will certainly
draw up the precious metal. Since, as Democritus affirmed,
and Theophrastus believed and experienced, that there was an
herb at whose single touch an iron wedge, though never so
far driven into a huge log of the hardest wood that is, would
presently come out; and it is this same herb your hickways, alias
woodpeckers, use, when with some mighty axe any one stops
up the hole of their nests, which they industriously dig and make
in the trunk of some sturdy tree. Since stags and hinds, when
deeply wounded with darts, arrows, and bolts, if they do but
meet the herb called dittany, which is common in Candia, and
eat a little of it, presently the shafts came out, and all is well
again; even as kind Venus cured her beloved by-blow Æneas,
when he was wounded on the right thigh with an arrow by
Juturna, Turnus's sister. Since the very wind of laurels, fig-
trees, or sea claves, makes the thunder sheer off insomuch that
it never strikes them. Since at the sight of a ram, mad elephants
recover their former senses. Since mad bulls coming near wild
fig-trees, called caprifici, grow tame, and will not budge a foot,
as if they had the cramp. Since the venomous rage of vipers

is assuaged if you but touch them with a beechen bough. Since also Euphorion writes, that in the Isle of Samos, before Juno's temple was built there, he has seen some beasts called neades, whose voice made the neighbouring places gape and sink into a chasm and abyss. In short, since elders grow of a more pleasing sound, and fitter to make flutes, in such places where the crowing of cocks is not heard, as the ancient sages have writ, and Theophrastus relates: as if the crowing of a cock dulled, flattened, and perverted the wood of the elder, as it is said to astonish and stupify with fear that strong and resolute animal, a lion. I know that some have understood this of wild elder, that grows so far from towns or villages, that the crowing of cocks cannot reach near it; and doubtless that sort ought to be preferred to the stenching common elder, that grows about decayed and ruined places; but others have understood this in a higher sense, not literal, but allegorical, according to the method of the Pythagoreans: as when it was said that Mercury's statue could not be made of every sort of wood; to which sentence they gave this sense; that God is not to be worshipped in a vulgar form, but in a chosen and religious manner. In the same manner by this elder, which grows far from places where cocks are heard, the ancients meant, that the wise and studious ought not to give their minds to trivial or vulgar music, but to that which is celestial, divine, angelical, more abstracted, and brought from remoter parts, that is, from a region where the crowing of cocks is not heard: for, to denote a solitary and unfrequented place, we say, cocks are never heard to crow there.

CHAPTER LXIII

How Pantagruel fell asleep near the Island of Chaneph, and of the problems proposed to be solved when he waked

THE next day, merrily pursuing our voyage, we came in sight of the Island of Cheneph, where Pantagruel's ship could not arrive, the wind chopping about, and then failing us so that we were becalmed, and could hardly get ahead, tacking about from starboard to larboard, and larboard to starboard, though to our sails we added drabblers.

With this accident we were all out of sorts, moping, drooping, metagrabolized, as dull as dun in the mire, in C sol fa ut flat, out of tune, off the hinges, and I-don't-know-howish, without caring to speak one single syllable to each other.

Pantagruel was taking a nap, slumbering and nodding on the quarter deck, by the cuddy, with an Heliodorus in his hand; for still it was his custom to sleep better by book than by heart.

Epistemon was conjuring, with his astrolabe, to know what latitude we were in.

Friar John was got into the cook-room, examining, by the ascendant of the spirits, and the horoscope of ragouts and fricassees, what time of day it might then be.

Panurge (sweet baby!) held a stalk of Pantagruelion, alias hemp, next his tongue, and with it made pretty bubbles and bladders.

Gymnast was making tooth pickers with lentisk.

Ponocrates, dozing, dozed, and dreaming, dreamed; tickled himself to make himself laugh, and with one finger scratched his noddle where it did not itch.

Carpalim, with a nut-shell, and a trencher of verne, (that's a card in Gascony,) was making a pretty little merry windmill, cutting the card longways into four slips, and fastening them with a pin to the convex of the nut, and its concave to the tarred side of the gunnel of the ship.

Eusthenes, bestriding one of the guns, was playing on it with his fingers, as if it had been a trump-marine.

Rhizotomus, with the soft coat of a field tortoise, alias ycleped a mole, was making himself a velvet purse.

Xenomanes was patching up an old weather-beaten lantern, with a hawk's jesses.

Our pilot (good man!) was pulling maggots out of the seamen's noses.

At last Friar John, returning from the forecastle, perceived that Pantagruel was awake. Then breaking this obstinate silence, he briskly and cheerfully asked him how a man should kill time, and raise good weather, during a calm at sea?

Panurge, whose belly thought his throat cut, backed the motion presently, and asked for a pill to purge melancholy.

Epistemon also came on, and asked how a man might be ready to bepiss himself with laughing, when he has no heart to be merry?

Gymnast, arising, demanded a remedy for a dimness of eyes.

Ponocrates, after he had a while rubbed his noddle, and shaken his ears, asked, how one might avoid dog-sleep? Hold, cried Pantagruel, the Peripatetics have wisely made a rule, that all problems, questions, and doubts, which are offered to be solved, ought to be certain, clear, and intelligible. What do you mean by dog's-sleep? I mean, answered Ponocrates, to sleep fasting in the sun at noon-day as the dogs do.

Rhizotomus, who lay stooping on the pump, raised his drowsy head, and lazily yawning, by natural sympathy, set almost every one in the ship a yawning too: then he asked for a remedy against oscitations and gapings.

Xenomanes, half puzzled, and tired out with new vamping his antiquated lantern, asked, how the hold of the stomach might be so well ballasted and freighted from the keel to the main hatch, with stores well stowed, that our human vessels might not heel, or be walt, but well trimmed and stiff?

Carpalim, twirling his diminutive windmill, asked how many motions are to be felt in nature, before a gentleman may be said to be hungry?

Eusthenes, hearing them talk, came from between decks, and from the capstern called out to know why a man that is fasting bit by a serpent also fasting, is in greater danger of death, than when man and serpent have eat their breakfasts? Why a man's fasting-spittle is poisonous to serpents and venomous creatures?

One single solution may serve for all your problems, gentlemen, answered Pantagruel, and one single medicine for all such symptoms and accidents. My answer shall be short, not to tire you with a long needless train of pedantic cant. The belly has no ears, nor is it to be filled with fair words: you shall be answered to content by signs and gestures. As formerly at Rome, Tarquin the proud, its last king, sent an answer by signs to his son Sextus, who was among the Gabii at Gabii. (Saying this, he pulled the string of a little bell, and Friar John hurried away to the cookroom.) The son having sent his father a messenger to know how he might bring the Gabii (Gabini) under a close subjection; the king, mistrusting the messenger, made him no answer, and only took him into his privy garden, and in his presence, with his sword, lopped off the heads of the tall poppies that were there. The express returned without any other dispatch: yet having related to the prince what he had seen his father do, he easily understood that by those signs he advised him to cut off the heads of the chief men in the town, the better to keep under the rest of the people

CHAPTER LXIV

How Pantagruel gave no answer to the problems

PANTAGRUEL then asked what sort of people dwelt in that damned island? They are, answered Xenomanes, all hypocrites, holy mountebanks, tumblers of Ave Marias, spiritual comedians, sham saints, hermits, all of them poor rogues, who like the hermit of Lormont between Blaye and Bordeaux, live wholly on alms given them by passengers. Catch me there if you can, cried Panurge! may the devil's head-cook conjure my bum-gut into a pair of bellows, if ever you find me among them. Hermits, sham saints, living forms of mortification, holy mountebanks, avaunt, in the name of your father Satan, get out of my sight: when the devil's a hog, you shall eat bacon. I shall not forget yet awhile our fat Concilipetes of Chesil. O that Beelzebub and Astorath had counselled them to hang themselves out of the way, and they had done it! we had not then suffered so much by devilish storms as we did for having seen them. Hark ye me, dear rogue, Xenomanes, my friend, I prithee are these hermits, hypocrites, and eaves-droppers, maids or married? Is there anything of the feminine gender among them? Could a body hypocritically take there a small hypocritical touch? Will they lie backwards, and let out their fore-rooms? There's a fine question to be asked, cried Pantagruel. Yes, yes, answered Xenomanes; you may find there many goodly hypocritesses, jolly spiritual actresses, kind hermitesses, women that have a plaguy deal of religion: then there's the copies of them, little hypocritillons, sham sanctitos, and hermetillons. Foh! away with them, cried Friar John; a young saint, an old devil! (Mark this, an old saying, and as true a one as a young whore an old saint.) Were there not such, continued Xenomanes, the Isle of Chaneph, for want of a multiplication of progeny, had long ere this been desert and desolate.

Pantagruel sent them by Gymnast, in the pinnace, seventy-eight thousand fine pretty little gold half-crowns, of those that are marked with a lantern. After this he asked, What's o'clock? Past nine, answered Epistemon. It is then the best time to go to dinner, said Pantagruel: for the sacred line, so celebrated by Aristophanes in his play called *Concionatores*, is at hand, never failing when the shadow is decempedal.

Formerly, among the Persians, dinner time was at a set hour only for kings: as for all others, their appetite and their belly was their clock; when that chimed, they thought it time to go to dinner. So we find in Plautus a certain parasite making a heavy do, and sadly railing at the inventors of hour-glasses and dials, as being unnecessary things, there being no clock more regular than the belly.

Diogenes, being asked at what times a man ought to eat, answered, The rich when he is hungry, the poor when he has anything to eat. Physicians more properly say, that the canonical hours are,

> To rise at five, to dine at nine,
> To sup at five, to sleep at nine.

The famous king Petosiris's magic was different,—Here the officers for the gut came in, and got ready the tables and cupboards; laid the cloth, whose sight and pleasant smell were very comfortable; and brought plates, napkins, salts, tankards, flagons, tall-boys, ewers, tumblers, cups, goblets, basons, and cisterns.

Friar John, at the head of the stewards, sewers, yeomen of the pantry, and of the mouth, tasters, carvers, cup-bearers, and cupboard-keepers, brought four stately pasties so huge, that they put me in mind of the four bastions at Turin. Odsfish, how manfully did they storm them! What havoc did they make with the long train of dishes that came after them! How bravely did they stand to their pan-puddings, and paid off their dust! How merrily did they soak their noses!

The fruit was not yet brought in, when a fresh gale at west and by north began to fill the main course, missen-sail, fore-sail, tops, and top-gallants: for which blessing they all sung divers hymns of thanks and praise.

When the fruit was on the table, Pantagruel asked: Now tell me, gentlemen, are your doubts fully resolved or no? I gape and yawn no more, answered Rhizotomus. I sleep no longer like a dog, said Ponocrates. I have cleared my eyesight, said Gymnast. I have broke my fast, said Eusthenes: so that for this whole day shall be secure from the danger of my spittle:

Asps.	Apimaos.	Spiders.
Amphisbenes.	Alhatrabans.	Starry lizards.
Amerudutes.	Aractes.	Attelabes.
Abedissimons.	Asterions.	Ascalabotes.
Alhartafs.	Alcharates.	Hæmorrhoids.
Ammobates.	Arges.	Basilisks.

Fitches.
Sucking water-snakes.
Black wag-leg flies.
Spanish flies.
Catoblepes.
Horned snakes.
Caterpillars.
Crocodiles.
Toads.
Night-mares.
Mad dogs.
Colotes.
Cychriodes.
Cafezates.
Cauhares.
Snakes.
Cuhersks, two-tongued
　　adders.
Amphibious serpents.
Cenchres.
Cockatrices.
Dipsades.
Domeses.
Dryinades.
Dragons.
Elopes.

Enhydrides.
Falvises.
Galeotes.
Harmenes.
Handons.
Icles.
Jarraries.
Ilicines.
Pharaoh's mice.
Kesudures.
Sea-hares.
Chalcidic newts.
Footed serpents.
Manticores.
Molures.
Mouse-serpents.
Shrew-mice.
Miliares.
Megalaunes.
Spitting-asps.
Porphyri.
Pareades.
Phalanges.
Penphredons.
Pine-tree-worms.
Rutulæ.

Worms.
Rhagions.
Rhaganes.
Salamanders.
Slow-worms.
Stellions.
Scorpenes.
Scorpions.
Horn-worms.
Scalavotins.
Solofuidars.
Deaf-asps.
Horse-leeches.
Salt-haters.
Rot-serpents.
Stink-fish.
Stuphes.
Sabrins.
Blood-sucking flies
Hornfretters.
Scolopendres.
Tarantulas.
Blind worms.
Tetragnathias.
Teristales.
Vipers, etc.

CHAPTER LXV

How Pantagruel passed the time with his servants

IN what hierarchy of such venomous creatures do you place
Panurge's future spouse? asked Friar John. Art thou speaking
ill of women, cried Panurge, thou mangy scoundrel, thou
sorry, noddy - peaked shaveling monk? By the cenomanic
paunch and gixie, said Epistemon, Euripides has written, and
makes Andromache say it, that by industry, and the help of the
gods, men had found remedies against all poisonous creatures;
but none was yet found against a bad wife.

This flaunting Euripides, cried Panurge, was gabbling against
women every foot, and therefore was devoured by dogs, as a
judgment from above; as Aristophanes observes.—Let us go
on. Let him speak that is next. I can leak now like any
stone-horse, said then Epistemon. I am, said Xenomanes,
full as an egg and round as a hoop; my ship's hold can hold
no more, and will now make shift to bear a steady sail. Said
Carpalim, A truce with thirst, a truce with hunger; they are
strong, but wine and meat are stronger. I am no more in the
dumps, cried Panurge; my heart is a pound lighter. I am in
the right cue now, as brisk as a body-louse, and as merry as a

beggar. For my part, I know what I do when I drink; and it is a true thing (though it is in your Euripides) that is said by that jolly toper Silenus of blessed memory, that

> The man's emphatically mad,
> Who drinks the best, yet can be sad.

We must not fail to return our humble and hearty thanks to the Being, who, with this good bread, this cool delicious wine, these good meats and rare dainties, removes from our bodies and minds these pains and perturbations, and at the same time fills us with pleasure and with food.

But methinks, sir, you did not give an answer to Friar John's question; which, as I take it, was how to raise good weather? Since you ask no more than this easy question, answered Pantagruel, I will strive to give you satisfaction; some other time we will talk of the rest of the problems if you will.

Well then, Friar John asked how good weather might be raised. Have we not raised it? Look up and see our full top-sails: Hark! how the wind whistles through the shrouds, what a stiff gale it blows; observe the rattling of the tacklings, and see the sheets, that fasten the mainsail behind; the force of the wind puts them upon the stretch. While we passed our time merrily, the dull weather also passed away; and while we raised the glasses to our mouths, we also raised the wind by a secret sympathy in nature.

Thus Atlas and Hercules clubbed to raise and underprop the falling sky, if you will believe the wise mythologists; but they raised it some half an inch too high; Atlas, to entertain his guest Hercules more pleasantly, and Hercules to make himself amends for the thirst which sometimes before had tormented him in the deserts of Africa.—Your good father, said Friar John, interrupting him, takes care to free many people from such an inconveniency; for I have been told by many venerable doctors, that his chief butler, Turelupin, saves above eighteen hundred pipes of wine yearly, to make servants, and all comers and goers, drink before they are a-dry.—As the camels and dromedaries of a caravan, continued Pantagruel, used to drink for the thirst that is past, for the present, and for that to come; so did Hercules: and being thus excessively raised, this gave new motion to the sky, which is that of *titubation and trepidation*, about which our crack-brained astrologers make such a pother.—This, said Panurge, makes the saying good,

> While jolly companions carouse it together,
> A fig for the storm, it gives way to good weather.

Nay, continued Pantagruel, some will tell you, that we have not only shortened the time of the calm, but also much disburthened the ship; not like Æsop's basket, by easing it of the provisions, but by breaking our fasts; and that a man is more terrestrial and heavy when fasting, than when he has eaten and drank, even as they pretend that he weighs more dead than living. However it is, you will grant they are in the right, who take their morning's draught, and breakfast before a long journey; then say that the horses will perform the better, and that a spur in the head is worth two in the flank; or, in the same horse dialect,

> That a cup in the pate
> Is a mile in the gate.

Don't you know that formerly the Amycleans worshipped the noble Bacchus above all other gods, and gave him the name of Psila, which in the Doric dialect signifies wings: for, as the birds raise themselves by a towering flight with their wings above the clouds; so, with the help of soaring Bacchus, the powerful juice of the grape, our spirits are exalted to a pitch above themselves, our bodies are more sprightly, and their earthly parts become soft and pliant.

CHAPTER LXVI

How, by Pantagruel's order, the Muses were saluted near the Isle of Ganabim

THIS fair wind and as fine talk brought us in the sight of a high land, which Pantagruel discovering afar off, showed it Xenomanes, and asked him, Do you see yonder to the leeward a high rock, with two tops much like Mount Parnassus in Phocis? I do plainly, answered Xenomanes; it is the Isle of Ganabim. Have you a mind to go ashore there? No, returned Pantagruel. You do well indeed, said Xenomanes; for there is nothing worth seeing in the place. The people are all thieves: yet there is the finest fountain in the world, and a very large forest towards the right top of the mountain. Your fleet may take in wood and water there.

He that spoke last, spoke well, quoth Panurge; let us not by any means be so mad as to go among a parcel of thieves and sharpers. You may take my word for it, this place is just such another as, to my knowledge, formerly were the islands of Sark and

Herm, between the smaller and the greater Britain; such as was
the Poneropolis of Philip in Thrace; islands of thieves, banditti,
picaroons, robbers, ruffians, and murderers, worse than raw-
head and bloody-bones, and full as honest as the senior fellows
of the college of iniquity, the very outcasts of the county gaol's
common-side. As you love yourself, do not go among them: if
you go, you will come off but bluely, if you come off at all.
If you will not believe me, at least believe what the good and
wise Xenomanes tells you: for may I never stir if they are not
worse than the very cannibals: they would certainly eat us alive.
Do not go among them, I pray you; it were safer to take a
journey to hell. Hark, by cod's body, I hear them ringing the
alarm bell most dreadfully as the Gascons about Bordeaux used
formerly to do against the commissaries and officers for the
tax on salt, or my ears tingle. Let's sheer off.

Believe me, sir, said Friar John, let's rather land; we will
rid the world of that vermin, and inn there for nothing. Old
Nick go with thee for me, quoth Panurge. This rash hairbrained devil of a friar fears nothing, but ventures and runs on
like a mad devil as he is, and cares not a rush what becomes
of others; as if every one was a monk, like his friarship. A pox
on grinning honour, say I. Go to, returned the friar, thou
mangy noddy-peak! thou forlorn druggle-headed sneaksby!
and may a million of black devils anatomize thy cockle brain.
The hen-hearted rascal is so cowardly, that he bewrays himself
for fear every day. If thou art so afraid, dunghill, do not go,
stay here and be hanged, or go and hide thy loggerhead under
Madam Proserpine's petticoat.

Panurge hearing this, his breech began to make buttons: so
he slunk in in an instant, and went to hide his head down in
the bread-room among the musty biscuits, and the orts and
scraps of broken bread.

Pantagruel in the meantime said to the rest, I feel a pressing
retraction, in my soul, which like a voice admonishes me not
to land there. Whenever I have felt such a motion within
me, I have found myself happy in avoiding what it directed me
to shun, or in undertaking what it prompted me to do; and never
had occasion to repent following its dictates.

As much, said Epistemon, is related of the dæmon of Socrates,
so celebrated among the Academics. Well then, sir, said Friar
John, while the ship's crew water, have you a mind to have
good sport? Panurge is got down somewhere in the hold, where
he is crept into some corner, and lurks like a mouse in a cranny;

let them give the word for the gunner to fire yon gun over the round-house on the poop: this will serve to salute the Muses of this Anti-parnassus: besides, the powder does but decay in it. You are in the right, said Pantagruel: here, give the word for the gunner.

The gunner immediately came, and was ordered by Pantagruel to fire the gun, and then charge it with fresh powder; which was soon done. The gunners of the other ships, frigates, galleons and galleys of the fleet, hearing us fire, gave every one a gun to the island: which made such a horrid noise, that you would have sworn heaven had been tumbling about our ears.

CHAPTER LXVII

How Panurge bewrayed himself for fear; and of the huge cat Rodilardus, which he took for a puny devil

PANURGE, like a wild, addle-pated, giddy goat, sallies out of the bread-room in his shirt, with nothing else about him but one of his stockings, half on half off, about his heel, like a rough footed pigeon; his hair and beard all be-powdered with crumbs of bread, in which he had been over head and ears, and a huge and mighty puss partly wrapped up in his other stocking. In this equipage, his chops moving like a monkey's who is a louse-hunting, his eyes staring like a dead pig's, his teeth chattering, and his bum quivering, the poor dog fled to Friar John, who was then sitting by the chain-wales of the starboard side of the ship, and prayed him heartily to take pity on him, and keep him in the safe-guard of his trusty bilbo; swearing, by his share of Papimany, that he had seen all hell broke loose.

Woe is me, my Jacky, cried he, my dear Johnny, my old crony, my brother, my ghostly father! all the devils keep holiday, all the devils keep their feast to-day, man: pork and peas choke me, if ever thou sawest such preparations in thy life for an infernal feast. Dost thou see the smoke of hell's kitchens? (This he said, showing him the smoke of the gunpowder above the ships.) Thou never sawest so many damned souls since thou wast born; and so fair, so bewitching they seem, that one would swear they are Stygian ambrosia. I thought at first, God forgive me, that they had been English souls; and I don't know, but that this morning the Isle of Horses, near Scotland, was sacked, with all the English who had surprised it, by the lords of Termes and Essay.

Friar John, at the approach of Panurge, was entertained with a kind of smell that was not like that of gunpowder, nor altogether so sweet as musk; which made him turn Panurge about, and then he saw that his shirt was dismally bepawed, and bewrayed with fresh sir-reverence. The retentive faculty of the nerve, which restrains the muscle called sphincter (it is the arse-hole, and it please you) was relaxed by the violence of the fear which he had been in during his fantastic visions. Add to this, the thundering noise of the shooting, which seems more dreadful between decks than above. Nor ought you to wonder at such a mishap; for one of the symptoms and accidents of fear is, that it often opens the wicket of the cupboard wherein second-hand meat is kept for a time. Let us illustrate this noble theme with some examples.

Messer Pantolfe de la Cassina, of Sienna, riding post from Rome, came to Chamberry, and alighting at honest Vinet's, took one of the pitchforks in the stable; then turning to the inn-keeper, said to him, *"Da Roma in qua, io non son andato del corpo. Di gratia piglia in mano questa forcha, et fa mi paura."* I have not had a stool since I left Rome. I pray thee take this pitchfork, and fright me. Vinet took it, and made several offers, as if he would in good earnest have hit the signor, but did not: so the Sienese said to him, *"Si tu non fai altramente, tu non fai nulla: pero sforzati di adoperarli più guagliardamente."* If thou dost not go another way to work, thou hadst as good do nothing: therefore try to bestir thyself more briskly. With this, Vinet lent him such a swinging stoater with the pitchfork souce between the neck and the collar of his jerkin, that down fell signore on the ground arsyversy, with his spindle shanks wide straggling over his pole. Then mine host sputtering, with a full-mouthed laugh, said to his guest, By Beelzebub's bum-gut, much good may it do you, Signore Italiano. Take notice this is *datum Camberiaci*, given at Chamberry. It was well the Sienese had untrussed his points, and let down his drawers: for this physic worked with him as soon as he took it; and as copious was the evacuation, as that of nine buffaloes and fourteen missificating arch-lubbers. Which operation being over, the mannerly Sienese courteously gave mine host a whole bushel of thanks, saying to him, *"Io ti ringratio, bel messere; così facendo tu m'ai esparmiata la speza d'un servitiale."* I thank thee, good landlord; by this thou hast even saved me the expense of a clyster.

I will give you another example of Edward V, king of England.

Master Francis Villon, being banished France, fled to him, and got so far into his favour, as to be privy to all his household affairs. One day the king, being on his close stool, showed Villon the arms of France, and said to him, Dost thou see what respect I have for thy French kings? I have none of their arms any where but in this backside, near my close stool. Odd's life, said the buffoon, how wise, prudent, and careful of your health, your highness is! How carefully your learned doctor, Thomas Linacer, looks after you! He saw that, now you grow old, you are inclined to be somewhat costive, and every day were fain to have an apothecary; I mean, a suppository or clyster thrust into your royal nockandroe; so he has, much to the purpose, induced you to place here the arms of France; for the very sight of them puts you into such a dreadful fright, that you immediately let fly, as much as would come from eighteen squattering *bonasi* of Pæonia. And if they were painted in other parts of your house, by jingo, you would presently conskite yourself wherever you saw them. Nay, had you but here a picture of the great oriflamb of France, odds bodikins, your tripes and bowels would be in no small danger of dropping out at the orifice of your posteriors. But henh, henh, *atque iterum* henh.

> A silly cockney am I not,
>   As ever did from Paris come?
> And with a rope and sliding knot
>   My neck shall know what weighs my bum.

A cockney of short reach, I say, shallow of judgment, and judging shallowly, to wonder, that you should cause your points to be untrussed in your chamber before you come into this closet. By our lady, at first I thought your close stool had stood behind the hangings of your bed; otherwise it seemed very odd to me you should untruss so far from the place of evacuation. But now I find I was a gull, a wittal, a woodcock, a mere ninny, a dolt-head, a noddy, a changeling, a calf-lolly, a doddipole. You do wisely, by the mass, you do wisely; for had you not been ready to clap your hind face on the mustard-pot as soon as you came within sight of these arms, mark ye me, cop's body, the bottom of your breeches had supplied the office of a close stool.

Friar John, stopping the handle of his face with his left hand, did, with the fore-finger of the right, point out Panurge's shirt to Pantagruel, who, seeing him in this pickle, scared, appalled, shivering, raving, staring, bewrayed, and torn with the claws of the famous cat Rodilardus, could not choose but laugh, and said to him, Prythee what wouldst thou do with this cat? With this cat, quoth Panurge, the devil scratch me, if I did not think it had been a young soft-chinned devil, which, with this same stocking instead of mitten, I had snatched up in the great hutch of hell, as thievishly as any sizar of Montague college could have done. The devil take Tybert: I feel it has all be-pinked my poor hide, and drawn on it to the life I do not know how many lobsters' whiskers. With this he threw his boar-cat down.

Go, go, said Pantagruel, be bathed and cleaned, calm your fears, put on a clean shift, and then your clothes. What! do you think I am afraid cried Panurge. Not I, I protest: by the testicles of Hercules, I am more hearty, bold, and stout, though I say it that should not, than if I had swallowed as many flies as are put into plum-cakes, and other paste at Paris, from Midsummer to Christmas. But what is this? hah! oh, ho! how the devil came I by this? Do you call this what the cat left in the malt, filth, dirt, dung, dejection, fæcal matter, excrement, stercoration, sir-reverence, ordure, second-hand meats, fumets, stronts, scybal, or spyrathe? 'Tis Hibernian saffron, I protest. Hah, hah, hah! it is Irish saffron, by Shaint Pautrick, and so much for this time. Selah. Let us drink.

BOOK V

TREATING OF THE HEROIC DEEDS AND SAYINGS OF THE
GOOD PANTAGRUEL

THE AUTHOR'S PROLOGUE

INDEFATIGABLE topers, and you thrice precious martyrs of the smock, give me leave to put a serious question to your worships, while you are idly striking your codpieces, and I myself not much better employed: Pray, why is it that people say that men are not such sots now-a-days as they were in the days of yore? Sot is an old word, that signifies a dunce, dullard, jolt-head, gull, wittal, or noddy, one without guts in his brains, whose cockloft is unfurnished, and, in short, a fool. Now would I know, whether you would have us understand by this same saying, as indeed you logically may, that formerly men were fools, and in this generation are grown wise? How many and what dispositions made them fools? How many and what dispositions were wanting to make them wise? Why were they fools? How should they be wise? Pray, how came you to know that men were formerly fools? How did you find that they are now wise? Who the devil made them fools? Who in God's name made them wise? Who do you think are most, those that loved mankind foolish, or those that love it wise? How long has it been wise? How long otherwise? Whence proceeded the foregoing folly? Whence the following wisdom? Why did the old folly end now, and no later? Why did the modern wisdom begin now, and no sooner? What were we the worse for the former folly? What the better for the succeeding wisdom? How should the ancient folly be come to nothing? How should this same new wisdom be started up and established?

Now answer me, an' it please you: I dare not adjure you in stronger terms, reverend sirs, lest I make your pious fatherly worships in the least uneasy. Come, pluck up a good heart; speak the truth and shame the devil, that enemy to paradise, that enemy to truth: be cheery, my lads; and if you are for me, take me off three or five bumpers of the best, while I make a halt at the first part of the sermon; then answer my question. If you are not for me, avaunt! avoid Satan! For I swear by my great-grandmother's placket, that if you do not help me to solve that puzzling problem, I will, nay, I already do repent having proposed it: for still I must remain nettled and gravelled, and a devil a bit I know how to get off. Well, what say you?

In faith, I begin to smell you out.   You are not yet disposed to
give me an answer: nor I neither, by these whiskers.   Yet to
give some light into the business, I will even tell you what had
been anciently foretold in the matter, by a venerable doctor,
who being moved by the spirit in a prophetic vein, wrote a
book ycleped the Prelatical Bagpipe.   What do you think the
old fornicator saith?   Hearken, you old noddies, hearken now
or never.

> The jubilee's year, when all, like fools were shorn,
> Is about thirty [trente] supernumerary.
> O want of veneration! fools they seem'd,
> But, persevering, with long breves, at last
> No more they shall be gaping greedy fools.
> For they shall shell the shrub's delicious fruit,
> Whose flow'r they in the spring so much had fear'd.

Now you have it, what do you make of it?   The seer is ancient,
the style laconic, the sentences dark, like those of Scotus,
though they treat of matters dark enough in themselves.   The
best commentators on that good father take the jubilee after
the thirtieth, to be the years that are included in this present
age till 1550, [there being but one jubilee every fifty years.]   Men
shall no longer be thought fools next green pease season.

The fools, whose number, as Solomon certifies, is infinite,
shall go to pot like a parcel of mad bedlamites as they are; and
all manner of folly shall have an end, that being also numberless,
according to Avicenna, *maniæ infinitæ sunt species*.   Folly
having been driven back and hidden towards the centre, during
the rigour of the winter, it is now to be seen on the surface, and
buds out like the trees.   This is as plain as a nose in a man's
face: you know it by experience; you see it.   And it was
formerly found out by that great good man Hippocrates,
Aphorism. Veræ etenim maniæ, etc.   This world therefore
wisifying itself, shall on longer dread the flower and blossoms of
every coming spring, that is, as you may piously believe, bumper
in hand, and tears in eyes, in the woeful time of Lent, which used
to keep them company.

Whole cartloads of books, that seemed florid, flourishing and
flowery, gay and gaudy as so many butterflies; but in the
main were tiresome, dull, soporiferous, irksome, mischievous,
crabbed, knotty, puzzling, and dark as those of whining Heraclitus, as unintelligible as the numbers of Pythagoras, that
king of the bean, according to 1, 2, *sat.* 6, Horace: those books,
I say, have seen their best days, and shall soon come to nothing,
being delivered to the executing worms, and merciless petty

chandlers: such was their destiny, and to this they were pre-destinated.

In their stead beans in cod are started up; that is, these merry and fructifying Pantagruelian books, so much sought now-a-days, in expectation of the following jubilee's period: to the study of which writings all people have given their minds, and accordingly have gained the name of wise.

Now, I think, I have fairly solved and resolved your problem: then reform, and be the better for it. Hem once or twice, like hearts of oak; stand to your pan-puddings, and take me off your bumpers, nine go-downs, and huzza! since we are like to have a good vintage, and misers hang themselves. Oh! they will cost me an estate in hempen collars if fair weather hold. For I hereby promise to furnish them with twice as much as will do their business, on free cost, as often as they will take the pains to dance at a rope's end, providently to save charges, to the no small disappointment of the finisher of the law.

Now my friends, that you may put in for a share of this new wisdom, and shake off the antiquated folly this very moment, scratch me out of your scrolls, and quite discard the symbol of the old philosopher with the golden thigh, by which he has forbidden you to eat beans: for you may take it for a truth, granted among all professors in the science of good eating, that he enjoined you not to taste of them, only with the same kind intent with the fresh water physician, Amer, late Lord of Camelotaire, kinsman to the lawyer of that name, who forbad his patients the wing of the partridge, the rump of the chicken, and the neck of the pigeon, saying, *Ala mala, rumpum dubium, collum bonum, pelle remotâ.* For the dunsical dog-leech was so selfish as to reserve them for his own dainty chops, and allowed his poor patients little more than the bare bones to pick, lest they should over-load their squeamish stomachs.

To the heathen philosopher succeeded a pack of Capucions, monks, who forbid us the use of beans, that is, Pantagruelian books. They seem to follow the example of Philoxenus and Gnatho, one of whom was a Sicilian, of fulsome memory, the ancient master-builders of their monastic cram-gut voluptuousness, who, when some dainty bit was served up at a feast, filthily used to spit on it, that none but their nasty selves might have the stomach to eat of it, though their liquorish chops watered never so much after it.

So those hideous, snotty, pthisicky, eves-dropping, musty, moving forms of mortification, both in public and private, curse

those dainty books, and like toads spit their venom upon
them.

Now though we have in our mother-tongue several excellent
works in verse and prose, and, heaven be praised, but little left
of the trash and trumpery stuff of those dunsical mumblers of
Ave Maries, and the barbarous foregoing Gothic age; I have made
bold to choose to chirrup and warble my plain ditty, or, as they
say, to whistle like a goose among the swans, rather than be
thought deaf among so many pretty poets and eloquent orators.
And thus I am prouder of acting the clown, or any other under
part, among the many ingenious actors in this noble play, than
of herding among those mutes, who, like so many shadows and
cyphers, only serve to fill up the house, and make up a number;
gaping and yawning at the flies, and pricking up their lugs, like
so many Arcadian asses, at the striking up of the music; thus
silently giving to understand, that their fopships are tickled in
the right place.

Having taken this resolution, I thought it would not be amiss
to move my Diogenical tub, that you might not accuse me of
living without example. I see a swarm of our modern poets
and orators, your Colinets, Marots, Herouets, Saint Gelias,
Salels, Masuels, and many more; who, having commenced
masters in Apollo's academy on Mount Parnassus, and drunk
brimmers at the Cabalian fountain, among the nine merry Muses,
have raised our vulgar tongue, and made it a noble and everlasting structure. Their works are all Parian marble, alabaster,
porphyry, and royal cement: they treat of nothing but heroic
deeds, mighty things, grave and difficult matters; and this in
a crimson, alamode, rhetorical style. Their writings are all
divine nectar, rich, racy, sparkling, delicate, and luscious wine.
Nor does our sex wholly engross this honour; ladies have had
their share of the glory: one of them, of the royal blood of
France, whom it were a profanation but to name here, surprises
the age at once by the transcendent and inventive genius in
her writings, and the admirable graces of her style. Imitate
those great examples, if you can; for my part, I cannot. Every
one, you know, cannot go to Corinth. When Solomon built
the temple, all could not give gold by handfuls; each offered a
shekel of gold.

Since, then, it is not in my power to improve our architecture
as much as they, I am even resolved to do like Renault of
Montauban: I will wait on the masons, set on the pot for the
masons, cook for the stone-cutters; and since it was not my

good luck to be cut out for one of them, I will live and die the admirer of their divine writings.

As for you, little envious prigs, snarling bastards, puny Zoiluses, you will soon have railed your last: go hang yourselves, and choose you out some well-spread oak, under whose shade you may swing in state, to the admiration of the gaping mob; you shall never want rope enough. While I here solemnly protest before my Helicon, in the presence of my nine mistresses the Muses, that if I live yet the age of a dog, eked out with that of three crows, sound wind and limbs, like the old Hebrew captain Moses, Xenophilus the musician, and Demonax the philosopher; by arguments no ways impertinent, and reasons not to be disputed, I will prove, in the teeth of a parcel of brokers and retailers of ancient rhapsodies, and such mouldy trash, that our vulgar tongue is not so mean, silly, inept, poor, barren, and contemptible, as they pretend. Nor ought I to be afraid of I know not what botchers of old thread-bare stuff, a hundred and a hundred times clouted up, and pieced together; wretched bunglers, that can do nothing but new-vamp old rusty saws; beggarly scavengers, that rake even the muddiest canals of antiquity for scraps and bits of Latin, as insignificant as they are often uncertain. Beseeching our grandees of Witland, that, as when formerly Apollo had distributed all the treasures of his poetical exchequer to his favourites, little hulch-backed Æsop got for himself the office of apologue-monger: in the same manner, since I do not aspire higher, they would not deny me that of puny rhyparographer, or riff-raff follower of Pyreicus.

I dare swear they will grant me this: for they are all so kind, so good-natured, and so generous, that they will never boggle at so small a request. Therefore both dry and hungry souls, pot and trencherman, fully enjoying those books, perusing, quoting them in their merry conventicles, and observing the great mysteries of which they treat, shall gain a singular profit and fame: as in the like case was done by Alexander the Great, with the books of prime philosophy composed by Aristotle.

O rare! belly on belly! what swillers, what twisters will there be!

Then be sure all you that take care not to die of the pip, be sure, I say, you take my advice, and stock yourselves with good store of such books, as soon as you meet with them at the booksellers; and do not only shell those beans, but even swallow them down like an opiate cordial, and let them be in you; I say, let them be within you; then you shall find, my beloved, what good they do to all clever shellers of beans.

Here is a good handsome basketful of them, which I here lay before your worships; they were gathered in the very individual garden whence the former came. So I beseech you, reverend sirs, with as much respect as was ever paid by dedicating author, to accept of the gift, in hopes of somewhat better against next visit the swallows give us.

CHAPTER I

How Pantagruel arrived at the Ringing Island, and of the noise that we heard

PURSUING our voyage, we sailed three days, without discovering anything; on the fourth, we made land. Our pilot told us that it was the Ringing Island, and indeed we heard a kind of a confused and often repeated noise, that seemed to us, at a great distance, not unlike the sound of great, middle-sized, and little bells, rung all at once, as it is customary at Paris, Tours, Gergeau, Nantes, and elsewhere, on high holidays; and the nearer we came to the land, the louder we heard that jangling.

Some of us doubted that it was the Dodonian kettle, or the portico called Heptaphone, in Olympia, or the eternal humming of the Colossus raised on Memnon's tomb, in Thebes of Egypt, or the horrid din that used formerly to be heard about a tomb at Lipara, one of the Æolian Islands. But this did not square with chorography.

I do not know, said Pantagruel, but that some swarms of bees hereabouts may be taking a ramble in the air, and so the neighbourhood make this dingle dangle with pans, kettles, and basons, the corybantine cymbals of Cybele, grandmother of the gods, to call them back. Let us hearken. When we were nearer, among the everlasting ringing of these indefatigable bells, we heard the singing, as we thought, of some men. For this reason, before we offered to land on the Ringing Island, Pantagruel was of opinion that we should go in the pinnace to a small rock, near which we discovered an hermitage, and a little garden. There we found a diminutive old hermit, whose name was Braguibus, born at Glenay. He gave us a full account of all the jangling, and regaled us after a strange sort of fashion: four live-long days did he make us fast, assuring us that we should not be admitted into the Ringing Island otherwise, because it was then one of the four fasting, or ember weeks. As I love my belly, quoth Panurge, I by no means understand this riddle: methinks, this should rather be one of the four windy weeks; for while we fast we are only puffed up with wind. Pray now, good father hermit, have not you here

some other pastime besides fasting? Methinks it is somewhat
of the leanest: we might well enough be without so many palace
holidays, and those fasting times of yours. In my Donatus,
quoth Friar John, I could find yet but three times or tenses,
the preterit, the present, and the future, and therefore I make
a donative of the fourth (i.e. the fast of the quatre-tems) to be
kept by my footman. That time or tense, said Epistemon, is
aorist, derived from the preter-imperfect tense of the Greeks,
admitted in variable and uncertain times. Patience perforce
is a remedy for a mad dog. Saith the hermit, it is as I told you,
fatal to go against this: whoever does it is a rank heretic, and
wants nothing but fire and faggot, that is certain. To deal
plainly with you, my dear pater, cried Panurge, being at sea,
I much more fear being wet than being warm, and being drowned
than being burned.

Well, however, let us fast in God's name; yet I have fasted
so long, that it has quite undermined my flesh, and I fear that
at last the bastions of this bodily fort of mine will fall to ruin.
Besides, I am much more afraid of vexing you in this same trade
of fasting; for the devil a bit I understand anything in it, and
it becomes me very scurvily, as several people have told me,
and I am apt to believe them. For my part I do not much
mind fasting: for alas! it is as easy as pissing a bed, and a trade
of which any body may set up; there needs no tools. I am much
more inclined not to fast for the future: for to do so, there is
some stock required, and some tools are set to work. No matter,
since you are so stedfast, and would have us fast, let us fast as
fast as we can, and then breakfast in the name of famine. Now
we are come to these esurial idle days. I vow I had quite put
them out of my head long ago. If we must fast, said Pantagruel,
I see no other remedy but to get rid of it as soon as we can, as
we would out of a bad way. I will in that space of time somewhat look over my papers, and examine whether the marine
study be as good as ours at land. For Plato, to describe a
silly, raw, ignorant fellow, compares him to those that are bred
on shipboard, as we would do one bred up in a barrel, who
never saw anything but through the bung-hole.

To tell you the short and the long of the matter, our fasting
was most hideous and terrible; for, the first day we fasted at
fisticuffs, the second at cudgels, the third at sharps and the
fourth at blood and wounds: such was the order of the fairies.

CHAPTER II

How the Ringing Island had been inhabited by the Siticines, who were become birds

HAVING fasted as aforesaid, the hermit gave us a letter from one whom he called Albian Camar, master Ædituus of the Ringing Island: but Panurge greeting him, called him Master Antitus. He was a little queer old fellow, bald-pated, with a snout where-at you might easily have lighted a card match, and a phiz as red as a cardinal's cap. He made us all very welcome, upon the hermit's recommendation, hearing that we had fasted, as I have told you.

When we had well stuffed our puddings, he gave us an account of what was remarkable in the island, affirming that it had been first inhabited by the Siticines; but that, according to the course of nature, as all things, you know, are subject to change, they were become birds.

There I had a full account of all that Atteius Capito, Pollux, Marcellus, A. Gellius, Athenæus, Suidas, Ammonius, and others had writ of the Siticines; and then we thought we might as easily believe the transmutations of Nectymene, Progné, Itys, Alcyone, Antigone, Tereus, and other birds. Nor did we think it more reasonable to doubt of the transmogrification of the Macrobian children into swans, or that of the men of Pallene in Thrace into birds, as soon as they had bathed themselves in the Tritonic lake. After this the devil a word could we get out of him but of birds and cages.

The cages were spacious, costly, magnificent and of an admirable architecture. The birds were large, fine, and neat accordingly; looking as like the men in my country, as one pea does like another: for they eat and drank like men, muted like men, digested like men, but stunk like devils; slept, billed, and trod their females like men, but somewhat oftener: in short, had you seen and examined them from top to toe, you would have laid your head to a turnip that they had been mere men. However, they were nothing less, as Master Ædituus told us; assuring us, at the same time, that they were neither secular nor laic: and the truth is, the diversity of their feathers and plumes did not a little puzzle us.

Some of them were all over as white as swans, others as black as crows, many as grey as owls, others black and white like magpies, some all red like red-birds, and others purple and white like some pigeons. He called the males clerg-hawks, monk-hawks, abbot-hawks, bish-hawks, cardin-hawks, and one pope-hawk, who is a species by himself. He called the females clerg-kites, nun-kites, priest-kites, abbess-kites, bis-kites, cardin-kites, and pope-kites.

However, said he, as hornets and drones will get among the bees, and there do nothing but buzz, eat, and spoil every thing; so, for these last three hundred years, a vast swarm of biggot-telloes flocked, I do not know how, among these goodly birds every fifth full moon, and have bemuted, bewrayed, and con-skited the whole island. They are so hard-favoured and monstrous, that none can abide them. For their wry necks make a figure like a crooked billet; their paws are hairy, like those of rough-footed pigeons; their claws and pounces, belly and breech, like those of the stymphalid harpies. Nor is it possible to root them out: for if you get rid of one, straight four and twenty new ones fly thither.

There has been need of another monster-hunter, such as was Hercules; for Friar John had like to have run distracted about it, so much he was nettled and puzzled in the matter. As for the good Pantagruel, he was even served, as was Messer Priapus, contemplating the sacrifices of Ceres, for want of skin.

CHAPTER III

How there is but one Popehawk in the Ringing Island

WE then asked Master Ædituus why there was but one pope-hawk among such venerable birds, multiplied in all their species? He answered, that such was the first institution and fatal destiny of the stars: that the clerg-hawks begot the priest-hawks and monk-hawks, without carnal copulation, as some bees are born of a young bull: the priest hawks begat the bis-hawks, the bish-hawks the stately cardin-hawks, and the stately cardin-hawks, if they live long enough, at last come to be pope-hawk.

Of this last kind, there never is more than one at a time; as in a bee-hive there is but one king, and in the world but one sun.

When the pope-hawk dies, another rises in his stead out of the whole brood of cardin-hawks; that is, as you must understand it all along without carnal copulation. So that there is in that species an individual unity, with a perpetuity of succession, neither more or less than in the Arabian phœnix.

It is true, that about two thousand seven hundred and sixty moons, ago, two pope-hawks were seen upon the face of the earth: but then you never saw in your lives such a woeful rout and hurly-burly as was all over this island. For all these same birds did so peck, clapperclaw, and maul one another all that time, that there was the devil and all to do, and the island was in a fair way of being left without inhabitants. Some stood up for this pope-hawk, some for the other. Some, struck with a dumbness, were as mute as so many fishes; the devil a note was to be got out of them; part of the merry bells here were as silent as if they had lost their tongues, I mean their clappers.

During these troublesome times, they called to their assistance the emperors, kings, dukes, earls, barons, and commonwealths of the world that live on the other side the water; nor was this schism and sedition at an end, till one of them died, and the plurality was reduced to a unity.

We then asked, what moved those birds to be thus continually chaunting and singing? He answered, that it was the bells that hung on the top of their cages. Then he said to us, Will you have me make these monkhawks, whom you see bardoculated with a bag, such as you use to strain Hippocras wine through, sing like any wood-larks? Pray do, said we. He then gave half a dozen pulls to a little rope, which caused a diminutive bell to give so many tingtangs; and presently a parcel of monkhawks ran to him, as if the devil had drove them, and fell a singing like mad.

Pray, master, cried Panurge, if I also rang this bell, could I make those other birds yonder, with red-herring-coloured feathers, sing? Aye, marry would you, returned Ædituus. With this Panurge hanged himself (by the hands, I mean) at the bell-rope's end, and no sooner made it speak, but those smoked birds hied them thither, and began to lift up their voices, and make a sort of untowardly hoarse noise, which I grudge to call singing. Ædituus indeed told us, that they fed on nothing but fish, like the herons and cormorants of the world, and that they were a fifth kind of cucullati newly stamped.

He added, that he had been told by Robert Valbringue, who lately passed that way in his return from Africa, that a sixth kind was to fly hither out of hand, which he called capushawks, more grum, vinegar-faced, brain-sick, forward, and loathsome, than any kind whatsoever in the whole island. Africa, said Pantagruel, still uses to produce some new and monstrous thing.

CHAPTER IV

How the birds of the Ringing Island were all passengers

Since you have told us, said Pantagruel, how the popehawk is
begot by the cardinhawks, the cardinhawks by the bishhawks,
and the bishhawks by the priesthawks, and the priesthawks
by the clerghawks, I would gladly know whence you have these
same clerghawks. They are all passengers, or travelling birds,
returned Ædituus, and come hither from the other world; part
out of a vast country, called Want-o'-bread, the rest out of
another towards the west, which they style, Too-many-of-'em.
From these two countries flock hither, every year, whole legions
of these clerghawks, leaving their fathers, mothers, friends,
and relations.

This happens when there are too many children, whether male
or female, in some good family of the latter country; insomuch
that the house would come to nothing, if the paternal estate
were shared among them all; (as reason requires, nature directs,
and God commands.) For this cause parents used to rid themselves of that inconveniency, by packing off the younger fry,
and forcing them to seek their fortune in this isle Bossart,
(or humpy island). I suppose he means L'isle Bouchart, near
Chinon, cried Panurge. No, replied the other, I mean Bossart
(crooked) for there is not one in ten among them, but is either
crooked, crippled, blinking, limping, ill-favoured, deformed, or
an unprofitable load to the earth.

It was quite otherwise among the heathens, said Pantagruel,
when they used to receive a maiden among the number of
vestals: for Leo Antistius affirms, that it was absolutely forbidden
to admit a virgin into that order, if she had any vice in her soul,
or defect in her body, though it were but the smallest spot on
any part of it. I can hardly believe, continued Ædituus, that
their dams on the other side the water go nine months with
them; for they cannot endure them nine years, nay, scarce
seven, sometimes in the house; but by putting only a shirt over
the other clothes of the young urchins, and lopping off I do not
well know how many hairs from their crowns, mumbling certain apostrophised and expiatory words, they visibly, openly,
and plainly, by a Pythagorical metempsychosis, without the
least hurt, transmogrify them into such birds as you now see;
much after the fashion of the Egyptian heathens, who used to
constitute isiacs, by shaving them, and making them put on

certain linostoles, or surplices. However, I do not know my
good friends, but that these she-things, whether clergkites,
monkites, and abbesskites, instead of singing pleasant motets
and charisteres, such as used to be sung to Oromasis by Zoro-
aster's institution, may be bellowing out such cataretes and
scythropys, (cursed lamentable, and wretched imprecations,)
as were usually offered to the Arimanian demon; being thus
in continual devotion for their kind friends and relations, that
transformed them into birds, whether when they were maids,
or thornbacks, in their prime, or at their last prayers.

But the greatest numbers of our birds came out of Want-o'-
bread, which, though a barren country, where the days are of
a most tedious lingering length, overstocks this whole island with
the lower class of birds. For hither fly the asapheis that inhabit that land, either when they are in danger of passing their
time scurvily for want of belly-timber, being unable, or what
is more likely, unwilling to take heart of grace, and follow some
honest lawful calling, or too proud-hearted and lazy to go to
service in some sober family. The same is done by our frantic
inamoradoes, who, when crossed in their wild desires, grow
stark staring mad, and choose this life suggested to them by
their despair [too cowardly to make them swing, like their
brother Iphis of doleful memory.] There is another sort, that
is, your gaol birds, who, having done some rogue's trick, or
other heinous villany, and being sought up and down to be
trussed up, and made to ride the two or three-legged mare that
groans for them, warily scour off, and come here to save their
bacon; because all these sorts of birds are here provided for,
and grow in an instant as fat as hogs, though they came as lean
as rakes; for having the benefit of the clergy, they are as safe
as thieves in a mill within this sanctuary.

But, asked Pantagruel, do these birds never return to the
world where they were hatched? Some do, answered Ædituus;
formerly some few, but very late and very unwillingly; however,
since some certain eclipses, by the virtue of the celestial constellations, a great crowd of them fled back to the world. Nor
do we fret or vex ourselves a jot about it: for those that stay,
wisely sing, the fewer the better cheer; and all those that fly away
first cast off their feathers here among these nettles and briars.

Accordingly we found some thrown by there; and as we
looked up and down, we chanced to light on what some people
will hardly thank us for having discovered; and thereby hangs
a tale.

CHAPTER V

Of the dumb knighthawks of the Ringing Island

THESE words were scarce out of his mouth, when some five-and-twenty or thirty birds flew towards us: they were of a hue and feather like which we had not seen any thing in the whole island. Their plumes were as changeable as the skin of the chameleon, and the flower of tripolion, or teucrion. They had all under the left wing, a mark like two diameters dividing a circle into equal parts, or if you had rather have it so, like a perpendicular line falling on a right line. The marks which each of them bore, were much of the same shape, but of different colours; for some were white, others green, some red, others purple, and some blue. Who are those, asked Panurge, and how do you call them? They are mongrels, quoth Ædituus.

We call them knighthawks, and have a great number of rich commanderies (fat livings) in your world. Good, your worship, said I, make them give us a song, an' it please you, that we may know how they sing. They scorn your words, cried Ædituus, they are none of your singing birds; but, to make amends, they feed as much as the best two of them all. Pray, where are their hens? where are their females? said I. They have none, answered Ædituus. How comes it to pass, then, asked Panurge, that they are thus bescabbed, bescurfed, all embroidered over the phiz with carbuncles, pushes, and pock-royals, some of which undermine the handles of their faces. This same fashionable and illustrious disease, quoth Ædituus, is common among that kind of birds, because they are pretty apt to be tossed on the salt deep.

He then acquainted us with the occasion of their coming. This next to us, said he, looks so wistfully upon you, to see whether he may not find among your company a stately gaudy kind of huge dreadful birds of prey, which yet are so untoward, that they never could be brought to the lure nor to perch on the glove. They tell us that there are such in your world, and that some of them have goodly garters below the knee, with an inscription about them, which condemns him (*qui mal y pense*) who shall think ill of it, to be bewrayed and conskited. Others are said to wear the devil in a string before their paunches; and others a ram's skin. All that is true enough, good master Ædituus, quoth Panurge; but we have not the honour to be acquainted with their knightships.

Come on, cried Ædituus, in a merry mood, we have had chat enough of conscience! let's even go drink.——And eat, quoth Panurge. Eat, replied Ædituus, and drink bravely, old boy; twist like plough jobbers, and swill like tinkers; pull away and save tide, for nothing is so dear and precious as time, therefore, we will be sure to put it to a good use.

He would fain have carried us first to bathe in the bagnios of the cardinhawks, which are goodly delicious places, and have us licked over with precious ointments by the alyptes, alias rubbers, as soon as we should come out of the bath. But Pantagruel told him, that he could drink but too much without that. He then led us into a spacious delicate refectory, or fratrie-room, and told us: Braguibus, the hermit, made you fast four days together; now contrariwise, I will make you eat and drink of the best four days through stitch, before you budge from this place. But hark-ye-me, cried Panurge, may not we take a nap in the meantime? Ay, ay, answered Ædituus, that is as you shall think good; for he that sleeps, drinks. Good Lord! how we lived! what good bub! what dainty cheer! O what an honest cod was this same Ædituus.

CHAPTER VI

How the birds are crammed in the Ringing Island

PANTAGRUEL looked I do not know howish, and seemed not very well pleased with the four days' junketing which Ædituus enjoined us. Ædituus, who soon found it out, said to him, You know, sir, that seven days before winter, and seven days after, there is no storm at sea: for then the elements are still, out of respect for the halcyons, or king-fishers, birds sacred to Thetis, which then lay their eggs and hatch their young near the shore. Now here the sea makes itself amends for this long calm; and whenever any foreigners come hither it grows boisterous and stormy for four days together. We can give no other reason for it, but that it is a piece of its civility, that those who come among us may stay whether they will or no, and be copiously feasted all the while with the incomes of the ringing. Therefore pray to not think your time lost; for, willing, nilling, you will be forced to stay; unless you are resolved

to encounter Juno, Neptune, Doris, Æolus, and his fluster-
busters; and, in short, all the pack of ill-natured left-handed
godlings and vejoves. Do but resolve to be cheery, and fall
to briskly.

After we had pretty well staid our stomachs with some tight
snatches, Friar John said to Ædituus, For aught I see, you have
none but a parcel of birds and cages in this island of yours, and
the devil-a-bit of one of them all that sets his hand to the plough,
or tills the land, whose fat he devours: their whole business is
to be frolic, to chirp it, to whistle it, to warble it: tossing it,
and roaring it merry night and day: pray then, if I may be
so bold, whence comes this plenty and overflowing of all dainty
bits and good things, which we see among you? From all the
other world, returned Ædituus, if you except some part of the
northern regions, who of late years have stirred up the jakes.
Mum! they may chance ere long to rue the day they did so;
their cows shall have porridge, and their dogs oats; there will
be work made among them, that there will: come, a fig for it,
let us drink.——But pray what countrymen are you? Touraine
is our country, answered Panurge. Cod so, cried Ædituus,
you were not then hatched of an ill bird, I will say that for
you, since the blessed Touraine is your mother: for from thence
there comes hither every year such a vast store of good things,
that we were told by some folks of the place, that happened
to touch at this island, that your Duke of Touraine's income will
not afford him to eat his belly full of beans and bacon, (a good
dish spoiled between Moses and Pythagoras,) because his pre-
decessors have been more than liberal to these most holy birds
of ours, that we might here munch it, twist it, cram it, gorge
it, craw it, riot it, junket it, and tickle it off; stuffing our puddings
with dainty pheasants, partridges, pullets with eggs, fat capons
of Loudunois, and all sort of vension and wild fowl. Come,
box it about, tope on my friends: pray do you see yon jolly
birds that are perched together, how fat, how plump, and in
good case they look, with the incomes that Touraine yields us!
And in faith they sing rarely for their good founders, that is
the truth on it. You never saw any Arcadian birds mumble
more fairly than they do over a dish, when they see these two
gilt batons, or when I ring for them those great bells that you
see above their cages. Drink on, sirs, whip it away: verily,
friends, it is very fine drinking to-day, and so it is every day
of the week; then drink on, toss it about, here is to you with
all my soul; you are most heartily welcome: never spare it,

I pray you; fear not we should ever want good bub, and belly timber; for, look here, though the sky were of brass, and the earth of iron, we should not want wherewithal, to stuff the gut, though they were to continue so seven or eight years longer than the famine in Egypt. Let us then, with brotherly love and charity, refresh ourselves here with the creature.

Woons man, cried Panurge, what a rare time you have of it in this world! Pshaw, returned Ædituus, this is nothing to what we shall have in the other: the Elysian fields will be the least that can fall to our lot. Come, in the meantime let us drink here; come, here is to thee, old fuddlecap.

Your first siticines, said I, were superlatively wise, in devising thus a means for you to compass whatever all men naturally covet so much; and so few, or, to speak more properly, none can enjoy together: I mean, a paradise in this life, and another in the next. Sure you were born wrapt in your mother's smickets! O happy creatures! O more than men! Would I had the luck to fare like you!

CHAPTER VII

How Panurge related to Master Ædituus the fable of the horse and the ass

WHEN we had crammed and crammed again, Ædituus took us into a chamber that was well furnished, hung with tapestry, and finely gilt. Thither he caused to be brought store of mirobolans, cashou, green ginger preserved with plenty of hippocras, and delicious wine. With those antidotes, that were like a sweet Lethe, he invited us to forgot the hardships of our voyage; and at the same time he sent plenty of provisions on board our ship that rid in the harbour. After this, we then jogged to bed for that night; but the devil a bit poor pilgarlic could sleep one wink: the everlasting jingle jangle of the bells kept me awake whether I would or no.

About midnight Ædituus came to wake us, that we might drink. He himself showed us the way, saying; You men of the other world say that ignorance is the mother of all evil, and so far you are right; yet for all that, you do not take the least care to get rid of it, but still plod on, and live in it, with it, and by it; for which a plaguy deal of mischief lights on you every day, and you are right enough served: you are perpetually

ailing somewhat, making a moan and never right. It is what
I was ruminating upon just now. And, indeed, ignorance
keeps you here fastened in bed, just as that bully-rock Mars
was detained by Vulcan's art: for all the while you do not mind,
that you ought to spare some of your rest, and be as lavish as
you can of the goods of this famous island. Come, come, you
should have eaten three breakfasts already: and take this from
me for a certain truth, That if you would consume the mouth-
ammunition of this island, you must rise betimes; eat them,
they multiply; spare them, they diminish.

For example: mow a field in due season, and the grass will
grow thicker and better; do not mow it, and in a short time it
will be floored with moss. Let us drink, and drink again, my
friends: come let us all carouse it. The leanest of our birds
are now singing to us all; we will drink to them, if you please,
Let us take off one, two, three, nine bumpers. *Non zelus,
sed charitas*.

At the break of day, he waked us again to take a dish of
monastical brewess. From that time we made but one meal,
that only lasted the whole day: so that I cannot well tell how
I may call it, whether dinner, supper, nunchion, or after-supper;
only to get a stomach, we took a turn or two in the island, to
see and hear the blessed singing birds.

At night Panurge said to Ædituus, Give me leave, sweet sir,
to tell you a merry story of something that happened some
three and twenty moons ago, in the country of Chastelleraud.

One day in April, a certain gentleman's groom, Roger by
name, was walking his master's horses in some fallow ground:
there it was his good fortune to find a pretty shepherdess,
feeding her bleating sheep and harmless lambkins, on the brow
of a neighbouring mountain, in the shade of an adjacent grove:
near her, some frisking kids tripped it over a green carpet of
nature's own spreading: and to complete the landscape, there
stood an ass. Roger, who was a wag, had a dish of chat with
her, and after some ifs, ands, and buts, hems and heighs on her
side, got her in the mind to get up behind him, to go and see his
stable, and there take a bit by the bye in a civil way. While
they were holding a parley, the horse, directing his discourse
to the ass, (for all brute beasts spoke that year in divers places,)
whispered these words in his ear: Poor ass, how I pity thee! thou
slavest like any hack, I read it on thy crupper: thou dost well,
however, since God has created thee to serve mankind; thou art
a very honest ass: but not to be better rubbed down, curri-

combed, traped, and fed, than thou art, seems to me indeed to
be too hard a lot. Alas! thou art all rough-coated, in ill plight;
jaded, foundered, crest-fallen, and drooping, like a mooting
duck, and feedest here on nothing but coarse grass, or briars
and thistles: therefore do but pace it along with me, and thou
shalt see how we noble steeds, made by nature for war, are
treated. Come, thou wilt lose nothing by coming; I will get
thee a taste of my fare. In troth, sir, I can but love you and
thank you, returned the ass; I will wait on you, good Mr. Steed.
Methinks, gaffer ass, you might as well have said Sir Grandpaw
Steed. O! cry mercy, good Sir Grandpaw, returned the ass; we
country clowns are somewhat gross, and apt to knock words out
of joint. However, if it please you, I will come after your worship
at some distance, lest for taking this run, my side should chance
to be firked and curried with a vengeance, as it is but too often,
the more is my sorrow.

The shepherdess being got behind Roger, the ass followed,
fully resolved to bait like a prince with Roger's steed; but
when they got to the stable, the groom, who spied the grave
animal, ordered one of his underlings to welcome him with a
pitchfork, and curricomb him with a cudgel. The ass, who
heard this, recommended himself mentally to the god Neptune,
and was packing off, thinking, and syllogising within himself
thus: Had not I been an ass, I had not come here among great
lords, when I must needs be sensible that I was only made for
the use of the small vulgar. Æsop had given me a fair warning
of this in one of his fables. Well, I must e'en scamper, or take
what follows. With this he fell a trotting, and wincing, and
yerking, and calcitrating, alias, kicking, and farting, and funking,
and curvetting, and bounding, and springing, and galloping
full drive, as if the devil had come for him in *propriâ personâ*.

The shepherdess, who saw her ass scour off, told Roger that
it was her cattle, and desired he might be kindly used, or else
she would not stir her foot over the threshold. Friend Roger
no sooner knew this, but he ordered him to be fetched in, and
that my master's horses should rather chop straw for a week
together, than my mistress's beast should want his belly-full
of corn.

The most difficult point was to get him back; for in vain the
youngsters complimented and coaxed him to come. I dare
not, said the ass, I am bashful. And the more they strove by
fair means to bring him with them, the more the stubborn
thing was untoward, and flew out at heels; insomuch that they

might have been there to this hour, had not his mistress advised them to toss oats in a sieve, or in a blanket, and call him; which was done, and made him wheel about, and say, Oats by mackins! oats shall go to pot. *Adveniat;* oats will do, there is evidence in the case: but none of the rubbing down, none of the firking. Thus melodiously singing (for, as you know, that Arcadian bird's note is very harmonious) he came to the young gentleman of the horse, alias, black garb, who brought him to the stable.

When he was there, they placed him next to the great horse, his friend, rubbed him down, curricombed him, laid clean straw under him up to the chin, and there he lay at rack and manger; the first stuffed with sweet hay, the latter with oats: which when the horse's *valet-de-chambre* sifted, he clapped down his lugs, to tell them by signs that he could eat it but too well without sifting, and that he did not deserve so great an honour.

When they had well fed, quoth the horse to the ass: Well, poor ass, how is it with thee now? How dost thou like this fare? Thou wert so nice at first, a body had much ado to get thee hither. By the fig, answered the ass, which, one of our ancestors eating, Philemon died laughing, this is all sheer ambrosia, good Sir Grandpaw; but what would you have an ass say? Methinks all this is yet but half cheer. Do not your worships here now and then use to take a leap? What leaping dost thou mean? asked the horse, the devil leap thee; dost thou take me for an ass? In troth, Sir Grandpaw, quoth the ass, I am somewhat a blockhead, you know, and cannot, for the heart's blood of me, learn so fast the court way of speaking of you gentlemen horses; I mean, don't you stallionize it sometimes here among your mettled fillies? Tush, whispered the horse, speak lower; for, by Bucephalus, if the grooms but hear thee, they will maul and belam thee thrice and threefold; so that thou wilt have but little stomach to a leaping bout. Cod so, man, we dare not so much as grow stiff at the tip of the lowermost snout, though it were but to leak or so, for fear of being jirked and paid out of our lechery. As for any thing else, we are as happy as our master, and perhaps more. By this packsaddle, my old acquaintance, quoth the ass, I have done with you; a fart for thy litter and hay, and a fart for thy oats; give me the thistles of our fields, since there we leap when we list: eat less, and leap more, I say: it is meat, drink, and cloth to us. Ah! friend Grandpaw, it would do thy heart good to see us at a fair, when we hold our provincial chapter! Oh!

how we leap it, while our mistresses are selling their goslings and other poultry! With this they parted. Dixi: I have done.

Panurge then held his peace. Pantagruel would have had him to have gone on to the end of the chapter: but Ædituus said, A word to the wise is enough; I can pick out the meaning of that fable, and know who is that ass, and who the horse; but you are a bashful youth, I perceive. Well, know that there is nothing for you here; scatter no words. Yet, returned Panurge, I saw but even now a pretty kind of a cooing abbess-kite as white as a dove, and her I had rather ride than lead. May I never stir if she is not a dainty bit, and very well worth a sin or two. Heaven forgive me! I meant no more harm in it than you; may the harm I meant in it befal me presently.

CHAPTER VIII

How with much ado we got a sight of the Popehawk

OUR junketing and banqueting held on at the same rate the third day, as the two former. Pantagruel then earnestly desired to see the pope-hawk: but Ædituus told him it was not such an easy matter to get a sight of him. How, asked Pantagruel, has he Plato's helmet on his crown, Gyges's ring on his pounces, or a chameleon on his breast, to make him invisible when he pleases? No, sir, returned Ædituus; but he is naturally of pretty difficult access: however, I will see and take care that you may see him, if possible. With this he left us piddling: then within a quarter of an hour came back, and told us the pope-hawk is now to be seen: so he led us, without the least noise, directly to the cage wherein he sat, drooping with his feathers staring about him, attended by a brace of little cardin-hawks, and six lusty bish-hawks.

Panurge stared at him like a dead pig, examining exactly his figure, size, and motions. Then with a loud voice he said, A curse light on the hatcher of the ill bird; on my word this is a filthy whoophooper. Hush, speak softly, said Ædituus; by G— he has a pair of ears, as formerly Michael de Matiscome remarked. What then, returned Panurge, so hath a whoopcat. Whist, said Ædituus, if he but hear you speak such another blasphemous word, you had as good be damned; do you see that bason yonder in his cage? Out of it shall sally thunderbolts and lightnings, storms, bulls, and the devil and all, that will sink you down to Peg Trantum's, an hundred fathom under ground. It were better to drink and be merry, quoth Friar John.

Panurge was still feeding his eyes with the sight of the pope-hawk and his attendants, when somewhere under his cage he perceived a madgehowlet. With this he cried out, By the devil's maker, master, there is roguery in the case; they put tricks upon travellers here more than any where else, and would make us believe that a t—d is a sugar loaf. What damned cozening, gulling, and cony-catching have we here! Do you see this madgehowlet? By Minerva, we are all beshit. Od-soons, said Ædituus, speak softly, I tell you: it is no madge-howlet, no she-thing on my honest word; but a male, and a noble bird.

May we not hear the pope-hawk sing? asked Pantagruel. I dare not promise that, returned Ædituus; for he only sings and eats at his own hours. So do not I, quoth Panurge; poor pilgarlic is fain to make every body's time his own: come, then let us go drink if you will. Now this is something like a tansy, said Ædituus, you begin to talk somewhat like; still speak in that fashion, and I will secure you from being thought a heretic. Come on, I am of your mind.

As we went back to have the other fuddling bout, we spied an old green-headed bish-hawk, who sat moping with his mate and three jolly bittern attendants, all snoring under an arbour. Near the old cuff stood a buxom abbess-kite, that sung like any linnet; and we were so mightily tickled with her singing, that I vow and swear we could have wished all our members but one turned into ears, to have had more of the melody. Quoth Panurge, This pretty cherubim of cherubims is here breaking her head with chaunting to this huge, fat, ugly face, who lies grunting all the while like a hog as he is. I will make him change his note presently in the devil's name. With this he rang a bell that hung over the bish-hawk's head; but though he rang and rang again, the devil a bit bish-hawk would hear; the louder the sound, the louder his snoring. There was no making him sing. By G—, quoth Panurge, you old buzzard, if you will not sing by fair means, you shall by foul. Having said this, he took up one of St. Stephen's loaves, alias a stone, and was going to hit him with it about the middle. But Ædituus cried to him, Hold, hold, honest friend! strike, wound, poison, kill, and murder all the kings and princes in the world, by treachery or how thou wilt, and as soon as thou wouldest, unnestle the angels from their cockloft; pope-hawk will pardon thee all this: but never be so mad as to meddle with these sacred birds, as much as thou lovest the profit, welfare, and life not only of thyself, and thy friends and relations alive or dead, but also of those that may be born hereafter to the thousandth generation; for so long thou wouldest entail misery upon them. Do but look upon that bason. Catso, let us rather drink, then, quoth Panurge. He that spoke last, spoke well, Mr. Antitus, quoth Friar John: while we are looking on these devilish birds, we do nothing but blaspheme; and while we are taking a cup, we do nothing but praise God. Come on, then, let us go drink; how well that word sounds!

The third day (after we had drank, as you must understand) Ædituus dismissed us. We made him a present of a pretty little Pergois knife, which he took more kindly than Artaxerxes did the cup of cold water that was given him by a clown. He most courteously thanked us, and sent all sorts of provisions aboard our ships, wished us a prosperous voyage, and success in our undertakings, and made us promise and swear by Jupiter of stone to come back by his territories. Finally he said to us, Friends, pray note, that there are many more stones in the world than men; take care you do not forget it.

CHAPTER IX

How we arrived at the Island of Tools

HAVING well ballasted the holds of our human vessels, we weighed anchor, hoised up sail, stowed the boats, set the land, and stood for the offing with a fair loom gale, and for more haste unparalleled the mizen-yard, and launched it and the sail over the lee-quarter, and fitted gyves to keep it steady, and boomed it out: so in three days we made the Island of Tools, that is altogether uninhabited. We saw there a great number of trees which bore mattocks, pickaxes, crows, weeding-hooks, scythes, sickles, spades, trowels, hatchets, hedging-bills, saws, adzes, bills, axes, shears, pincers, bolts, piercers, augers, and wimbles.

Others bore dags, daggers, poniards, bayonets, square-bladed tucks, stilettoes, poinadoes, skenes, penknives, puncheons, bodkins, swords, rapiers, back-swords, cutlasses, scymetars, hangers, falchions, glaives, raillons, whittles, and whinyards.

Whoever would have any of these, needed but to shake the tree, and immediately they dropped down as thick as hops, like so many ripe plums; nay, what is more, they fell on a kind of grass called scabbard, and sheathed themselves in it cleverly. But when they came down, there was need of taking care lest they happened to touch the head, feet, or other parts of the body. For they fell with the point downwards, and in they stuck, or slit the continuum of some member, or lopped it off like a twig; either of which generally was enough to have killed a man, though he were a hundred years old, and worth as many thousand spankers, spur-royals, and rose nobles.

Under some other trees, whose names I cannot justly tell you, I saw some certain sorts of weeds that grew and sprouted like pikes, lances, javelins, javelots, darts, dartlets, halberts, boar-spears, eel-spears, partizans, tridents, prongs, troutstaves, spears, halfpikes, and hunting staffs. As they sprouted up and chanced to touch the tree, straight they met with their heads, points, and blades, each suitable to its kind, made ready for them by the trees over them, as soon as every individual weed was grown up, fit for its steel: even like the children's coats, that are made for them as soon as they wear them, and you wean them of their swaddling clothes. Nor do you mutter, I pray you, at what Plato, Anaxagoras, and Democritus have said: od's fish! they were none of your lower-form gimcracks, were they?

Those trees seemed to us terrestrial animals, in no wise so different from brute beasts as not to have skin, fat, flesh, veins, arteries, ligaments, nerves, cartilages, kernals, bones, marrow, humours, matrices, brains, and articulations; for they certainly have some, since Theophrastus will have it so: but in this point they differed from other animals, that their heads, that is, the part of their trunks next to the root, are downwards; their hair, that is their roots, in the earth; and their feet, that is their branches, upside down: as if a man should stand on his head with outstretched legs. And as you, battered sinners, on whom Venus has bestowed something to remember her, feel the approach of rains, winds, cold, and every change of weather, at your ischiatic legs, and your omoplates, by means of the perpetual almanack which she has fixed there: so these trees have notice given them, by certain sensations which they have at their roots, stocks, gums, paps, or marrow, of the growth of the staffs under them; and accordingly they prepare suitable points and blades for them beforehand. Yet as all things, except God, are sometimes subject to error, nature itself not free from it, when it produceth monstrous things; likewise I observed something amiss in these trees. For a halfpike, that grew up high enough to reach the branches of one of these instrumentiferous trees, happened no sooner to touch them, but instead of being joined to an iron head, it impaled a stub broom at the fundament. Well, no matter, it will serve to sweep the chimney. Thus a partizan met with a pair of garden shears. Come, all is good for something, it will serve to nip off little twigs, and destroy caterpillars. The staff of a halbert got the blade of a scythe, which made it look like a herma-phrodite. Happy-be-lucky, it is all a case, it will serve for some mower. Oh, it's a great blessing to put our trust in the Lord! As we went back to our ships, I spied behind I do not what bush, I do not know what folks, doing I do not know what business, in I do not know what posture, scouring I do not know what tools, in I do not know what manner, and I do not know what place.

CHAPTER X

How Pantagruel arrived at the Island of Sharping (or gaming)

WE left the Island of Tools to pursue our voyage, and the next day stood in for the Island of Sharping, the true image of Fontainbleau: for the land is so very lean, that the bones, that is, the rocks, shoot through its skin. Besides, it is sandy, barren, unhealthy, and unpleasant. Our pilot showed us there two little square rocks, which had eight equal points in the shape of a cube. They were so white, that I might have mis-taken them for alabaster or snow, had he not assured us they were made of bone.

He told us that twenty-one chance devils very much feared in our country, dwelt there in six different stories, and that the biggest twins or braces of them were called sixes, and the smallest amb's-ace; the rest cinques, quatres, treys, and duces. When they were conjured up, otherwise coupled, they were called either sice cinque, sice quatre, sice trey, sice duce, and sice ace; or cinque quatre, cinque trey, and so forth. I made there a shrewd observation: would you know what it is, game-sters? It is, that there are very few of you in the world, but what call upon and invoke the devils. For the dice are no sooner thrown on the board, and the greedy gazing sparks

have hardly said, Two sixes, Frank; but Six devils damn it!
cry as many of them. If amb's-ace, then, A brace of devils
broil me, will they say. Quarter duce, Tom, The duce take it,
cries another. And so on to the end of the chapter. Nay,
they do not forget sometimes to call the black cloven-footed
gentlemen by their christian-names and surnames: and what is
stranger yet, they use them as the greatest cronies, and make
them so often the executors of their wills; not only giving themselves, but every body, and every thing, to the devil, that there
is no doubt but he takes care to seize, soon or late, what is so
zealously bequeathed him. Indeed, it is true, Lucifer does not
always immediately appear by his lawful attornies; but alas!
it is not for want of good-will: he is really to be excused for his
delay: for what the devil would you have a devil do? He and
his blackguards are then at some other places, according to the
priority of the persons that call on them: therefore, pray let
none be so venturesome as to think, that the devils are deaf
and blind.

He then told us that more wrecks had happened about those
square rocks, and a greater loss of body and goods, than about
all the Syrtes, Scyllas and Charibdes, Sirens, Strophades, and
gulfs in the universe. I had not much ado to believe it, remem-
bering that formerly, among the wise Egyptians, Neptune was
described in hieroglyphics for the first cube, Apollo by an ace,
Diana by a duce, Minerva by seven, and so forth.

He also told us that there was a phial of sang-real, a most
divine thing, and known to a few. Panurge did so sweeten up
the syndics of the place, that they blessed us with a sight of it:
but it was with three times more pother and ado, with more
formalities and antic-tricks, than they show the pandects of
Justinian at Florence, or the holy Veronica at Rome. I never
saw such a sight of flambeaux, torches, and hagios, and sanctified tapers, in my whole life. After all, that which was shown
us was only the ill-faced countenance of a roasted coney.

All that we saw there worth speaking of, was a good face
set upon an ill game, and the shells of the two eggs formerly
laid up and hatched by Leda, out of which came Castor and
Pollux, fair Helen's brothers. These same syndics sold us a
piece of them for a song, I mean, for a morsel of bread. Before
we went, we bought a parcel of hats and caps of the manufacture
of the place; which, I fear, will turn to no very good account:
nor are those who shall take them off our hands, more likely
to commend their wearing.

CHAPTER XI

*How we passed through the wicket, inhabited by Gripe-men-all,
Arch-duke of the Furred Law-cats*

FROM thence Condemnation was passed by us. It is another
damned barren island, whereat none for the world cared to
touch. Then we went through the wicket: but Pantagruel
had no mind to bear us company; and it was well he did not,
for we were nabbed there, and clapped into lob's pound by
order of Gripe-men-all, Arch-duke of the Furred Law-cats,
because one of our company would have put upon a serjeant
some hats of the Sharping Island.

The Furred Law-cats are most terrible and dreadful monsters,
that devour little children, and trample over marble stones.
Pray tell me, noble topers, do they not deserve to have their
snouts slit? The hair of their hides does not lie outwards;
and every mother's son of them for his device wears a gaping
pouch, but not all in the same manner: for some wear it tied
to their neck scarf-wise, others upon the breech, some on the
paunch, others on the side, and all for a cause, with reason
and mystery. They have claws so very strong, long, and sharp,
that nothing can get from them what is once fast between
their clutches. Sometimes they cover their heads with mortar-
like caps, at other times with mortified caparisons.

As we entered their den, said a common mumper, to whom
we had given half a teston, Worshipful culprits, God send you
a good deliverance. Examine well, said he, the countenance
of these stout props and pillars of this catch-coin law and
iniquity: and pray observe, that if you still live but six olympiads,
and the age of two dogs more, you will see these Furred Law-cats
lords of all Europe, and in peaceful possession of all the estates
and dominions belonging to it: unless, by divine providence,
what is got over the devil's back, is spent under his belly; or
the goods which they unjustly get, perish with their prodigal
heirs. Take this from an honest beggar.

Among them reigns the sixth essence; by the means of which
they gripe all, devour all, conskite all, burn all, draw all, hang
all, quarter all, behead all, murder all, imprison all, waste all,
and ruin all, without the least notice of right or wrong: for among
them vice is called virtue; wickedness, piety; treason, loyalty;
robbery, justice. Plunder is their motto, and when acted by
them, is approved by all men, except the heretics: and all this

they do, because they dare; their authority is sovereign and irrefragable. For a sign of the truth of what I tell you, you will find, that there the mangers are above the racks. Remember hereafter, that a fool told you this; and if ever plague, famine, war, fire, earthquakes, inundations, or other judgments befal the world, do not attribute them to the aspects and conjunctions of the malevolent planets, to the abuses of the court of Romania, or the tyranny of secular kings and princes: to the impostures of the false zealots of the cowl, heretical bigots, false prophets, and broachers of sects; to the villany of griping usurers, clippers, and coiners; nor to the ignorance, impudence, and imprudence of physicians, surgeons, and apothecaries: nor to the lewdness of adultresses, and destroyers of by-blows; but charge them all, wholly and solely to the inexpressible, incredible, and inestimable wickedness and ruin, which is continually hatched, brewed, and practised in the den or shop of those Furred Law-cats. Yet it is no more known in the world than the cabala of the Jews; the more is the pity; and, therefore, it is not detested, chastised, and punished, as it is fit it should be. But should all their villany be once displayed in its true colours, and exposed to the people; there never was, is, nor will be any spokesman so sweet-mouthed, whose fine colloguing tongue could save them; nor any law so rigorous and draconic, that could punish them as they deserve: nor yet any magistrate so powerful, as to hinder their being burnt alive in their coneyburrows without mercy. Even their own furred kittlings, friends, and relations would abominate them.

For this reason, as Hannibal was solemnly sworn by his father Amilcar to pursue the Romans with the utmost hatred, as long as ever he lived: so, my late father has enjoined me to remain here without, till God Almighty's thunder reduce them there within to ashes, like other presumptuous Titans, prophane wretches, and opposers of God: since mankind is so inured to their oppressions, that they either do not remember, foresee, or have a sense of the woes and miseries which they have caused; or if they have, either will not, dare not, or cannot root them out.

How, said Panurge, say you so? Catch me there and hang me! Damme, let us march off! This noble beggar has scared me worse than thunder in autumn. Upon this we were filing off; but alas! we found ourselves trapped: the door was double locked and barricadoed. Some messengers of ill news told us, it was full as easy to get in there as into hell, and no less hard to get out. Ay, there indeed lay the difficulty, for there is no getting loose without a pass and discharge in due course from the bench. This for no other reason than because folks go easier out of a church than out of a spunging-house, and because they could not have our company when they would. The worst of it was when we got through the wicket: for we were carried, to get out our pass or discharge, before a more dreadful monster than ever was read of in the legends of knight errantry. They called him Gripe-men-all. I cannot tell what to compare it to, better than to a chimera, a Sphynx, a Cerberus; or to the image of Osiris, as the Egyptians represented him, with three heads, one of a roaring lion, the other of a fawning cur, and the last of a howling, prowling wolf, twisted about with a dragon biting his tail, surrounded with fiery rays. His hands were full of gore, his talons like those of the harpies, his snout like a hawk's bill, his fangs or tusks like those of an overgrown brindled wild boar; his eyes were flaming, like the jaws of hell, all covered with mortars interlaced with pestles, and nothing of his arms was to be seen, but his clutches. His hutch, and that of the warren-cats his collaterals, was a long, spick-and-span new rack, a-top of which (as the mumper told us) some large, stately mangers were fixed in the reverse. Over the chief seat was the picture of an old woman, holding the case or scabbard of a sickle in her right hand, a pair of scales in her left, with spectacles on her nose: the cups or scales of the balance were a pair of velvet pouches: the one full of bullion, which over-poised the other, empty and long, hoisted higher than the middle of the beam. I am of opinion it was the true effigies of Justice Gripe-men-all; far different from the institution of the ancient Thebans, who set up the statues of their dicasts without hands, in marble, silver, or gold, according to their merit, even after their death.

When we made our personal appearance before him, a sort of I do not know what men, all clothed with I do not know what bags and pouches, with long scrolls in their clutches, made us sit down upon a cricket: [such as criminals sit on when tried in France.] Quoth Panurge to them, Good my lords, I am very well as I am; I would as lieve stand, if it please you. Besides, this same stool is somewhat of the lowest for a man that has new breeches and a short doublet. Sit you down, said Gripe-men-all again, and look that you do not make the court bid you twice. Now, continued he, the earth shall immediately open its jaws, and swallow you up to quick damnation if you do not answer as you should.

CHAPTER XII

How Gripe-men-all propounded a riddle to us

WHEN we were sate, Gripe-men-all, in the middle of his furred
cats, called to us in a hoarse dreadful voice, Well, come on, give
me presently—an answer. Well, come on, muttered Panurge
between his teeth, give, give me presently—a comforting dram.
Hearken to the court, continued Gripe-men-all.

AN ENIGMA

A young tight thing—as fair as may be,
Without a dad conceived a baby;
And brought him forth without the pother
In labour made by teeming mother.
Yet the cursed brat feared not to gripe her,
But gnawed, for haste, her sides like viper.
Then the black upstart boldly sallies,
And walks and flies o'er hills and vallies.
Many fantastic sons of wisdom,
Amazed, foresaw their own in his doom;
And thought, like an old Grecian noddy,
A human spirit moved his body.

Give, give me out of hand—an answer to this riddle, quoth
Gripe-men-all. Give, give me—leave to tell you, good, good,
my lord, answered Panurge, that if I had but a sphynx at home,
as Verres, one of your precursors had, I might then solve your
enigma presently: but verily, good my lord, I was not there:
and, as I hope to be saved, am as innocent in the matter as the
child unborn. Foh, give me—a better answer, cried Gripe-
men-all; or, by gold, this shall not serve your turn: I will not
be paid in such coin: if you have nothing better to offer, I will
let your rascalship know, that it had been better for you to have
fallen into Lucifer's own clutches, than into ours. Dost thou
see them here, sirrah? hah? and dost thou prate here of thy
being innocent, as if thou couldest be delivered from our racks
and tortures for being so! Give me—Patience! thou widgeon.
Our laws are like cobwebs: your silly little flies are stopped,
caught, and destroyed therein; but your stronger ones break
them, and force and carry them which way they please. Likewise, do not think we are so mad as to set up your nets to snap
up your great robbers and tyrants: no, they are somewhat too
hard for us, there is no meddling with them; for they would
make no more of us than we make of the little ones: but you
paltry, silly, innocent wretches, must make us amends; and,

by gold, we will innocentise your fopship with a wannion; you never were so innocentised in your days; the devil shall sing mass among ye.

Friar John, hearing him run on at that mad rate, had no longer the power to remain silent, but cried to him, Heigh-dey! Pr'ythee, Mr. Devil in a coif, wouldest thou have a man tell thee more than he knows? Has not the fellow told you he does not know a word of the business? His name is Twyford. A plague rot you, will not truth serve your turns? Why, how now, Mr. Prate-apace, cried Gripe-men-all, taking him short, marry come up, who made you so saucy as to open your lips before you were spoken to? Give me—Patience! By gold! this is the first time, since I have reigned, that any one has had the impudence to speak before he was bidden. How came this mad fellow to break loose? (Villain, thou liest, said Friar John, without stirring his lips.) Sirrah, sirrah, continued Gripe-men-all, I doubt thou wilt have business enough on thy hands, when it comes to thy turn to answer. (Damme, thou liest, said Friar John, silently.) Dost thou think, continued my lord, thou art in the wilderness of your foolish university, wrangling and bawling among the idle, wandering searchers and hunters after truth? By gold, we have here other fish to fry; we go another gat's-way to work, that we do. By gold, people here must give categorical answers to what they don't know. By gold, they must confess they have done those things, which they have not nor ought to have done. By gold, they must protest that they know what they never knew in their lives; and, after all, patience, perforce, must be their only remedy, as well as a mad dog's. Here silly geese are plucked, yet cackle not. Sirrah, give me,—an account, whether you had a letter of attorney, or whether you were feed or no, that you offered to bawl in another man's cause? I see you had no authority to speak, and I may chance to have you wed to something you will not like. Oh, you devils, cried Friar John, proto-devils, panto-devils, you would wed a monk, would you? Ho hu! ho hu! A heretic! a heretic! I will give thee out for a rank heretic.

CHAPTER XIII

How Panurge solved Gripe-men-all's riddle

GRIPE-MEN-ALL, as if he had not heard what Friar John said, directed his discourse to Panurge, saying to him, Well, what have you to say for yourself, Mr. Rogue-enough, hah? Give, give me out of hand—an answer. Say? quoth Panurge, why, what would you have me say? I say, that we are damnably beshit, since you give no heed at all to the equity of the plea, and the devil sings among you: let this serve for all, I beseech you, and let us go out about our business; I am no longer able to hold out, as gad shall judge me.

Go to, go to, cried Gripe-men-all; when did you ever hear that for these three hundred years last past, anybody ever got out of this weal without leaving something of his behind him? No, no get out of the trap if you can without losing leather, life, or at least some hair, and you will have done more than ever was done yet. For why, this would bring the wisdom of the court into question, as if we had took you up for nothing, and dealt wrongfully by you. Well, by hook or by crook, we must have something out of thee. Look ye, it is a folly to make a rout for a fart and ado; one word is as good as twenty; I have no more to say to thee, but that as thou likest thy former entertainment, thou wilt tell me more of the next; for it will go ten times worse with thee, unless, by gold, you give me—a solution to the riddle I propounded. Give, give—it, without any more ado.

By gold, quoth Panurge, it is a black mite or weevil, which is born of a white bean, and sallies out at the hole which he makes, gnawing it: the mite, being turned into a kind of fly, sometimes walks and sometimes flies, over hills and dales. Now, Pythagoras, the Greek sage, and his sect, besides many others, wondering at its birth in such a place, (which makes some argue for equivocal generation,) thought that, by a metempsychosis, the body of that insect was the lodging of a human soul. Now, were you men here, after your welcome death, according to his opinion, your souls would most certainly enter into the body of mites or weevils; for, as in your present state of life, you are good for nothing in the world, but to gnaw, bite, eat, and devour all things; so in the next you will even gnaw and devour your mother's very sides, as the vipers do. Now, by gold, I think I have fairly solved and resolved your riddle.

May my bauble be turned into a nut-cracker, quoth Friar John, if I could not almost find in my heart to wish that what comes out at my bung-hole were beans, that these evil weevils might feed as they deserve.

Panurge then, without any more ado, threw a large leathern purse, stuffed with gold crowns (*escus au soleil*) among them.

The furred law-cats no sooner heard the jingling of the chink, but they all began to bestir their claws, like a parcel of fiddlers running a division: and then fell to it, squimble, squamble, catch that catch can. They all said aloud, These are the fees, these are the gloves; now, this is somewhat like a tansy. Oh! it was a pretty trial, a sweet trial, a dainty trial. On my word, they did not starve the cause: these are none of your snivelling *forma pauperis's*; no, they are noble clients, gentlemen every inch of them. By gold, it is gold, quoth Panurge, good old gold, I'll assure you.

Saith Gripe-men-all, The court, upon a full hearing, (of the gold, quoth Panurge,) and weighty reasons given finds the prisoners not guilty, and accordingly orders them to be discharged out of custody, paying their fees. Now, gentlemen, proceed, go forwards, said he to us: we have not so much of the devil in us as we have of his hue; though we are stout, we are merciful.

As we came out at the wicket, we were conducted to the port by a detachment of certain highland griffins, who advised us, before we came to our ships, not to offer to leave the place until we had made the usual presents, first to the Lady Gripe-men-all, then to all the furred law-pusses; otherwise we must return to the place from whence we came. Well, well, said Friar John, we will fumble in our fobs, examine everyone of us his concern, and even give the women their due; we will never boggle nor stick out on that account; as we tickled the men in the palm, we will tickle the women in the right place. Pray, gentlemen, added they, do not forget to leave somewhat behind you for us poor devils to drink your healths. O lawd! never fear, answered Friar John, I do not remember that I ever went any where yet, where the poor devils are not remembered and encouraged.

CHAPTER XIV

How the Furred Law-cats live on corruption

FRIAR JOHN had hardly said these words ere he perceived seventy-eight gallies and frigates just arriving at the port. So he hied him thither to learn some news; and as he asked what goods they had on board, he soon found that their whole cargo was venison, hares, capons, turkeys, pigs, swine, bacon, kids, calves, hens, ducks, teals, geese, and other poultry and wildfowl.

He also spied among these some pieces of velvet satin, and damask. This made him ask the new-comers, Whither, and to whom, they were going to carry those dainty goods? They answered, that they were for Gripe-men-all and the furred law-cats.

Pray, asked he, what is the true name of all these things in your country language? Corruption, they replied. If they live on corruption, said the Friar, they will perish with their generation. May the devil be damned, I have it now: their fathers devoured the good gentlemen, who, according to their state of life, used to go much a hunting and hawking, to be the better inured to toil in time of war; for hunting is an image of a martial life; and Xenophon was much in the right of it, when he affirmed that hunting had yielded a great number of excellent warriors, as well as the Trojan horse. For my part, I am no scholar, I have it but by hearsay, yet I believe it. Now, the souls of those brave fellows, according to Gripe-men-all's riddle, after their decease, enter into wild boars, stags, roebucks, herons, and such other creatures, which they loved, and in quest of which they went while they were men; and these furred law-cats, having first destroyed and devoured their castles, lands, demesnes, possessions, rents, and revenues, are still seeking to have their blood and soul in another life. What an honest fellow was that same mumper, who had forewarned us of all these things, and bid us take notice of the mangers above the racks!

But, said Panurge to the new-comers, how do you come by all this venison? Methinks the great king has issued out a proclamation, strictly inhibiting the destroying of stags, does, wild boars, roebucks, or other royal game, on pain of death. All this is true enough, answered one for the rest, but the great king is so good and gracious, you must know, and these furred law-cats so cursed and cruel, so mad, and thirsting after Christian blood, that we have less cause to fear in trespassing against that mighty sovereign's commands, than reason to hope to live, if we do not continually stop the mouths of these furred law-cats with such bribes and corruption. Besides, added he, to-morrow Gripe-man-all marries a furred law-puss of his to a high and mighty double-furred law-tybert. Formerly we used to call them chop-hay; but, alas! they are not such clean creatures now as to eat any, or chew the cud. We call them chop-hares, chop-partridges, chop-woodcocks, chop-pheasants, chop-pullets, chop-venison, chop-conies, chop-pigs, for they scorn to feed on coarser meat. A t—d for their chops, cried Friar John, next year we will have them called chop-dung, chop-stront, chop-filth.

Would you take my advice? added he to the company. What is it? answered we. Let us do two things, returned he. First, let us secure all this venison and wild fowl,—I mean paying well for them; for my part, I am but too much tired already with our salt meat, it heats my flanks, so horribly. In the next place, let us go back to the wicket, and destroy all these devilish furred law-cats. For my part, quoth Panurge, I know better things: catch me there, and hang me: no, I am somewhat more inclined to be fearful than bold; I love to sleep in a whole skin.

CHAPTER XV

How Friar John talks of rooting out the Furred Law-cats

VIRTUE of the frock, quoth Friar John, what kind of voyage are we making? A shitten one, on my word: the devil of anything we do, but fizzling, farting, funking, squattering, dozing, raving, and doing nothing. Odd's belly, it is not in my nature to lie idle; I mortally hate it: unless I am doing some heroic feat every foot, I cannot sleep one wink at nights. Damn it, did you then take me along with you for your chaplain, to sing mass and shrive you? By Maunday Thursday, the first of ye all that comes to me on such an account shall be fitted; for the only penance I will enjoin shall be, that he immediately throw himself headlong over-board into the sea, like a base cow-hearted son of ten fathers. This in deduction of the pains of purgatory.

What made Hercules such a famous fellow, do you think? Nothing, but that while he travelled, he still made it his business to rid the world of tyrannies, errors, dangers, and drudgeries; he still put to death all robbers, all monsters, all venomous serpents, and hurtful creatures. Why then do we not follow his example, doing as he did in the countries through which we pass? He destroyed the Stymphalides, the Lernæan hydra, Cacus, Antheus, the centaurs, and what not; I am no clericus, those that are such tell me so.

In imitation of that noble by-blow, let us destroy and root out these wicked furred law-cats, that are a kind of ravenous devils; thus we shall remove all manner of tyranny out of the land. Mahomet's tutor, swallow me body and soul, tripes and guts, if I would stay to ask your help or advice in the matter, were I but as strong as he was. Come, he that would be thought a gentleman, let him storm a town; well, then, shall we go? I dare swear we will do their business for them with a wet finger; they will bear it, never fear: since they could swallow down more foul language that came from us, than ten sows and their babies could swill hogwash. Damn them, they do not value all the ill words or dishonour in the world at a rush, so they but get the coin into their purses, though they were to have it in a shitten clout. Come, we may chance to kill them all, as Hercules would have done, had they lived in his time. We only want to be set to work by another Eurystheus, and nothing else for the present, unless it be what I heartily wish them, that Jupiter may give them a short visit, only some two or three hours long, and walk among their lordships in the same equipage that attended him when he came last to his Miss Semele, jolly Bacchus's mother.

It is a very great mercy, quoth Panurge, that you have got out of their clutches: for my part, I have no stomach to go there again; I am hardly come to myself yet, so scared and appalled I was; my hair still stands up on end when I think on it; and most damnably troubled I was there, for three very weighty reasons. First, because I was troubled. Secondly, because I was troubled. Thirdly and lastly, because I was troubled. Hearken to me as little on the right side, Friar John, my left cod, since thou wilt not hear at the other; whenever the maggot bites thee, to take a trip down to hell, and visit the tribunal of Minos, Æacus, Rhadamanthus, and Dis, do but tell me, and I will be sure to bear thee company, and never leave thee, as long as my name is Panurge, but will wade over Acheron,

Styx, and Cocytus, drink whole bumpers of Lethe's water,—
though I mortally hate that element,—and even pay thy passage
to that bawling, cross-grained ferryman, Charon. But as for
the damned wicket, if thou art so weary of thy life as to
go thither again, thou mayest even look for somebody else to
bear thee company, for I will not move one step that way:
even rest satisfied with this positive answer. By my good
will, I will not stir a foot to go thither as long as I live, any
more than Calpe will come over to Abyla. Was Ulysses so mad
as to go back into the cyclop's cave to fetch his sword? No,
marry was he not. Now, I have left nothing behind me at the
wicket through forgetfulness; why then should I think of
going thither?

Well, quoth Friar John, as good sit still as rise up and fall;
what cannot be cured must be endured. But, pr'ythee, let us
hear one another speak in turn. Come, wert thou not a wise
doctor to fling away a whole purse of gold on those mangy
scoundrels? Ha? A squinzy choke thee, we were too rich,
were we? Had it not been enough to have thrown the hell-
hounds a few cropt pieces of white cash?

How could I help it, returned Panurge? Did you not see
how Gripe-men-all held his gaping velvet pouch, and every
moment roared and bellowed, By gold, give me out of hand;
by gold, give, give, give me presently? Now, thought I to
myself, we shall never come off scot-free; I will even stop their
mouths with gold, that the wicket may be opened, and we may
get out; the sooner the better. And I judged that lousy silver
would not do the business; for, do you see, velvet pouches
do not use to gape for little paltry clipped silver and small
cash; no, they are made for gold, my friend John, that they
are, my dainty cod. Ah! when thou hast been larded, basted,
and roasted, as I was, thou wilt hardly talk at this rate, I doubt.
But now what is to be done?—We are enjoined by them to go
forwards.

The scabby slabberdegullions still waited for us at the port,
expecting to be greased in the fist as well as their masters.
Now, when they perceived that we were ready to put to sea,
they came to Friar John, and begged that we would not forget
to gratify the apparitors before we went off, according to the
assessment for the fees at our discharge. Hell and damnation,
cried Friar John, are ye here still, ye bloodhounds, ye citing,
scribbling imps of Satan? Rot you, am I not vexed enough
already, but you must have the impudence to come and

plague me, ye scurvy fly-catchers you? By cob's-body, I will
gratify your ruffianships as you deserve; I will apparatorize
you presently, with a wannion, that I will. With this he
lugged out his slashing cutlass, and, in a mighty heat, came
out of the ship, to cut the cozening varlets into steaks, but
they scampered away and got out of sight in a trice.

However, there was somewhat more to do, for some of our
sailors, having got leave of Pantagruel to go ashore, while we
were had before Gripe-men-all, had been at a tavern near the
haven, to make much of themselves, and roar it, as seamen
will do when they come into some port. Now I do not know
whether they had paid their reckoning to the full or no, but,
however it was, an old fat hostess, meeting Friar John on the
quay, was making a woeful complaint before a serjeant, son-in-
law to one of the furred law-cats, and a brace of bums, his
assistants.

The Friar, who did not much care to be tired with their impertinent prating said to them, Harkee me, ye lubberly gnat-snappers,
do ye presume to say, that our seamen are not honest men? I
will maintain they are, ye doterrels, and will prove it to your
brazen faces, by justice: I mean this trusty piece of cold iron by
my side. With this he lugged it out and flourished with it.
The forlorn lobcocks soon showed him their backs, betaking
themselves to their heels; but the old fusty landlady kept her
ground, swearing like any butter-whore, that the tarpaulins
were very honest cods, but that they only forgot to pay for
the bed on which they had lain after dinner, and she asked
fivepence French money, for the said bed. May I never sup,
said the Friar, if it be not dog-cheap; they are sorry guests,
and unkind customers, that they are; they do not know when
they have a pennyworth, and will not always meet with such
bargains; come, I myself will pay you the money, but I would
willingly see it first.

The hostess immediately took him home with her, and showed
him the bed, and having praised it for its good qualifications,
said, that she thought, as times went, she was not out of the way
in asking fivepence for it. Friar John then gave her the fivepence; and she no sooner turned her back, but he presently
began to rip up the ticking of the feather-bed and bolster, and
threw all the feathers out at the window. In the mean time
the old hag came down, and roared out for help, crying out
murder, to set all the neighbourhood in an uproar. Yet she
also fell to gathering the feathers that flew up and down in the

air, being scattered by the wind.   Friar John let her bawl on, and, without any further ado, marched off with the blanket, quilt, and both the sheets, which he brought aboard undiscovered, for the air was darkened with the feathers, as it uses sometimes to be with snow.   He gave them away to the sailors, then said to Pantagruel, that beds were much cheaper at that place than in Chinnonois, though we have there the famous geese of Pautilé; for the old beldam had asked him but fivepence for a bed, which in Chinnonois, had been worth about twelve francs. [As soon as Friar John and the rest of the company were embarked, Pantagruel set sail.   But there arose a southeast wind, which blew so vehemently they lost their way, and in a manner going back to the country of the furred law-cats, they entered into a huge gulf, where the sea ran so high and terrible, that the ship-boy on the top of the mast cried out, he again saw the habitation of Gripe-men-all; upon which Panurge, frightened almost out of his wits, roared out, Dear master, in spite of the wind and waves, change your course, and turn the ship's head about: O my friend, let us come no more into that cursed country, where I left my purse.   So the wind carried them near an island where, however, they did not dare at first to land, but entered about a mile off.]

CHAPTER XVI

How Pantagruel came to the Island of the Apedefts, or Ignoramuses, with long claws and crooked paws, and of terrible adventures and monsters there

(This chapter is not in early edition, 1707)

As soon as they had cast anchor, and had moored the ship, the pinnace was put over the ship's side, and manned by the cockswain's crew.   When the good Pantagruel had prayed publicly, and given thanks to the Lord, that had delivered him from so great a danger, he stepped into the pinnace with his whole company, to go on shore, which was no ways difficult to do, for, as the sea was calm, and the winds laid, they soon got to the cliffs.   When they were set on shore, Epistemon, who was admiring the situation of the place, and the strange shape of the rocks, discovered some of the natives.   The first he met had on a short purple gown, a doublet cut in panes, like a Spanish leather jerkin, half sleeves of satin, and the upper part of them leather, a coif like a black pot tipped with tin.   He was a good likely sort of a body, and his name, as we heard afterwards, was Double-fee. Epistemon asked him, How they called those strange craggy rocks and deep valleys? He told them it was a colony, brought out of Attorneyland, and called Process; and that if we forded the river somewhat further beyond the rocks, we should come into the island of the Apedefts. By the sacred memory of the decretals, said Friar John, tell us, I pray you, what you honest men here live on? Could not a man take a chirping bottle with you, to taste your wine? I can see nothing among you, but parchment, ink-horns, and pens. We live on nothing else, returned Double-fee; and all who live in this place must come through my hands. How, quoth Panurge, are you a shaver, then? Do you fleece them? Ay, ay, their purse, answered Double-fee, nothing else. By the foot of Pharaoh, cried Panurge, the devil a sous will you get of me. However, sweet sir, be so kind as to show an honest man the way to those Apedefts, or ignorant people, for I come from the land of the learned, where I did not learn over much.

Still talking on, they got to the island of the Apedefts, for they were soon got over the ford. Pantagruel was not a little taken up with admiring the structure and habitation of the people of the place. For they live in a swingeing wine-press, fifty steps up to it. You must know there are some of all sorts, little, great, private, middle-sized, and so forth. You go through a large peristyle, alias a long entry set about with pillars, in which you see, in a kind of landscape, the ruins of almost the whole world; besides so many gibbets for great robbers, so many gallows and racks, that it is enough to fright you out of your seven senses. Double-fee perceiving that Pantagruel was taken up with contemplating those things, Let us go further, sir, said he to him, all this is nothing yet. Nothing, quotha, cried Friar John; by the soul of my overheated codpiece, friend Panurge and I here shake and quiver for mere hunger. I had rather be drinking, than staring on these ruins. Pray come along, sir, said Double-fee. He then led us into a little wine-press, that lay backwards in a blind corner, and was called Pithies in the language of the country. You need not ask whether Master John and Panurge made much of their sweet selves there; it is enough that I tell you there was no want of Bolonia sausages, turkey-pouts, capons, bustards, malmsey-wine, and all other sorts of good belly-timber, very well dressed.

A pimping son of ten fathers, who, for want of a better, did the office of a butler, seeing that Friar John had cast a sheep's eye at a choice bottle that stood near a cupboard by itself, at some distance from the rest of the bottellic magazine, like a jack-in-an-office, said to Pantagruel, Sir, I perceive that one of your men here is making love to this bottle: he ogles it, and would fain caress it; but I beg that none offer to meddle with it; for it is reserved for their worships. How, cried Panurge, there are some grandees here then I see. It is vintage time with you, I perceive.

Then Double-fee led up to a private stair-case, and showed us into a room, whence, without being seen, out at a loop-hole, we could see their worships in the great wine-press, where none could be admitted without their leave. Their worships, as he called them, were about a score of fusty, crack-ropes and gallow-clappers, or rather more, all posted before a bar, and staring at each other like so many dead pigs: their paws or hands were as long as a crane's leg, and their claws or nails four and twenty inches long at least; for you must know, they are enjoined never to pare off the least chip of them, so that they grow as crooked as a Welch hook, or a hedging-bill.

We saw a swingeing bunch of grapes, that are gathered and squeezed in that country, brought in by them. As soon as it was laid down, they clapped it into the press, and there was not a bit of it out of which each of them did not squeeze some oil of gold. Insomuch that the poor grape was tried with a witness, and brought off so drained and picked, and so dry that there was not the least moisture, juice, or substance left in it; for they had pressed out its very quintessence.

Double-fee told us, they had not often such huge bunches; but, let the worst come to the worst, they were sure never to be without others in their press. But hark you me, master of mine, asked Panurge, have they not some of different growth? Ay marry have they, quoth Double-fee. Do you see there this little bunch, to which they are going to give the other wrench? It is of tythe-growth, you must know; they crushed, wrung, squeezed, and strained out the very heart's blood of it but the other day: but it did not bleed freely; the oil came hard, and smelt of the priest's chest; so that they found there was not much good to be got out of it. Why then, said Pantagruel, do they put it again into the press? Only, answered Double-fee, for fear there should still lurk some juice among the husks and hullings, in the mother of the grape. The devil be damned, cried Friar John, do you call these same folks illiterate lobcocks, and dunsical doddipoles? May I be broiled like a red herring, if

I do not think they are wise enough to skin a flint, and draw
oil out of a brick wall. So they are, said Double-fee; for they
sometimes put castles, parks, and forests into the press, and
out of them all extract *aurum potabile*. You mean *portabile*,
I suppose, cried Epistemon, such as may be borne. I mean as
I said, replied Double-fee, *potabile*, such as may be drunk;
for it makes them drink many a good bottle more than otherwise
they should.

But I cannot better satisfy you as to the growth of the vine-
tree syrup that is here squeezed out of grapes, than in desiring
you to look yonder in that back-yard, where you will see above
a thousand different growths that lie waiting to be squeezed
every moment. Here are some of the public and some of the
private growth; some of the fortifications, loans, gifts and
gratuities, escheats, forfeitures, fines, and recoveries, penal
statutes, crown lands, and demesne, privy purse, post-offices,
offerings, lordships of manors, and a world of other growths, for
which we want names. Pray, quoth Epistemon, tell me of
what growth is that great one, with all those little grapelings
about it. Oh, oh! returned Double-fee, that plump one is of
the treasury, the very best growth in the whole country. Whenever any one of that growth is squeezed there is not one of their
worships but gets juice enough of it to soak his nose six months
together. When their worships were up, Pantagruel desired
Double-fee to take us into that great wine-press, which he
readily did. As soon as we were in, Epistemon, who understood all sorts of tongues, began to show us many devices on
the press, which was large and fine, and made of the wood of
the cross—at least Double-fee told us so. On each part of it
were names of every thing in the language of the country.
The spindle of the press was called receipt; the trough, costs
and damages; the hole for the vice-pin, state; the side-boards,
money paid into the office; the great beam, respite of homage;
the branches, *radietur*; the side-beams, *recuperetur*; the fats,
ignoramus; the two-handled basket, the rolls; the treading-
place, acquittance; the dossers, validation; the panniers,
authentic decrees; the pailes, *potentials*; the funnels, *quietus est*.

By the Queen of the Chitterlings, quoth Panurge, all the
hieroglyphics of Egypt are mine a— to this jargon. Why!
here are a parcel of words full as analogous as chalk and cheese
or a cat and a cart wheel! But why, pr'ythee, dear Double-fee,
do they call these worshipful dons of yours ignorant fellows?
Only, said Double-fee, because they neither are, nor ought to

be, clerks, and all must be ignorant as to what they transact here; nor is there to be any other reason given, but, The court hath said it; The court will have it so; The court has decreed it. Cop's body, quoth Pantagruel, they might full as well have called them necessity; for necessity has no law.

From thence, as he was leading us to see a thousand little puny presses, we spied another paltry bar, about which sat four or five ignorant waspish churls, of so testy, fuming a temper, like an ass with squibs and crackers tied to its tail, and so ready to take pepper in the nose for yea and nay, that a dog would not have lived with them. They were hard at it with the lees and dregs of the grapes, which they griped over and over again, might and main, with their clenched fists. They were called contractors, in the language of the country. These are the ugliest, misshapen, grim-looking scrubs, said Friar John, that ever were beheld, with or without spectacles. Then we passed by an infinite number of little pimping wine-presses, all full of vintage-mongers, who were picking, examining, and raking the grapes with some instruments, called bills of charge.

Finally we came into a hall down stairs, where we saw an overgrown cursed mangy cur, with a pair of heads, a wolf's belly, and claws like the devil of hell. The son of a bitch was fed with costs, for he lived on a multiplicity of fine amonds and amerciaments, by order of their worships, to each of whom the monster was worth more than the best farm in the land. In their tongue of ignorance they called him Twofold. His dam lay by him, and her hair and shape were like her whelp's, only she had four heads, two male and two female, and her name was Fourfold. She was certainly the most cursed and dangerous creature of the place, except her grandam, which we saw, and had been kept locked up in a dungeon, time out of mind, and her name was Refusing-of-fees.

Friar John, who had always twenty yards of gut ready empty, to swallow a gallimaufry of lawyers, began to be somewhat out of humour, and desired Pantagruel to remember he had not dined, and bring Double-fee along with him. So away we went, and as we marched out at the back-gate, whom should we meet but an old piece of mortality in chains. He was half ignorant and half learned, like an hermaphrodite of Satan. The fellow was all caparisoned with spectacles, as a tortoise is with shells, and lived on nothing but a sort of food which, in their gibberish, was called appeals. Pantagruel asked Double-fee of what breed was that prothonotary, and what name they

gave him? Double-fee told us that time out of mind, he had
been kept there in chains, to the great grief of their worships,
who starved him, and his name was Review. By the pope's
sanctified two-pounders, cried Friar John, I do not much wonder
at the meagre cheer which this old chuff finds among their
worships. Do but look a little on the weather-beaten scratch-
toby, friend Panurge; by the sacred tip of my cowl, I will lay
five pounds to a hazel-nut, the foul thief has the very looks of
Gripe-men-all. These same fellows here, ignorant as they be,
are as sharp and knowing as other folks. But were it my case,
I would send him packing with a squib in his breech, like a
rogue as he is. By my oriental barnacles, quoth Panurge,
honest Friar, thou art in the right, for if we but examine that
treacherous Review's ill-favoured phiz, we find that the filthy
snudge is yet more mischievous and ignorant than these ignorant
wretches here, since they (honest dunces) grapple and glean
with as little harm and pother as they can, without any long
fiddle-cum-farts or tantalizing in the case; nor do they dally
and demur in your suit, but, in two or three words, whip-stitch,
in a trice, they finish the vintage of the close, bating you all
these damned tedious interlocutories, examinations, and
appointments, which fret to the heart's blood your furred
law-cats.

CHAPTER XVII

How we went Forwards, and how Panurge had like to have been killed

WE put to sea that very moment, steering our course forwards,
and gave Pantagruel a full account of our adventures, which
so deeply struck him with compassion, that he wrote some
elegies on that subject, to divert himself during the voyage.
When we were safe in the port we took some refreshment, and
took in fresh water and wood. The people of the place, who had
the countenance of jolly fellows, and boon companions, were
all of them forward folks, bloated and puffed up with fat; and
we saw some who slashed and pinked their skins, to open a
passage to the fat, that it might swell out at the slits and gashes
which they made; neither more nor less than the shit-breech
fellows in our country bepink and cut open their breeches, that
the taffety on the inside may stand out and be puffed up. They
said, that what they did was not out of pride or ostentation, but

because otherwise their skins would not hold them without
much pain. Having thus slashed their skin, they used to grow
much bigger, like the young trees, on whose barks the gardeners
make incisions, that they may grow the better.

Near the haven there was a tavern, which forwards seemed
very fine and stately. We repaired thither, and found it filled
with people of the forward nation, of all ages, sexes, and conditions; so that we thought some notable feast or other was
getting ready, but we were told that all that throng were invited
to the bursting of mine host, which caused all his friends and
relations to hasten thither.

We did not understand that jargon, and, therefore, thought
in that country, by that bursting they meant some merry
meeting or other, as we do in ours by betrothing, wedding,
groaning, christening, churching (of women), shearing (of sheep),
reaping (of corn, or harvest-home), and many other junketing
bouts that end in ing. But we soon heard that there was no
such matter in hand.

The master of the house, you must know, had been a good
fellow in his time, loved heartily to wind up his bottom, to
bang the pitcher, and lick his dish: he used to be a very fair
swallower of gravy soup, a notable accountant in matter of
hours, and his whole life was one continual dinner, like mine
host at Rouillac [in Perigord]. But now, having farted out
much fat for ten years together, according to the custom of
the country, he was drawing towards the bursting hour; for
neither the inner thin caul wherewith the entrails are covered,
nor his skin that had been jagged and mangled so many years,
were able to hold and enclose his guts any longer, or hinder
them from forcing their way out. Pray, quoth Panurge, is
there no remedy, no help for the poor man, good people? Why
do you not swaddle him round with good tight girths, or secure
his natural tub with a strong sorb-apple-tree hoop? Nay, why
do you not iron-bind him, if needs be? This would keep the
man from flying out and bursting. The word was not yet out
of his mouth, when we heard something give a loud report, as
if a huge sturdy oak had been split in two. Then some of the
neighbours told us, that the bursting was over, and that the
clap or crack, which we heard, was the last fart, and so there
was an end of mine host.

This made me call to mind a saying of the venerable abbot of
Castilliers, the very same who never cared to humph his chamber-
maids, but when he was *in pontificalibus*. That pious person,

being much dunned, teased, and importuned by his relations
to resign his abbey in his old age, said and professed, That he
would not strip till he was ready to go to bed, and that the last
fart which his reverend paternity was to utter, should be the
fart of an abbot.

CHAPTER XVIII

*How our ships were stranded, and we were relieved by some people
that were subject to Queen Whims (qui tenoient de la Quinte)*

WE weighed and set sail with a merry westerly gale, when
about seven leagues off (twenty-two miles), some gusts or scuds
of wind suddenly arose, and the wind veering and shifting
from point to point, was, as they say, like an old woman's
breech, at no certainty; so we first got our starboard tacks
aboard, and hauled off our lee-sheets.   Then the gusts increased,
and by fits blowed all at once from several quarters, yet we
neither settled not braided up close our sails, but only let fly
the sheets, not to go against the master of the ship's direction;
and thus having let go amain, lest we should spend our topsails,
or the ship's quick-side should lie in the water, and she be overset, we lay by and run adrift; that is, in a landloper's phrase, we
temporised it.   For he assured us that, as these gusts and
whirlwinds would not do much good, so they could not do us
much harm, considering their easiness and pleasant strife, as
also the clearness of the sky and calmness of the current.   So
that we were to observe the philosopher's rule, bear and forbear;
that is, trim, or go according to the time.

However, these whirlwinds and gusts lasted so long, that we
persuaded the master to let us go and lie at trie with our main
course: that is, to haul the tack aboard, the sheet close aft, the
bowline set up, and the helm tied close aboard; so, after a
stormy gale of wind, we broke through the whirlwind.   But it
was like falling into Scylla to avoid Charybdis, (out of the frying-
pan into the fire).   For we had not sailed a league, ere our
ships were stranded upon some sands, such as are the flats of
St. Maixant.

All our company seemed mightily disturbed, except Friar
John, who was not a jot daunted, and with sweet sugar-plum
words, comforted now one and then another, giving them
hopes of speedy assistance from above, and telling them that

he had seen Castor at the main-yard arm. Oh! that I were but now ashore, cried Panurge, that is all I wish for myself at present, and that you, who like the sea so well, had each man of you two hundred thousand crowns; I would fairly let you set up shop on these sands, and would get a fat calf dressed, and a hundred of faggots cooled for you against you come ashore. I freely consent never to mount a wife, so you but set me ashore, and mount me on a horse, that I may go home: no matter for a servant, I will be contented to serve myself; I am never better treated than when I am without a man. Faith old Plautus was in the right of it when he said, the more servants the more crosses; for such they are, even supposing they could want what they all have but too much of, a tongue, that most busy, dangerous, and pernicious member of servants: accordingly, it was for their sakes alone that the racks and tortures for confession were invented, though some foreign civilians in our time have drawn alogical and unreasonable consequences from it.

That very moment we spied a sail that made towards us. When it was close by us, we soon knew what was the lading of the ship, and who was aboard of her. She was full freighted with drums: I was acquainted with many of the passengers that came in her, who were most of them of good families; among the rest Harry Cotiral the chemist, an old toast, who had got a swingeing ass's touch-tripe (penis) fastened to his waist, as the good women's beads are to their girdle. In his left hand he held an old overgrown greasy foul cap, such as your scald-pated fellows wear, and in the right a huge cabbage-stump.

As soon as he saw me he was overjoyed, and bawled out to me, What cheer, ho? How dost like me now? Behold the true Algamana (this, he said, showing me the ass's ticklegizzard.) This doctor's cap is my true elixo; and this (continued he, shaking, the cabbage stump in his fist) is *lunaria major*; I have it, old boy, I have it; we will blow the coal when thou art come back. But pray, father, said I, whence come you? Whither go you? What is your lading? Have you smelt the sea? To these four questions he answered, From Queen Whims; for Touraine; alchymy; to the very bottom.

Whom have you got on board? said I. Said he, Astrologers, fortune-tellers, alchymists, rhymers, poets, painters, projectors, mathematicians, watchmakers, sing-songs, musicianers, and the devil and all of others that are subject to Queen Whims. They have very fair legible patents to show for it, as any body may

see. Panurge had no sooner heard this, but he was upon the
high-rope, and began to rail at them like mad. What the devil
do you mean, cried he, to sit idly here, like a pack of loitering
sneaksbies, and see us stranded, while you may help us, and
tow us off into the current! A plague on your whims; you can
make all things whatsoever, they say, so much as good weather
and little children; yet will not make haste to fasten some
hawsers and cables, and get us off. I was just coming to set
you afloat, quoth Harry Cotiral: by Trismegistus, I will clear
you in a trice. With this he caused 7,532,810 huge drums to
be unheaded on one side, and set that open side so that it faced
the end of the streamers and pendants; and having fastened
them to good tacklings, and our ship's head to the stern of
theirs, with cables fastened to the bits abaft the manger in the
ship's loof, they towed us off ground at one pull, so easily and
pleasantly, that you would have wondered at it, had you been
there. For the dub-o-dub rattling of the drums, with the soft
noise of the gravel, which murmuring disputed us our way, and
the merry cheers and huzzas of the sailors, made an harmony
almost as good as that of the heavenly bodies, when they roll
and are whirled round their spheres, which rattling of the
celestial wheels Plato said he heard some nights in his sleep.

We scorned to be behind-hand with them in civility, and
gratefully gave them store of our sausages and chitterlings,
with which we filled their drums; and we were just a-hoisting
two-and-sixty hogsheads of wine out of the hold, when two
huge whirlpools (physeteres) with great fury made towards
their ship; spouting more water than is in the river Vienne
(Vigenne), from Chinon to Saumur: to make short, all their
drums, all their sails, their concerns, and themselves, were
soused, and their very hose were watered by the collar.

Panurge was so overjoyed, seeing this, and laughed so
heartily, that he was forced to hold his sides, and it set him
into a fit of the cholic for two hours and more. I had a mind,
quoth he, to make the dogs drink, and those honest whirlpools,
egad, have saved me that labour and that cost. There's sauce
for them; ἄριστον μὲν ὕδωρ, Water is good, saith a poet; let
them Pindarise upon it: they never cared for fresh water, but
to wash their hands or their glasses. This good salt water will
stand them in good stead, for want of sal ammoniac and nitre
in Geber's kitchen.

We could not hold any further discourse with them; for the
former whirlpool hindered our ship from feeling the helm.

The pilot advised us henceforwards to let her run adrift, and follow the stream, not busying ourselves with anything, but making much of our carcasses. For our only way to arrive safe at the Queendom of Whims, was to trust to the whirlwind, and be led by the current.

CHAPTER XIX

How we arrived at the queendom of Whims, or kingdom of Quintessence, called Entelechy

WE did as he directed us for about twelve hours, and on the third day the sky seemed to us somewhat clearer, and we happily arrived at the port of Mateotechny, not far distant from the palace of Quintessence.

We met full-butt on the quay a great number of guards, and other military men that garrisoned the arsenal; and we were somewhat frighted at first, because they made us all lay down our arms, and, in a haughty manner, asked us whence we came?

Cousin, quoth Panurge to him that asked the question, we are of Touraine, and come from France, being ambitious of paying our respects to the Lady Quintessence, and visit this famous realm of Entelechy.

What do you say? cried they: do you call it Entelechy, or Endelechy? Truly, truly, sweet cousins, quoth Panurge, we are a silly sort of grout-headed lobcocks, an' it please you; be so kind as to forgive us if we chance to knock words out of joint: as for anything else, we are downright honest fellows, and true hearts.

We have not asked you this question without a cause, said they: for a great number of others, who have passed this way from your country of Touraine, seemed as mere joltheaded doddipoles as ever were scored over the coxcomb, yet spoke as correct as other folks. But there has been here from other countries a pack of I know not what overweening self-conceited prigs, as moody as so many mules, and as stout as any Scotch lairds, and nothing would serve these, forsooth, but they must wilfully wrangle and stand out against us at their coming; and much they got by it after all. Troth, we even fitted them, and clawed them off with a vengeance, for all they looked so big and so grum.

Pray tell me, does your time lie so heavy upon you in your world, that you do not know how to bestow it better than in thus impudently talking, disputing, and writing of our sovereign lady? There was much need that your Tully, the consul, should go and leave the care of his commonwealth to busy himself idly about her; and after him, your Diogenes Laertius, the biographer, and your Theodorus Gaza, the philosopher, and your Argiropilus, the emperor, and your Bessario, the cardinal, and your Politian, the pedant, and your Budæus, the judge, and your Lascaris, the ambassador, and the devil and all of those you call lovers of wisdom; whose number, it seems, was not thought great enough already, but lately your Scaliger, Bigot, Chambrier, Francis Fleury, and I cannot tell how many such other junior sneaking fly-blows, must take upon them to increase it.

A squincy gripe the cods-headed changelings at the swallow, and eke at the cover-weesel; we shall make them—But the deuce take them; (they flatter the devil here, and smoothify his name, quoth Panurge, between their teeth;) you do not come here, continued the captain, to uphold them in their folly, you have no commission from them to this effect; well then, we will talk no more of it.

Aristotle, that first of men, and peerless pattern of all philosophy, was our sovereign lady's godfather; and wisely and properly gave her the name of Entelechy. Her true name then is Entelechy, and may he be in tail beshit, and entail a shit-a-bed faculty, and nothing else on his family, who dares call her by any other name: for whoever he is, he does her wrong, and is a very impudent person. You are heartily welcome, gentlemen. With this they colled and clipt us about the neck, which was no small comfort to us, I will assure you.

Panurge then whispered me, Fellow-traveller, quoth he, hast thou not been somewhat afraid this bout? A little, said I. To tell you the truth of it, quoth he, never were the Ephraimites in a greater fear and quandary, when the Gileadites killed and drowned them for saying sibboleth instead of shibboleth; and among friends, let me tell you, that perhaps there is not a man in the whole country of Beauce, but might easily have stopt my bunghole with a cart-load of hay.

The captain afterwards took us to the queen's palace, leading us silently with great formality. Pantagruel would have said something to him; but the other, not being able to come up to his height, wished for a ladder, or a very long pair of stilts;

then said, Patience, if it were our sovereign lady's will, we would
be as tall as you; well, we shall, when she pleases.

In the first galleries, we saw great numbers of sick persons,
differently placed according to their maladies. The leprous
were apart; those that were poisoned on one side; those that
had got the plague, alias the pox, in the first rank accordingly.

CHAPTER XX

How the Quintessence cured the sick with a song

THE captain showed us the queen, attended with her ladies
and gentlemen in the second gallery. She looked young,
though she was at least eighteen hundred years old; and was
handsome, slender, and as fine as a queen, that is as hands
could make her. He then said to us, It is not yet a fit time
to speak to the queen; be you but mindful of her doings in the
meanwhile.

You have kings in your world that fantastically pretend to
cure some certain diseases; as for example, scrofula or wens,
swelled throats, nick-named the king's evil, and quartan agues,
only with a touch: now our queen cures all manner of diseases
without so much as touching the sick, but barely with a song,
according to the nature of the distemper. He then showed
us a set of organs, and said, that when it was touched by her,
those miraculous cures were performed. The organ was indeed
the strangest that ever eyes beheld; for the pipes were of cassia
fistula in the cod; the top and cornice of guiacum; the bellows
of rhubarb; the pedals of turbith, and the clavier or keys of
scammony.

While we were examining this wonderful new make of an
organ, the leprous were brought in by her abstractors, spodizators, masticators, pregustics, tabachins, chachanins, nee-
manins, rabrebans, nercins, rozuins, nebidins, tearins, segamions,
perarons, chasinins, sarins, soteins, aboth, enilins, archasdar-
penins, mebins, chabourins, and other officers, for whom I want
names; so she played them I do not know what sort of a tune,
or song, and they were all immediately cured.

Then those who were poisoned were had in, and she had no
sooner given them a song, but they began to find a use for their
legs, and up they got. Then came on the deaf, the blind, and
the dumb and they too were restored to their lost faculties and

senses with the same remedy; which did so strangely amaze us
(and not without reason, I think,) that down we fell on our
faces, remaining prostrate, like men ravished in ecstasy, and
were not able to utter one word through the excess of our
admiration, till she came, and having touched Pantagruel
with a fine fragrant nosegay of red roses, which she held in her
hand, thus made us recover our senses, and get up. Then she
made us the following speech in Byssin words, such as Parisatis
desired should be spoken to her son Cyrus, or at least of crimson
alamode.

The probity that scintillizes in the superfices of your persons,
informs my ratiocinating faculty, in a most stupendous manner,
of the radiant virtues, latent within the precious caskets and
ventricles of your minds. For, contemplating the mellifluous
suavity of your thrice discreet reverences, it is impossible not
to be persuaded with facility, that neither your affections nor
your intellects are vitiated with any defect, or privation of
liberal and exalted sciences: far from it, all must judge that in
you are lodged a cornucopia, an encyclopedia, an unmeasurable
profundity of knowledge in the most peregrine and sublime
disciplines, so frequently the admiration, and so rarely the
concomitants of the imperite vulgar. This gently compels
me, who in preceding times indefatigably kept my private
affections absolutely subjugated, to condescend to make my
application to you in the trivial phrase of the plebeian world;
and assure you, that you are well, more than most heartily
welcome.

I have no hand at making of speeches, quoth Panurge to me
privately: pr'ythee, man, make answer to her for us, if thou
canst. This would not work with me, however, neither did
Pantagruel return a word: so that Queen Whims, or Queen
Quintessence (which you please) perceiving that we stood as
mute as fishes, said: Your taciturnity speaks you not only
disciples of Pythagoras, from whom the venerable antiquity
of my progenitors, in successive propagation was emaned, and
derives its original; but also discovers, that through the revolu-
tion of many retrograde moons, you have in Egypt pressed the
extremities of your fingers, with the hard tenants of your
mouths, and scalptized your heads with frequent applications
of your unguicules. In the school of Pythagoras, taciturnity
was the symbol of abstracted and superlative knowledge; and
the silence of the Egyptians was agnized as an expressive manner
of divine adoration: this caused the pontiffs of Hierapolis to

sacrifice to the great deity in silence, impercussively, without any vociferous or obstreperous sound. My design is not to enter into a privation of gratitude towards you; but by a vivacious formality, though matter were too abstract itself from me, excentricate to you my cogitations.

Having spoken this, she only said to her officers, Tabachins, A panacea; and strait they desired us not to take it amiss, if the queen did not invite us to dine with her; for she never eat anything at dinner but some categories, jecabots, emnins, dimions, abstractions, harborins, chelemins, second intentions, carradoths, antitheses, metempsychoses, transcendent prolepsies, and such other light food.

Then they took us into a little closet, lined through with alarums, where we were treated God knows how. It is said that Jupiter writes whatever is transacted in the world, on the dipthera or skin of the Amalthæan goat that suckled him in Crete, which pelt served him instead of a shield against the Titans, whence he was nicknamed Ægiochos. Now as I hate to drink water, brother topers, I protest it would be impossible to make eighteen goat-skins hold the description of all the good meat they brought before us; though it were written in characters as small as those in which were penned Homer's Iliads, which Tully tells us he saw enclosed in a nutshell.

For my part, had I one hundred mouths, as many tongues, a voice of iron, a heart of oak, and lungs of leather, together with the mellifluous abundance of Plato; yet I never could give you a full account of a third part of a second of the whole.

Pantagruel was telling me, that he believed the queen had given the symbolic word used among her subjects, to denote sovereign good cheer, when she said to her tabachins, A panacea; just as Lucullus used to say, In Apollo, when he designed to give his friends a singular treat; though sometimes they took him at unawares, as, among the rest, Cicero and Hortensius sometimes used to do.

CHAPTER XXI

How the Queen passed her time after dinner

WHEN we had dined, a chachanin led us into the queen's hall, and there we saw how, after dinner, with the ladies and princes of her court, she used to sift, searse, boult, range, and pass away time with a fine large white and blue silk sieve. We also perceived how they revived ancient sports, diverting themselves together at

1. Cordax.	5. Persica.	9. Molossia.	12. Terminalia.
2. Emmelia.	6. Phrygia.	10. Cernopho-	13. Floralia.
3. Sicinnia.	7. Thracia.	rum.	14. Pyrrhice.
4. Jambics.	8. Calabrisme.	11. Monogas.	15. Nicatism.

And a thousand other dances.

Afterwards she gave orders that they should show us the apartments and curiosities in her palace; accordingly we saw there such new, strange, and wonderful things, that I am still ravished in admiration every time I think on it. However, nothing surprised us more than what was done by the gentlemen of her household, abstractors, parazons, nebidins, spodizators, and others, who freely, and without the least dissembling, told us, that the queen their mistress did all impossible things, and cured men of incurable diseases; and they, her officers, used to do the rest.

I saw there a young parazon cure many of the new consumption, I mean the pox, though they were never so peppered: had it been the rankest Roan ague, (Anglicé, the Covent-garden gout,) it was all one with him; touching only their dentiform vertebræ thrice with a piece of a wooden shoe, he made them as wholesome as so many sucking pigs.

Another did thoroughly cure folks of dropsies, tympanies, ascites, and hyposarcides, striking them on the belly nine times with a Tenedian hatchet, without any solution of the continuum.

Another cured all manner of fevers and agues on the spot, only with hanging a fox tail on the left side of the patient's girdle.

One removed the tooth-ache only with washing thrice the root of the aching tooth with elder-vinegar, and letting it dry half-an-hour in the sun.

Another the gout, whether hot or cold, natural or accidental, by barely making the gouty person shut his mouth, and open his eyes.

I saw another ease nine gentlemen of St. Francis's distemper, in a very short space of time, having clapped a rope about their necks, at the end of which hung a box with ten thousand gold crowns in it.

One with a wonderful engine, threw the houses out at the windows, by which means they were purged of all pestilential air.

Another cured all the three kinds of hectics, the tabid, atrophes, and emaciated, without bathing, without Tabian milk, dropax, alias depilatory, or other such medicaments; only turning the consumptive for three months into monks: and he assured me that if they did not grow fat and plump in a monastic way of living, they never would be fattened in this world, either by nature, or by art.

I saw another surrounded with a crowd of two sorts of women. Some were young, quaint, clever, neat, pretty, juicy, tight, brisk, buxom, proper, kind-hearted, and as right as my leg, to any man's thinking. The rest were old, weather-beaten, over-ridden, toothless, blear-eyed, tough, wrinkled, shrivelled, tawny, phthysicky, decrepit hags, beldams, and walking carcasses. We were told that this office was to cast anew those she-pieces of antiquity, and make them such as the pretty creatures whom we saw, who had been made young again that day, recovering at once the beauty, shape, size, and disposition, which they enjoyed at sixteen; except their heels, that were now much shorter than in their former youth.

This made them yet more apt to fall backwards, whenever any man happened to touch them, than they had been before. As for their counterparts, the old mother-scratch-tobies, they most devoutly waited for the blessed hour, when the batch that was in the oven was to be drawn, that they might have their turns, and in a mighty haste they were pulling and hauling the man like mad, telling him, that it is the most grievous and intolerable thing in nature for the tail to be on fire, and the head to scare away those who should quench it.

The officer had his hands full, never wanting patients; neither did his place bring him in little, you may swear. Pantagruel asked him whether he could also make old men young again? He said he could not. But the way to make them new men, was to get them to cohabit with a new-cast female: for thus they caught that fifth kind of crinckams, which some call pellade, in Greek, ὀφίασις, that makes them cast off their old hair and skin, just as the serpents do; and thus their youth is renewed like the Arabian phœnix's. This is the true fountain of youth, for there the old and decrepit become young, active, and lusty.

Just so, as Euripides tells us, Iolaus was transmogrified; and thus Phaon, for whom kind-hearted Sappho run wild, grew young again for Venus's use: so Tithon by Aurora's means; so Æson by Medæa, and Jason also, who, if you will believe Phere-cides and Simonides, was new-vamped and dy'd by that witch: and so were the nurses of jolly Bacchus, and their husbands, as Æschylus relates.

CHAPTER XXII

*How Queen Whim's officers were employed : and how the
said lady retained us among her abstractors*

I THEN saw a great number of the queen's officers, who made
black-a-moors white, as fast as hops, just rubbing their bellies
with the bottom of a pannier.

Others, with three couples of foxes in one yoke, ploughed a
sandy shore, and did not lose their seed.

Others washed burnt tiles, and made them lose their colour.

Others extracted water out of pumice-stones; braying them a
good while in a mortar, and changed their substance.

Others sheared asses, and thus got long fleece wool.

Others gathered off of thorns grapes, and figs off thistles.

Others stroked he-goats by the dugs, and saved their milk
in a sieve; and much they got by it.

Others washed asses' heads, without losing their soap.

Others taught cows to dance, and did not lose their fiddling.

Others pitched nets to catch the wind, and took cock lobsters
in them.

I saw a spodizator, who very artificially got farts out of a
dead ass, and sold them for five pence an ell.

Another did putrify beetles. O the dainty food!

Poor Panurge fairly cast up his accounts, and gave up his
half penny [i.e. vomited], seeing an archasdarpenin, who laid
a huge plenty of chamberlye to putrify in horse-dung, mismashed with abundance of christian sir-reverence. Pugh, fie
upon him, nasty dog! However, he told us, that with this
sacred distillation he watered kings and princes, and made
their sweet lives a fathom or two the longer.

Others built churches to jump over the steeples.

Others set carts before the horses, and began to flay eels
at the tail; neither did the eels cry before they were hurt, like
those of Melun.

Others out of nothing made great things, and made great
things return to nothing.

Others cut fire into steaks, with a knife, and drew water with
a fish net.

Others made chalk of cheese, and honey of a dog's t—d.

We saw a knot of others, about a baker's dozen in number,
tippling under an arbour. They toped out of jolly bottomless

cups, four sorts of cool, sparkling, pure, delicious, vine-tree syrup, which went down like mother's milk; and healths and bumpers flew about like lightning. We were told, that these true philosophers were fairly multiplying the stars by drinking till the seven were fourteen, as brawny Hercules did with Atlas.

Others made a virtue of necessity, and the best of a bad market, which seemed to me a very good piece of work.

Others made alchymy with their teeth, and clapping their hind retort to the recipient, made scurvy faces, and then squeezed.

Others, in a large grass plat, exactly measured how far the fleas could go at a hop, a step, and a jump; and told us, that this was exceedingly useful for the ruling of kingdoms, the conduct of armies, and the administration of common-wealths; and that Socrates, who first got philosophy out of heaven, and from idle and trifling, made it profitable and of moment, used to spend half his philosophising time in measuring the leaps of fleas, as Aristophanes, the quintessential, affirms.

I saw two gibroins by themselves, keeping watch on the top of a tower, and we were told, they guarded the moon from the wolves.

In a blind corner, I met four more very hot at it, and ready to go to loggerheads. I asked what was the cause of the stir and ado, the mighty coil and pother they made? And I heard that for four or five livelong days, those overwise roisters had been at it ding dong, disputing on three high, more than meta-physical propositions, promising themselves mountains of gold by solving them; the first was concerning a he-ass's shadow: the second, of the smoke of a lantern; and the third, of goat's hair, whether it were wool or no? We heard that they did not think it a bit strange, that two contradictions in mode, form, figure, and time, should be true. Though I will warrant the sophists of Paris had rather be unchristened than own so much.

While we were admiring all those men's wonderful doings, the evening star already twinkling; the queen (God bless her) appeared attended with her court, and again amazed and dazzled us. She perceived it, and said to us:

What occasions the aberrations of human cogitations through the perplexing labyrinths and abysses of admiration, is not the source of the effects, which sagacious mortals visibly experience to be the consequential result of natural causes: it is the novelty of the experiment which makes impressions on their concep-tive, cogitative faculties; that do not previse the facility of the operation adequately, with a subact and sedate intellection, associated with diligent and congruous study. Consequently let all manner of perturbation abdicate the ventricles of your brains, if any one has invaded them while they were contemplating what is transacted by my domestic ministers. Be spectators and auditors of every particular phenomenon, and every individual proposition, within the extent of my mansion; satiate yourselves with all that can fall here under the consideration of your visual or ascultating powers, and thus emancipate yourselves from the servitude of crassous ignorance. And that you may be induced to apprehend how sincerely I desire this in consideration of the studious cupidity that so demonstratively emicates at your external organs, from this present particle of time, I retain you as my abstractors: Geber, my principal talachin, shall register and initiate you at your departing.

We humbly thanked her queenship, without saying a word, accepting of the noble office she conferred on us.

CHAPTER XXIII

How the Queen was served at dinner, and of her way of eating

QUEEN WHIMS, after this, said to her gentlemen: The orifice of the ventricle; that ordinary embassador for the alimentation of all members, whether superior or inferior, importunes us to restore, by the apposition of idoneous sustenance, what was dissipated by the internal calidity's action on the radical humidity. Therefore spodizators, gesinins, memains, and parazons, be not culpable of dilatory protractions in the apposition of every re-roborating species, but rather let them pullulate and superabound on the tables. As for you, noblissim prægustators, and my gentilissim masticators, your frequently experimented industry, internected with perdiligent sedulity, and sedulous perdiligence, continually adjuvates you to perficiate all things in so expeditious a manner, that there is a necessity of exciting in you a cupidity to consummate them. Therefore I can only suggest to you still to operate, as you are assuefacted indefatigably to operate.

Having made this fine speech, she retired for a while with part of her women, and we were told, that it was to bathe, as the ancients did more commonly than we use now-a-days to wash our hands before we eat. The tables were soon placed, the cloth spread, and then the queen sat down. She eat nothing but celestial ambrosia, and drank nothing but divine nectar. As for the lords and ladies that were there, they as well as we, fared on as rare, costly, and dainty dishes, as ever Apicius wot or dreamed of in his life.

When we were as round as hoops, and as full as eggs, with stuffing the gut, an olla podrida was set before us, to force hunger to come to terms with us, in case it had not granted us a truce; and such a huge vast thing it was, that the golden platter which Pythius Althius gave King Darius, would hardly have covered it. The olla consisted of several sorts of pottages, salads, fricasees, saugrenees, cabirotadoes, roast and boiled meat, carbonadoes, swingeing pieces of powdered beef, good old hams, dainty deifical somates, cakes, tarts, a world of curds after the Moorish way, fresh cheese, jellies, and fruit of all sorts. All this seemed to me good and dainty: however the sight of it made me sigh; for alas, I could not taste a bit of it; so full I had filled my puddings before, and a bellyful is a bellyful you know. Yet I must tell you what I saw, that seemed to me odd enough of conscience: it was some pasties in paste; and what should those pasties in paste be, do you think, but pasties in pots? At the bottom I perceived store of dice, cards, tarots, luettes, chess-men and chequers, besides full bowls of gold crowns, for those who had a mind to have a game or two, and try their chance. Under this I saw a jolly company of mules in stately trappings, with velvet foot-cloths, and a troop of ambling nags, some for men and some for women; besides I do not know how many litters all lined with velvet, and some coaches of Ferrara make: all this for those who had a mind to take the air.

This did not seem strange to me: but if anything did, it was certainly the queen's way of eating; and truly it was very new, and very odd: for she chewed nothing the good lady; not but that she had good sound teeth, and her meat required to be masticated; but such was her highness's custom. When her prægustators had tasted the meat, her masticators took it and chewed it most nobly: for their dainty chops and gullets were lined through with crimson satin, with little welts, and gold purls, and their teeth were of delicate white ivory. Thus, when they had chewed the meat ready for her highness's maw, they poured it down her throat through a funnel of fine gold, and so on to her craw. For that reason, they told us, she never visited a close stool but by proxy.

CHAPTER XXIV

How there was a ball in the manner of a tournament, at which Queen Whims was present

AFTER supper there was a ball in the form of a tilt or a tournament, not only worth seeing, but also never to be forgotten. First, the floor of the hall was covered with a large piece of velveted white and yellow chequered tapestry, each chequer exactly square, and three full spans in breadth.

Then thirty-two young persons came into the hall; sixteen of them arrayed in cloth of gold; and of these, eight were young nymphs, such as the ancients described Diana's attendants: the other eight were a king, a queen, two wardens of the castle, two knights, and two archers. Those of the other band were clad in cloth of silver.

They posted themselves on the tapestry in the following manner: the kings on the last line of the fourth square; so that the golden king was on a white square, and the silvered king on a yellow square, and each queen by her king; the golden queen on a yellow square, and the silvered queen on a white one: and on each side stood the archers to guide their kings and queens; by the archers the knights, and the wardens by them. In the next row before them stood the eight nymphs; and between the two bands of nymphs four rows of squares stood empty.

Each band had its musicians, eight on each side, dressed in its livery; the one with orange-coloured damask, the other with white; and all played on different instruments most melodiously and harmoniously, still varying in time and measure as the figure of the dance required. This seemed to me an admirable thing, considering the numerous diversity of steps, back-steps, bounds, rebounds, jerks, paces, leaps, skips, turns, coupés, hops, leadings, risings, meetings, flights, ambuscades, moves, and removes.

I was also at a loss, when I strove to comprehend how the dancers could so suddenly know what every different note meant: for they no sooner heard this or that sound, but they placed themselves in the place which was denoted by the music, though their motions were all different. For the nymphs that stood in the first file, as if they designed to begin the fight, marched straight forwards to their enemies from square to square, unless it were the first step, at which they were free to move over the two steps at once. They alone never fall back, (which is not very natural to other nymphs) and if any of them is so lucky as to advance to the opposite king's row, she is immediately crowned queen of her king, and after that, moves with the same state, and in the same manner as the queen; but till that happens, they never strike their enemies but forwards, and obliquely in a diagonal line. However, they make it not their chief business to take their foes; for if they did, they would leave their queen exposed to the adverse parties, who then might take her.

The kings move and take their enemies on all sides square-ways, and only step from a white square into a yellow one, and vice versa, except at their first step the rank should want other officers than the wardens; for then they can set them in their place, and retire by him.

The queens take a greater liberty than any of the rest; for they move backwards and forwards all manner of ways, in a straight line, as far as they please, provided the place be not filled with one of their own party, and diagonally also, keeping to the colour on which they stand.

The archers move backwards or forwards, far and near, never changing the colour on which they stand. The knights move, and take in a lineal manner, stepping over one square, though a friend or foe stand upon it, posting themselves on the second square to the right or left, from one colour to another, which is very unwelcome to the adverse party, and ought to be carefully observed, for they take at unawares.

The wardens move, and take to the right or left, before or behind them, like the kings, and can advance as far as they find places empty; which liberty the kings take not.

The law which both sides observe, is, at the end of the fight, to besiege and enclose the king of either party, so that he may not be able to move; and being reduced to that extremity, the battle is over, and he loses the day.

Now, to avoid this, there is none of either sex of each party, but is willing to sacrifice his or her life, and they begin to take one another on all sides in time, as soon as the music strikes up. When anyone takes a prisoner, he makes his honours, and striking him gently in the hand, puts him out of the field and combat, and encamps where he stood.

If one of the kings chance to stand where he might be taken, it is not lawful for any of his adversaries that had discovered

him, to lay hold on him: far from it, they are strictly enjoined
humbly to pay him their respects, and give him notice, saying,
God preserve you, sir! that his officers may relieve and cover
him, or he may remove, if unhappily he could not be relieved.
However, he is not to be taken, but greeted with a Good-morrow,
the others bending the knee: and thus the tournament used
to end.

CHAPTER XXV

How the thirty-two persons at the ball fought

THE two companies having taken their stations, the music
struck up, and, with a martial sound, which had something of
horrid in it, like a point of war, roused and alarmed both parties,
who now began to shiver, and then soon were warmed with
warlike rage; and having got in readiness to fight desperately,
impatient of delay, stood waiting for the charge.

Then the music of the silvered band ceased playing, and the
instruments of the golden side alone were heard, which denoted
that the golden party attacked. Accordingly, a new movement
was played for the onset, and we saw the nymph, who stood
before the queen, turn to the left towards her king, as it were
to ask leave to fight: and thus saluting her company at the
same time, she moved two squares forwards, and saluted the
adverse party.

Now the music of the golden brigade ceased playing, and their
antagonists began again. I ought to have told you that the
nymph, who began by saluting her company, had by that
formality also given them to understand that they were to
fall on. She was saluted by them, in the same manner, with a
full turn to the left, except the queen, who went aside towards
her king to the right; and the same manner of salutation was
observed on both sides during the whole ball.

The silvered nymph that stood before her queen likewise
moved, as soon as the music of her party sounded a charge:
her salutations, and those of her side, were to the right, and
her queen's to the left. She moved in the second square forwards, and saluted her antagonists, facing the first golden
nymph: so that there was not any distance between them, and
you would have thought they two had been going to fight; but
they only strike sideways.

Their comrades, whether silvered or golden, followed them

in an intercalary figure, and seemed to skirmish a while, till the golden nymph, who had first entered the lists, striking a silvered nymph in the hand on the right, put her out of the field, and set herself in her place. But soon the music playing a new measure, she was struck by a silvered archer, who after that was obliged himself to retire. A silvered knight then sallied out, and the golden queen posted herself before her king.

Then the silvered king, dreading the golden queen's fury, removed to the right, to the place where his warden stood, which seemed to him strong and well guarded.

The two knights on the left, whether golden or silvered, marched up, and on either side, took up many nymphs, who could not retreat; principally the golden knight, who made this his whole business; but the silvered knight had greater designs, dissembling all along, and even sometimes not taking a nymph when he could have done it, still moving on till he was come up to the main body of the enemies, in such a manner, that he saluted their king with a God save you, sir!

The whole golden brigade quaked for fear and anger, those words giving notice of their king's danger; not but that they could soon relieve him, but because their king being thus saluted, they were to lose their warden on the right wing, without any hopes of a recovery. Then the golden king retired to the left, and the silver knight took the golden warden, which was a mighty loss to that party. However, they resolved to be revenged, and surrounded the knight that he might not escape. He tried to get off, behaving himself with a great deal of gallantry, and his friends did what they could to save him; but at last he fell into the golden queen's hands, and was carried off.

Her forces not yet satisfied, having lost one of their best men, with more fury than conduct moved about, and did much mischief among their enemies. The silvered party warily dissembled, watching their opportunity to be even with them, and presented one of their nymphs to the golden queen, having laid an ambuscade; so that the nymph being taken, a golden archer had like to have seized the silvered queen. Then the golden knight undertakes to take the silvered king and queen, and says, Good-morrow. Then the silvered archer salutes them, and was taken by a golden nymph, and she herself by a silvered one.

The fight was obstinate and sharp. The wardens left their posts, and advanced to relieve their friends. The battle was doubtful, and victory hovered over both armies. Now the silvered host charge and break through their enemy's ranks, as far as the golden king's tent, and now they are beaten back: the golden queen distinguishes herself from the rest by her mighty achievements, still more than by her garb and dignity; for at once she takes an archer, and going sideways, seizes a silvered warden. Which thing the silvered queen perceiving, she came forwards, and rushing on with equal bravery, takes the last golden warden, and some nymphs. The two queens fought a long while hand to hand; now striving to take each other by surprise, then to save themselves, and sometimes to guard their kings. Finally, the golden queen took the silvered queen; but presently after she herself was taken by the silvered archer.

Then the silvered king had only three nymphs, an archer, and a warden left, and the golden only three nymphs and the right knight, which made them fight more slowly and warily than before. The two kings seemed to mourn for the loss of their loving queens, and only studied and endeavoured to get new ones out of all their nymphs, to be raised to that dignity, and thus be married to them. This made them excite those brave nymphs to strive to reach the farthest rank, where stood the king of the contrary party, promising them certainly to have them crowned if they could do this. The golden nymphs were beforehand with the others, and out of their number was created a queen, who was dressed in royal robes, and had a crown set on her head. You need not doubt the silvered nymphs made also what haste they could to be queens: one of them was within a step of the coronation place; but there the golden knight lay ready to intercept her, so that she could go no further.

The new golden queen, resolved to show herself valiant, and worthy of her advancement to the crown, achieved great feats of arms. But, in the mean time, the silvered knight takes the golden warden who guarded the camp: and thus there was a new silvered queen, who, like the other, strove to excel in heroic deeds at the beginning of her reign. Thus the fight grew hotter than before. A thousand stratagems, charges, rallyings, retreats, and attacks, were tried on both sides; till at last the silvered queen, having by stealth advanced as far as the golden king's tent, cried, God save you, sir! Now none but his new queen could relieve him: so she bravely came and exposed herself to the utmost extremity to deliver him out of it. Then the silvered warden, with his queen, reduced the golden king to such a stress, that, to save himself, he was forced to lose his queen: but the golden king took him at last. However, the rest of the golden party were soon taken; and that king being left alone, the silvered party made him a low bow, crying, Good-morrow, sir! which denoted that the silvered king had got the day.

This being heard, the music of both parties loudly proclaimed the victory. And thus the first battle ended to the unspeakable joy of all the spectators.

After this the two brigades took their former stations, and began to tilt a second time, much as they had done before, only the music played somewhat faster than at the first battle, and the motions were altogether different. I saw the golden queen sally out one of the first, with an archer and a knight, as it were angry at the former defeat, and she had like to have fallen upon the silvered king in his tent among his officers; but having been baulked in her attempt, she skirmished briskly, and overthrew so many silvered nymphs and officers, that it was a most amazing sight. You would have sworn she had been another Penthesilea; for she behaved herself with as much bravery as that Amazonian queen did at Troy.

But this havoc did not last long; for the silvered party, exasperated by their loss, resolved to perish, or stop her progress; and having posted an archer in ambuscade, on a distant angle, together with a knight-errant, her highness fell into their hands, and was carried out of the field. The rest were soon routed after the taking of their queen, who, without doubt, from that time resolved to be more wary, and keep near her king, without venturing so far amidst her enemies, unless with more force to defend her. Thus the silver brigade once more got the victory.

This did not dishearten or deject the golden party: far from it, they soon appeared again in the field to face their enemies; and being posted as before, both the armies seemed more resolute and cheerful than ever. Now the martial concert began, and the music was above a hemiole the quicker, according to the warlike Phrygian mode, such as was invented by Marsyas.

Then our combatants began to wheel about, and charge with such a swiftness, that in an instant they made four moves, besides the usual salutations. So that they were continually in action, flying, hovering, jumping, vaulting, curvetting, with petauristical turns and motions, and often intermingled.

Seeing them then turn about on one foot after they had made their honours, we compared them to your tops or gigs, such as boys use to whip about; making them turn round so swiftly, that they sleep, as they call it, and motion cannot be perceived, but resembles rest, its contrary: so that if you make a point or mark on some part of one of those gigs, it will be perceived not as a point, but a continual line in a most divine manner, as Cusanus has wisely observed.

While they were thus warmly engaged, we heard continually the claps and episemapsies, which those of the two bands reiterated at the taking of their enemies; and this, joined to the variety of their motions and music, would have forced smiles out of the most severe Cato, the never-laughing Crassus, the Athenian man-hater, Timon: nay, even whining Heraclitus, though he abhorred laughing, the action that is most peculiar to man. For who could have forborn? seeing those young warriors, with their nymphs and queens, so briskly and gracefully advance, retire, jump, leap, skip, spring, fly, vault, caper, move to the right, to the left, every way still in time, so swiftly, and yet so dexterously, that they never touched one another but methodically.

As the number of the combatants lessened, the pleasure of the spectators increased; for the stratagems and motions of the remaining forces were more singular. I shall only add, that this pleasing entertainment charmed us to such a degree, that our minds were ravished with admiration and delight; and the martial harmony moved our souls so powerfully, that we easily believed what is said of Ismenias's having excited Alexander to rise from table and run to his arms, with such a warlike melody. At last the golden king remained master of the field: and while we were minding those dancers, Queen Whims vanished, so that we saw her no more from that day to this.

Then Geber's michelots conducted us, and we were set down among her abstractors, as her queenship had commanded. After that we returned to the port of Mateotechny, and thence straight aboard our ships: for the wind was fair, and had we not hoisted out of hand, we could hardly have got off in three quarters of a moon in the wane.

CHAPTER XXVI

How we came to the Island of Odes, where the ways go up and down

WE sailed before the wind, between a pair of courses, and in two days made the Island of Odes, at which place we saw a very strange thing. The ways there are animals; so true is Aristotle's saying, that all self-moving things are animals. Now the ways walk there. Ergo, they are then animals. Some of them are strange unknown ways, like those of the planets; others are highways, crossways, and bye-ways. I perceived that the travellers and inhabitants of that country asked— Whither does this way go? Whither does that way go? Some answered, between Midy and Fevrolles, to the parish church, to the city, to the river, and so forth. Being thus in their right way, they used to reach their journey's end without any farther trouble, just like those who go by water from Lyons to Avignon or Arles.

Now, as you know that nothing is perfect here below, we heard there was a sort of people whom they called highwaymen, way-beaters, and makers of inroads in roads; and that the poor ways were sadly afraid of them, and shunned them as you do robbers. For these used to waylay them, as people lay trains for wolves, and set gins for woodcocks. I saw one who was taken up with a lord chief justice's warrant, for having unjustly, and in spite of Pallas, taken the schoolway, which is the longest. Another boasted that he had fairly taken the shortest, and that doing so, he first compassed his design. Thus, Carpalim, meeting once Epistemon looking upon a wall with his fiddle-diddle, or live urinal, in his hand, to make a little maid's water, cried, that he did not wonder now how the other came to be still the first at Pantagruel's levee, since he held his shortest and least used.

I found Bourges highway among these. It went with the deliberation of an abbot, but was made to scamper at the approach of some waggoners, who threatened to have it trampled under their horses' feet, and make their waggons run over it, as Tullia's chariot did over her father's body.

I also espied there the old way between Peronne and St. Quentin, which seemed to me a very good, honest, plain way, as smooth as a carpet, and as good as ever was trod upon by shoe of leather.

Among the rocks I knew again the good old way to la Ferrare, mounted on a huge bear. This at a distance would have put me in mind of St. Jerome's picture, had but the bear been a lion; for the poor way was all mortified, and wore a long hoary beard uncombed and entangled, which looked like the picture of winter, or at least like a white-frosted bush.

On that way were store of beads or rosaries, coarsely made of wild pine-tree; and it seemed kneeling, not standing, nor lying flat; but its sides and middle were beaten with huge stones, insomuch that it proved to us at once an object of fear and pity.

While we were examining it, a runner, bachelor of the place, took us aside, and showing us a white smooth way, somewhat filled with straw, said, Henceforth, gentlemen, do not reject the opinion of Thales the Milesian, who said that water is the beginning of all things; nor that of Homer, who tells us that all things derive their original from the ocean: for this same way which you see here had its beginning from water, and is to return whence she came, before two months come to an end; now carts are driven here where boats used to be rowed.

Truly, said Pantagruel, you tell us no news; we see five hundred such changes, and more, every year, in our world. Then reflecting on the different manner of going of those moving ways, he told us he believed that Philolaus and Aristarchus had philosophized in this island, and that Seleucus, indeed, was of opinion, the earth turns round about its poles, and not the heavens, whatever we may think to the contrary: As, when we are on the river Loire, we think the trees and the shore moves, though this is only an effect of our boat's motion.

As we went back to our ships, we saw three waylayers, who, having been taken in ambuscado, were going to be broken on the wheel; and a huge fornicator was burned with a lingering fire, for beating away and breaking one of its sides: we were told it was the way of the banks of the Nile in Egypt.

CHAPTER XXVII

How we came to the Island of Sandals; and of the order of Semi-quaver Friars

THENCE we went to the Island of Sandals, whose inhabitants live on nothing but ling-broth. However, we were very kindly received and entertained by Benius the Third, king of the island, who, after he had made us drink, took us with him to

show us a spick-and-span new monastery, which he had contrived for the Semiquaver Friars: so he called the religious
men whom he had there. For he said that, on the other side
of the water lived friars who styled themselves her sweet lady-
ship's most humble servants. Item, the goodly Friar-minors,
who are semibreves of bulls; the smoked-herring tribe of Minim
Friars; then the Crotchet Friars. So that these diminutives
could be no more than Semiquavers. By the statutes, bulls,
and patents of Queen Whims, they were all dressed like so many
house-burners, except that, as in Anjou your tilers used to
quilt their knees when they tile houses, so these holy friars
had usually quilted bellies, and thick quilted paunches were
among them in much repute. Their codpieces were cut slipper-
fashion, and every monk among them wore two—one sewed
before and another behind—reporting that some certain dreadful
mysteries were duly represented by this duplicity of codpieces.

They wore shoes as round as basons, in imitation of those
who inhabit the sandy sea. Their chins were closed shaved,
and their feet iron-shod; and to show they did not value fortune,
Benius made them shave and poll the hind part of their poles,
as bare as a bird's arse, from the crown to the shoulder-blades;
but they had leave to let their hair grow before, from the two
triangular bones in the upper part of the skull.

Thus did they not value fortune a button, and cared no more
for the goods of this world than you or I do for hanging. And
to show how much they defied that blind jilt, all of them wore,
not in their hands like her, but at their waist, instead of beads,
sharp razors, which they used to new grind twice a-day, and
set thrice a-night.

Each of them had a round ball on their feet, because Fortune
is said to have one under hers.

The flap of their cowls hanged forward, and not backwards,
like those of others; thus, none could see their noses, and they
laughed without fear both at fortune and the fortunate; neither
more nor less than our ladies laugh at bare-faced trulls, when
they have those mufflers on, which they call masks, and which
were formerly much more properly called charity, because
they cover a multitude of sins.

The hind part of their faces were always uncovered, as are
our faces, which made them either go with the belly or the
arse foremost, which they pleased. When their hind face went
forwards, you would have sworn this had been their natural
gait, as well on account of their round shoes as of the double

codpiece, and their face behind, which was as bare as the back
of my hand, and coarsely daubed over with two eyes and a
mouth, such as you see on some Indian nuts. Now, if they
offered to waddle along with their bellies forwards, you would
have then thought they were playing at blindman's buff. May
I never be hanged if it was not a comical sight.

Their way of living was thus. About owl-light they charitably
began to boot and spur one another; this being done, the least
thing they did was to sleep and snore; and thus sleeping, they
had barnacles on the handles of their faces, or spectacles at most.

You may swear we did not a little wonder at this odd fancy:
but they satisfied us presently, telling us that the day of
judgment is to take mankind napping; therefore, to show they
did not refuse to make their personal appearance, as fortune's
darlings used to do, they were always thus booted and spurred,
ready to mount whenever the trumpet should sound.

At noon, as soon as the clock struck, they used to awake.
You must know that their clock-bell, church-bells, and refectuary
bells, were all made according to the pontial device, that is,
quilted with the finest down, and their clappers of fox-tails.

Having then make shift to get up at noon, they pulled off
their boots, and those that wanted to speak with a maid, alias
piss, pissed; those that wanted to scumber, scumbered; and
those that wanted to sneeze, sneezed. But all, whether they
would or no, (poor gentlemen!) were obliged largely and plentifully to yawn; and this was their first breakfast, (O rigorous
statute!) Methought it was very comical to observe their
transactions: for, having laid their boots and spurs on a rack,
they went into the cloisters; there they curiously washed their
hands and mouths, then sat them down on a long bench, and
picked their teeth till the provost gave the signal, whistling
through his fingers; then every he stretched out his jaws as
much as he could, and they gaped and yawned for about half
an hour, sometimes more, sometimes less, according as the
prior judged the breakfast to be suitable to the day.

After that they went in procession, two banners being carried
before them in one of which was the picture of Virtue, and
that of Fortune in the other. The last went before, carried
by a semiquavering-friar, at whose heels was another, with
the shadow or image of Virtue in one hand, and an holy-water-
sprinkle in the other; I mean of that holy mercurial-water,
which Ovid describes in his Fasti. And as the preceding
Semiquaver rang a hand-bell, this shaked the sprinkle with his

fist. With that, says Pantagruel, This order contradicts the rule which Tully and the academics prescribed that Virtue ought to go before, and Fortune follow. But they told us they did as they ought. seeing their design was to breech, lash, and bethwack Fortune.

During the processions, they trilled and quavered most melodiously betwixt their teeth, I do not know what antiphonies, or chauntings, by turns; for my part, it was all Hebrew-Greek to me, the devil a word I could pick out of it; at last, pricking up my ears, and intensely listening, I perceived they only sang with the tip of theirs. Oh, what a rare harmony it was! How well it was tuned to the sound of their bells! You will never find those to jar, that you will not. Pantagruel made a notable observation upon the processions: For, says he, have you seen and observed the policy of these Semiquavers? To make an end of their procession, they went out at one of their church doors and came in at the other; they took a deal of care not to come in at the place whereat they went out. On my honour, these are a subtle sort of people, quoth Panurge; they have as much wit as three folks, two fools and a madman; they are as wise as the calf that ran nine miles to suck a bull, and when he came there it was a steer. This subtlety and wisdom of theirs, cried Friar John, is borrowed from the occult philosophy: may I be gutted like an oyster if I can tell what to make of it. Then the more it is to be feared, said Pantagruel; for subtlety suspected, subtlety foreseen, subtlety found out, loses the essence and very name of subtlety, and only gains that of blockishness. They are not such fools as you take them to be; they have more tricks than are good, I doubt.

After the procession they went sluggingly into the fratry room, by the way of walk and healthful exercise, and there kneeled under the tables, leaning their breasts on lanterns. While they were in that posture, in came a huge Sandal, with a pitchfork in his hand, who used to baste, rib-roast, swaddle, and swinge them well favouredly, as they said, and in truth treated them after a fashion. They began their meal as you end yours—with cheese, and ended it with mustard and lettuce, as Martial tells us the ancients did. Afterwards, a platter full of mustard was brought before every one of them, and thus they made good the proverb—after meat comes mustard.

Their diet was this.

On Sundays they stuffed their puddings with puddings, chitterlings, links, Bolognia sausages, forced-meats, liverings, hogs'-haslets, young quails, and teals: you must also always add cheese for the first course, and mustard for the last.

On Mondays they were crammed with pease and pork, *cum commento*, and interlineary glosses.

On Tuesdays they used to twist store of holy-bread, cakes, buns, puffs, lenten loaves, jumbals, and biscuits.

On Wednesdays my gentlemen had fine sheep's-heads, calves'-heads, and brocks'-heads, of which there is no want in that country.

On Thursdays they guzzled down seven sorts of porridge, not forgetting mustard.

On Fridays they munched nothing but services or sorb-apples; neither were these full ripe, as I guessed by their complexion.

On Saturdays they gnawed bones; not that they were poor or needy, for every mother's son of them had a very good fat belly-benefice.

As for their drink, it was an antifortunal; thus they called I do not know what sort of a liquor of the place.

When they wanted to eat or drink, they turned down the back-points or flaps of their cowls forwards, below their chins, and that served them instead of gorgets or slabbering-bibs.

When they had well dined, they prayed rarely all in quavers and shakes; and the rest of the day, expecting the day of judgment, they were taken up with acts of charity, and particularly

On Sundays, rubbers at cuffs.

On Mondays, lending each other flirts and fillips on the nose.

On Tuesdays, clapperclawing one another.

On Wednesdays, sniting and fly-flapping.

On Thursdays, worming and pumping.

On Fridays, tickling.

On Saturdays, jirking and firking one another.

Such was their diet when they resided in the convent, and if the prior of the monk-house sent any of them abroad, then they were strictly enjoined neither to touch nor eat any manner of fish, as long as they were on sea or rivers, and to abstain from all manner of flesh whenever they were at land; that every one might be convinced that, while they enjoyed the object, they denied themselves the power, and even the desire, and were no more moved with it than the Marpesian rock.

All this was done with proper antiphones, still sung and chaunted by ear, as we have already observed.

When the sun went to bed, they fairly booted and spurred

each other as before, and having clapped on their barnacles, even jogged to bed too. At midnight the Sandal came to them, and up they got, and having well whetted and set their razors, and been a processioning, they clapped the tables over themselves, and like wire-drawers under their work, fell to it as aforesaid.

Friar John des Entoumeures, having shrewdly observed these jolly Semiquaver Friars, and had a full account of their statutes, lost all patience, and cried out aloud—Bounce tail and God have mercy guts; if every fool should wear a bauble, fuel would be dear. A plague rot it, we must know how many farts go to an ounce. Would Priapus were here, as he used to be at the nocturnal festivals in Crete, that I might see him play backwards and wriggle and shake to the purpose. Ay, ay, this is the world, and that other is the country; may I never piss if this be not an antichthonian land, and our very antipodes. In Germany they pull down monasteries and unfrockify the monks; here they do quite kam, and act clean contrary to others, setting new ones up, against the hair.

CHAPTER XXVIII

How Panurge asked a Semiquaver Friar many questions, and was only answered in monosyllables

PANURGE, who had since been wholly taken up with staring at these royal Semiquavers, at last pulled one of them by the sleeve, who was as lean as a rake, and asked him.—

Hearkee me, Friar Quaver, Semiquaver, Demisemiquavering quaver. where is the punk!

The Friar, pointing downwards, answered, There.

Pan. Pray, have you many? *Fri.* Few.

Pan. How many scores have you? *Fri.* One.

Pan. How many would you have? *Fri.* Five.

Pan. Where do you hide them? *Fri.* Here.

Pan. I suppose they are not all of one age; but, pray, how is their shape? *Fri.* Straight.

Pan. Their complexion? *Fri.* Clear.

Pan. Their hair? *Fri.* Fair.

Pan. Their eyes? *Fri.* Black.

Pan. Their features? *Fri.* Good.

Pan. Their brows? *Fri.* Soft.

Pan. Their graces? *Fri.* Ripe.
Pan. Their looks? *Fri.* Free.
Pan. Their feet? *Fri.* Flat.
Pan. Their heels? *Fri.* Short.
Pan. Their lower parts? *Fri.* Rare.
Pan. And their arms? *Fri.* Long.
Pan. What do they wear on their hands? *Fri.* Gloves.
Pan. What sort of rings on their fingers? *Fri.* Gold.
Pan. What rigging do you keep them in? *Fri.* Cloth.
Pan. What sort of cloth is it? *Fri.* New.
Pan. What colour? *Fri.* Shy.
Pan. What kind of cloth is it? *Fri.* Fine.
Pan. What caps do they wear? *Fri.* Blue.
Pan. What is the colour of their stockings? *Fri.* Red.
Pab. What wear they on their feet? *Fri.* Pumps.
Pan. How do they use to be? *Fri.* Foul.
Pan. How do they use to walk? *Fri.* Fast.
Pan. Now let us talk of the kitchen, I mean that of the
harlots, and without going hand over head, let us a little examine
things by particulars. What is in their kitchens? *Fri.* Fire.
Pan. What fuel feeds it? *Fri.* Wood.
Pan. What sort of wood is it? *Fri.* Dry.
Pan. And of what kind of trees? *Fri.* Yew.
Pan. What are the faggots and brushes of? *Fri.* Holme.
Pan. What wood do you burn in your chambers? *Fri.* Pine.
Pan. And of what other trees? *Fri.* Lime.
Pan. Hearkee me; as for the buttocks, I will go your halves:
pray, how do you feed them? *Fri.* Well.
Pan. First, what do they eat? *Fri.* Bread.
Pan. Of what complexion? *Fri.* White.
Pan. And what else? *Fri.* Meat.
Pan. How do they love it dressed? *Fri.* Roast.
Pan. What sort of porridge? *Fri.* None.
Pan. Are they for pies and tarts? *Fri.* Much.
Pan. Then I am their man. Will fish go down with them?
Fri. Well.
Pan. And what else? *Fri.* Eggs.
Pan. How do they like them? *Fri.* Boiled.
Pan. How must they be done? *Fri.* Hard.
Pan. Is this all they have? *Fri.* No.
Pan. What have they besides, then? *Fri.* Beef.
Pan. And what else? *Fri.* Pork.
Pan. And what more? *Fri.* Geese.

Pan. What then? *Fri.* Ducks.

Pan. And what besides? *Fri.* Cocks.

Pan. What do they season their meat with? *Fri.* Salt.

Pan. What sauce are they most dainty for? *Fri.* Must.

Pan. What is their last course? *Fri.* Rice.

Pan. And what else? *Fri.* Milk.

Pan. What besides? *Fri.* Peas.

Pan. What sort? *Fri.* Green.

Pan. What do they boil with them? *Fri.* Pork.

Pan. What fruit do they eat? *Fri.* Good.

Pan. How? *Fri.* Raw.

Pan. What do they end with? *Fri.* Nuts.

Pan. How do they drink? *Fri.* Neat.

Pan. What liquor? *Fri.* Wine.

Pan. What sort? *Fri.* White.

Pan. In winter? *Fri.* Strong.

Pan. In the spring? *Fri.* Brisk.

Pan. In summer? *Fri.* Cool.

Pan. In autumn? *Fri.* New.

Buttock of a monk! cried Friar John, how plump these plaguy trulls, these arch Semiquavering strumpets must be! That damned cattle are so high fed that they must needs be high-mettled, and ready to wince, and give two ups for one go-down, when any one offers to ride them below the crupper.

Pr'ythee, Friar John, quoth Panurge, hold thy prating tongue, stay till I have done.

Till what time do the doxies sit up? *Fri.* Night.

Pan. When do they get up? *Fri.* Late.

Pan. May I ride on a horse that was foaled of an acorn, if this be not as honest a cod as ever the ground went upon, and as grave as an old gate-post into the bargain. Would to the blessed St. Semiquaver, and the blessed worthy virgin St. Semiquavera, he were lord chief president (justice) of Paris. Odsbodikins, how he would dispatch! With what expedition would he bring disputes to an upshot! What an abbreviator and clawer of law-suits, reconciler of differences, examiner and fumbler of bags, peruser of bills, scribbler of rough drafts, and engrosser of deeds, would he not make! Well, Friar, spare your breath to cool your porridge: come, let us now talk with deliberation, fairly and softly, as lawyers go to heaven. Let us know how you victual the venereal camp. How is the snatchblatch? *Fri.* Rough.

Pan. How is the gate-way? *Fri.* Free.

Pan. And how is it within? *Fri.* Deep.

Pan. I mean, what weather is it there? *Fri.* Hot.

Pan. What shadows the brooks? *Fri.* Groves.

Pan. Of what is the colour of the twigs? *Fri.* Red.

Pan. And that of the old? *Fri.* Grey.

Pan. How are you when you shake? *Fri.* Brisk.

Pan. How is their motion? *Fri.* Quick.

Pan. Would you have them vault or wriggle more? *Fri.* Less.

Pan. What kind of tools are yours? *Fri.* Big.

Pan. And in their helves? *Fri.* Round.

Pan. Of what colour is the tip? *Fri.* Red.

Pan. When they have been used, how are they? *Fri.* Shrunk.

Pan. How much weighs each bag of tools? *Fri.* Pounds.

Pan. How hang your pouches? *Fri.* Tight.

Pan. How are they when you have done? *Fri.* Lank.

Pan. Now, by the oath you have taken, tell me, when you have a mind to cohabit, how you throw them? *Fri.* Down.

Pan. And what do they say then? *Fri.* Fie.

Pan. However, like maids, they say nay, and take it; and speak the less, but think the more; minding the work in hand: do they not? *Fri.* True.

Pan. Do they get you bairns? *Fri.* None.

Pan. How do you pig together? *Fri.* Bare.

Pan. Remember you are upon your oath, and tell me justly, and bona fide, how many times a day you monk it? *Fri.* Six.

Pan. How many bouts a-nights? *Fri.* Ten.

Cat so, quoth Friar John, the poor fornicating brother is bashful, and sticks at sixteen, as if that were his stint. Right, quoth Panurge, but couldst thou keep pace with him, Friar John, my dainty cod? May the devil's dam suck my teat, if he does not look as if he had got a blow over the nose with a Naples cowl-staff.

Pan. Pray, Friar Shakewell, does your whole fraternity quaver and shake at that rate? *Fri.* All.

Pan. Who of them is the best cock of the game? *Fri.* I.

Pan. Do you never commit dry-bobs or flashes in the pan? *Fri.* None.

Pan. I blush like any black dog, and could be as testy as an old cook, when I think on all this; it passes my understanding. But, pray, when you have been pumped dry one day, what have you got the next? *Fri.* More.

Pan. By Priapus, they have the Indian herb, of which Theophrastus spoke, or I am much out. But hearkee me, thou man of brevity, should some impediment, honestly, or otherwise, impair your talents, and cause your benevolence to lessen, how would it fare with you, then? *Fri.* Ill.

Pan. What would the wenches do? *Fri.* Rail.

Pan. What if you skipped, and let them fast a whole day? *Fri.* Worse.

Pan. What do you give them then? *Fri.* Thwacks.

Pan. What say they to this? *Fri.* Bawl.

Pan. And what else? *Fri.* Curse.

Pan. How do you correct them? *Fri.* Hard.

Pan. What do you get out of them then? *Fri.* Blood.

Pan. How is their complexion then? *Fri.* Odd.

Pan. What do they mend it with? *Fri.* Paint.

Pan. Then, what do they do? *Fri.* Fawn.

Pan. By the oath you have taken, tell me truly, what time of the year do you do it least in? *Fri.* Now.

Pan. What season do you do it best in? *Fri.* March.

Pan. How is your performance the rest of the year? *Fri.* Brisk.

Then, quoth Panurge, sneering, Of all, and of all, commend me to ball; this is the friar of the world for my money: you have heard how short, concise, and compendious he is in his answers? Nothing is to be got out of him but monosyllables? By jingo, I believe he would make three bites of a cherry.

Damn him, cried Friar John, that is as true as I am his uncle: the dog yelps at another gat's rate when he is among his bitches; there he is polysyllable enough, my life for yours. You talk of making three bites of a cherry! God send fools more wit, and us more money; may I be doomed to fast a whole day, if I do not verily believe he would not make above two bites of a shoulder of mutton, and one swoop of a whole pottle of wine; zoons, do but see how down of the mouth the cur looks! He is nothing but skin and bones, he has pissed his tallow.

Truly, truly, quoth Epistemon, this rascally monastical vermin all over the world mind nothing but their gut, and are as ravenous as any kites, and then, forsooth, they tell us they have nothing but food and raiment in this world: 'sdeath, what more have kings and princes?

CHAPTER XXIX

How Epistemon disliked the institution of Lent

PRAY did you observe, continued Epistemon, how this damned ill-favoured Semiquaver mentioned March as the best month for caterwauling. True, said Pantagruel, yet Lent and March always go together, and the first was instituted to macerate and bring down our pampered flesh, to weaken and subdue its lusts, and to curb and assuage the venereal rage.

By this, said Epistemon, you may guess what kind of a pope it was who first enjoined it to be kept, since this filthy wooden-shoed Semiquaver owns that his spoon is never oftener nor deeper in the porringer of lechery than in Lent. Add to this, the evident reasons given by all good and learned physicians, affirming, that throughout the whole year no food is eaten, that can prompt mankind to lascivious acts, more than at that time.

As for example, beans, peas, phasels, or long-peason, ciches, onions, nuts, oysters, herrings, saltmeats, garum, (a kind of anchovy), and salads, wholly made up of venereous herbs and fruits, as,

Rocket,	Parsley,	Hop-buds,
Nose-smart,	Rampions,	Figs,
Taragon,	Poppy,	Rice,
Cresses,	Celery,	Raisins, and others.

It would not a little surprise you, said Pantagruel, should a man tell you, that the good pope, who first ordered the keeping of Lent, perceiving that at that time of the year the natural heat (from the centre of the body, whither it was retired during the winter's cold) diffuses itself, as the sap does in trees, through the circumference of the members, did therefore in a manner prescribe that sort of diet to forward the propagation of mankind. What makes me think so, is, that by the registers of christenings at Touars, it appears that more children are born in October and November than in the other ten months of the year, and, reckoning backwards, it will be easily found that they were all made, conceived, and begotten in Lent.

I listen to you with both my ears, quoth Friar John, and that with no small pleasure, I assure you. But I must tell you, that the vicar of Jambert ascribed this copious prolification of the women, not to that sort of food that we chiefly eat in Lent, but to the little licensed stooping members, your little-booted Lent-preachers, your little draggle-tailed father confessors, who, during all that time of their reign, damn all husbands that run astray, three fathoms and a half below the very lowest pit of hell. So the silly cod's-headed brothers of the noose dare not then stumble any more at the truckle-bed, to the no small discomfort of their maids, and are even forced, poor souls, to take up with their own bodily wives. Dixi, I have done.

You may descant on the institution of Lent as much as you please, cried Epistemon; so many men so many minds; but certainly all the physicians will be against its being suppressed, though I think that time is at hand: I know they will, and have heard them say, were it not for Lent, their art would soon fall into contempt, and they would get nothing, for hardly anybody would be sick.

All distempers are sowed in Lent; it is the true seminary and native bed of all diseases: nor does it only weaken and putrify bodies, but also makes souls mad and uneasy. For then the devils do their best, and drive a subtle trade, and the tribe of canting dissemblers come out of their holes. It is then term-time with your cucullated pieces of formality, that have one face to God and the other to the devil; and a wretched clutter they make with their sessions, stations, pardons, syntereses, confessions, whippings, anathematizations, and much prayer, with as little devotion. However, I will not offer to infer from this that the Arimaspians are better than we are in that point; yet I speak to the purpose.

Well, quoth Panurge to the Semiquaver friar, who happened to be by, dear bumbasting, shaking, trilling, quavering cod, what thinkest thou of this fellow? Is he not a rank heretic? *Fri.* Much.

Pan. Ought he not to be singed? *Fri.* Well.

Pan. As soon as may be? *Fri.* Right.

Pan. Should not he be scalded first? *Fri.* No.

Pan. How then, should he be roasted? *Fri.* Quick.

Pan. Till at last he be? *Fri.* Dead.

Pan. What has he made you? *Fri.* Mad.

Pan. What do you take him to be? *Fri.* Damned.

Pan. What place is he to go to? *Fri.* Hell.

Pan. But, first, how would you have him served here? *Fri.* Burnt.

Pan. Some have been served so? *Fri.* Store.

Pan. That were heretics? *Fri.* Less.

Pan. And the number of those that are to be warmed thus hereafter is? *Fri.* Great.

Pan. How many of them do you intend to save? *Fri.* None.
Pan. So you would have them burned? *Fri.* All.

I wonder, said Epistemon to Panurge, what pleasure you can find in talking thus with this lousy tatterdemallion of a monk; I vow, did I not know you well, I might be ready to think you had no more wit in your head, than he has in both his shoulders. Come, come, scatter no words, returned Panurge, every one as they like, as the woman said when she kissed her cow. I wish I might carry him to Gargantua: when I am married he might be my wife's fool. And make you one, cried Epistemon. Well said, quoth Friar John: now, poor Panurge, take that along with thee, thou art even fitted; it is a plain case thou wilt never escape wearing the bull's feather; thy wife will be as common as the highway, that is certain.

CHAPTER XXX

How we came to the land of Satin

HAVING pleased ourselves with observing that new order of Semiquaver Friars, we set sail, and in three days our skipper made the finest and most delightful island that ever was seen; he called it the Island of Frize; for all the ways were of frize.

In that island is the land of Satin, so celebrated by our court pages. Its trees and herbage never lose their leaves or flowers, and are all damask and flowered velvet. As for the beasts and birds, they are all of tapestry work. There we saw many beasts, birds on trees, of the same colour, bigness, and shape, of those in our country; with this difference, however, that these did eat nothing, and never sung, or bit like ours: and we also saw there many sorts of creatures which we never had seen before.

Among the rest, several elephants in various postures; twelve of which were the six males and six females that were brought to Rome by their governor in the time of Germanicus, Tiberius's nephew: some of them were learned elephants, some musicians, others philosophers, dancers, and shewers of tricks; and all sat down at table in good order, silently eating and drinking like so many fathers in a fratry-room.

With their snouts or proboscises, some two cubits long, they draw up water for their own drinking, and take hold of palm leaves, plums, and all manner of edibles, using them offensively or defensively, as we do our fists; with them tossing men high into the air in fight, and making them burst with laughing when they come to the ground.

They have joints in their legs, whatever some men who never saw any but painted, may have written to the contrary. Between their teeth they have two huge horns: thus Juba called them, and Pausanias tells us, they are not teeth, but horns: however, Philostratus will have them to be teeth, and not horns. It is all one to me, provided you will be pleased to own them to be true ivory. These are some three or four cubits long, and are fixed in the upper jaw-bone, and consequently not in the lowermost. If you hearken to those who will tell you to the contrary, you will find yourself damnably mistaken, for that is a lie with a latchet: though it were Ælian, that long-bow man, that told you so, never believe him, for he lies as fast as a dog can trot. It was in this very island that Pliny, his brother tell-truth, had seen some elephants dance on the rope with bells, and whip over the tables, presto, begone, while people were at feasts, without so much as touching the toping topers, or the topers toping.

I saw a rhinoceros there, just such a one as Harry Clerberg had formerly showed me: methought it was not much unlike a certain boar which I had formerly seen at Limoges, except the sharp horn on its snout, that was about a cubit long; by the means of which that animal dares encounter with an elephant, that is sometimes killed with its point thrust into its belly, which is its most tender and defenceless part.

I saw there two and thirty unicorns. They are a cursed sort of creatures, much resembling a fine horse, unless it be that their heads are like a stag's, their feet like an elephant's, their tails like a wild boar's, and out of each of their foreheads sprouts a sharp black horn, some six or seven feet long; commonly it dangles down like a turkey-cock's comb. When a unicorn has a mind to fight, or put it to any other use, what does he do but make it stand, and then it is as straight as an arrow.

I saw one of them, which was attended with a throng of other wild beasts, purify a fountain with its horn. With that Panurge told me, that this prancer, alias his nimble-wimble, was like the unicorn, not altogether in length indeed, but in virtue and propriety: for as the unicorn purified pools and fountains from filth and venom, so that other animals came and drank securely there afterwards; in the like manner, others might water their nags, and dabble after him without fear of shankers, carnosities, gonorrhœas, buboes, crinkams, and such other plagues, caught by those who venture to quench their amorous thirst in a common puddle; for with his nervous horn he removed all the infection that might be lurking in some blind cranny of the mephitic sweet-scented hole.

Well, quoth Friar John, when you are sped, that is when you are married, we will make a trial of this on thy spouse, merely for charity-sake, since you are pleased to give us so beneficial an instruction.

Aye, aye, returned Panurge, and then immediately I will give you a pretty gentle aggregative pill of God, made up of two and twenty kind stabs with a dagger, after the Cæsarian way. Cat so, cried Friar John, I had rather take off a bumper of good cool wine.

I saw there the golden fleece, formerly conquered by Jason, and can assure you on the word of an honest man, that those who have said it was not a fleece, but a golden pippin, because μῆλον signifies both an apple and a sheep, were utterly mistaken.

I saw also a chameleon, such as Aristotle describes it, and like that which had been formerly shown me by Charles Maris, a famous physician of the noble city of Lyons on the Rhone: and the said chameleon lived on air, just as the other did.

I saw three hydras, like those I had formerly seen. They are a kind of serpent, with seven different heads.

I saw also fourteen phœnixes. I had read in many authors that there was but one in the whole world in every century; but, if I may presume to speak my mind, I declare that those who said this had never seen any, unless it were in the land of tapestry; though it were vouched by Lactantius Firmianus.

I saw the skin of Apuleius's golden ass.

I saw three hundred and nine pelicans.

Item, six thousand and sixteen Seleucid birds marching in battalia, and picking up straggling grasshoppers in corn-fields.

Item, some cynamologi, argatiles, caprimulgi, thynnunculs, onocrotals, or bitterns, with their wide swallows, stymphalides, harpies, panthers, dorcasses, or bucks, cemades, cynocephalises, satyrs, cartasans, tarands, uri, monopses, pegasi, neades, cepes, marmosets, or monkeys, presteres, bugles, musimons, byturoses, ophyri, screech owls, goblins, fairies, and griffins.

I saw Mid-Lent on horseback, with Mid-August and Mid-March holding its stirrups.

I saw some mankind wolves, centaurs, tigers, leopards, hyænas, camelopardels, and orixes, or huge wild goats with sharp horns.

I saw a remora, a little fish called echineis by the Greeks, and
near it a tall ship, that did not get ahead an inch, though she
was in the offing with top and top-gallants spread before the
wind.   I am somewhat inclined to believe, that it was the very
numerical ship in which Periander the tyrant happened to be,
when it was stopped by such a little fish in spite of wind and
tide.   It was in this land of Satin, and in no other, that Mutianus
had seen one of them.

Friar John told us, that in the days of yore, two sorts of
fishes used to abound in our courts of judicature, and rotted the
bodies and tormented the souls of those who were at law, whether
noble or of mean descent, high or low, rich or poor; the first
were your April fish or mackerel, [pimps, panders, and bawds;]
the others your beneficial remoras, that is, the eternity of law-
suits; the needless lets that keep them undecided.

I saw some sphynges, some raphes, some ounces, and some
cepphi, whose fore-feet are like hands, and their hind-feet like
men's feet.

Also some crocutas and some eali as big as sea-horses, with
elephants' tails, boars' jaws and tusks, and horns as pliant as
an ass's ears.

The leucrocutes, most fleet animals, as big as our asses of
Mirebalais, have necks, tails, and breasts like a lion's, legs like
a stag's, the mouth up to the ears, and but two teeth, one above
and one below; they speak with human voices, but when they
do, they say nothing.

Some people say, that none ever saw an eyry, or nest of
sakers; if you will believe me, I saw no less than eleven, and
I am sure I reckoned right.

I saw some left-handed halberts, which were the first that
I had ever seen.

I saw some manticores, a most strange sort of creatures,
which have the body of a lion, red hair, a face and ears like a
man's, three rows of teeth which close together, as if you joined
your hands with your fingers between each other; they have a
sting in their tails like a scorpion's, and a very melodious voice.

I saw some catablepases, a sort of serpents, whose bodies
are small, but their heads large without any proportion, so that
they have much ado to lift them up; and their eyes are so
infectious, that whoever sees them, dies upon the spot, as if
he had seen a basilisk.

I saw some beasts with two backs, and those seemed to me
the merriest creatures in the world: they were most nimble at

wriggling the buttocks, and more diligent in tail-wagging than
any water-wagtails, perpetually jogging and shaking their
double rumps.

I saw there some milched craw-fish, creatures that I never
heard of before in my life; these moved in very good order, and
it would have done your heart good to have seen them.

CHAPTER XXXI

How in the land of Satin we saw Hearsay, who kept a school of vouching

WE went a little higher up into the country of Tapestry, and
saw the Mediterranean Sea open to the right and left, down to
the very bottom; just as the Red Sea very fairly left its bed at
the Arabian Gulf, to make a lane for the Jews, when they
left Egypt.

There I found Triton winding his silver shell instead of a
horn, and also Glaucus, Proteus, Nereus, and a thousand other
godlings and sea monsters.

I also saw an infinite number of fish of all kinds, dancing,
flying, vaulting, fighting, eating, breathing, billing, shoving,
milting, spawning, hunting, fishing, skirmishing, lying in
ambuscado, making truces, cheapening, bargaining, swearing,
and sporting.

In a blind corner we saw Aristotle holding a lantern, in the
posture in which the hermit uses to be drawn near St. Christopher, watching, prying, thinking, and setting every thing
down in writing.

Behind him stood a pack of other philosophers, like so many
bums by a head bailiff; as Appian, Heliodorus, Athenæus,
Porphyrius, Pancrates, Arcadian, Numenius, Possidonius,
Ovidius, Oppianus, Olympius, Seleucus, Leonides, Agathocles,
Theophrastus, Damostratus, Mutianus, Nymphodorus, Ælian,
and five hundred other such plodding dons, who were full of
business, yet had little to do; like Chrysippus or Aristarchus of
Soli, who for eight and fifty years together did nothing in the
world but examine the state and concerns of bees.

I spied Peter Gilles among them, with an urinal in his hand,
narrowly watching the water of those goodly fishes.

When we had long beheld every thing in this land of Satin,
Pantagruel said, I have sufficiently fed my eyes, but my belly

is empty all this while, and chimes to let me know it is time to go to dinner: let us take care of the body, lest the soul abdicate it; and to this effect, let us taste some of these ancampserotes that hang over our heads. Pshaw, cried one, they are mere trash, stark naught on my word, they are good for nothing.

I then went to pluck some myrobolans off of a piece of tapestry, whereon they hung, but the devil a bit I could chew or swallow them; and had you had them betwixt your teeth, you would have sworn they had been thrown silk; there was no manner of savour in them.

One might be apt to think Heliogabalus had taken a hint from thence, to feast those whom he had caused to fast a long time, promising them a sumptuous, plentiful, and imperial feast after it; for all the treat used to amount to no more than several sorts of meat in wax, marble, earthenware, painted and figured tablecloths.

While we were looking up and down to find some more substantial food, we heard a loud various noise, like that of papermills, or women bucking of linen: so with all speed we went to the place whence the noise came, where we found a diminutive, monstrous, mis-shapen old fellow, called Hearsay. His mouth was slit up to his ears, and in it were seven tongues, each of them cleft into seven parts. However he chattered, tattled, and prated with all the seven at once, of different matters, and in divers languages.

He had as many ears all over his head, and the rest of his body, as Argus formerly had eyes; and was as blind as a beetle, and had the palsy in his legs.

About him stood an innumerable number of men and women, gaping, listening, and hearing very intensely; among them I observed some who strutted like crows in a gutter, and principally a very handsome bodied man in the face, who held then a map of the world, and with little aphorisms compendiously explained every thing to them; so that those men of happy memories grew learned in a trice, and would most fluently talk with you of a world of prodigious things, the hundredth part of which would take up a man's whole life to be fully known.

Among the rest, they descanted with great prolixity on the pyramids and hieroglyphics of Egypt, of the Nile, of Babylon, of the Troglodytes, the Hymantopodes, or crump-footed nation, the Blemiæ, people that wear their heads in the middle of their breasts, the Pigmies, the Cannibals, the Hyperborei and their mountains, the Egypanes with their goat's feet, and the devil and all of others; every individual word of it by hear-say.

I am much mistaken if I did not see among them Herodotus, Pliny, Solinus, Borosus, Philostratus, Pomponius Mela, Strabo, and God knows how many other antiquaries.

Then Albert, the great Jacobin friar, Peter Tesmoin, alias Witness, Pope Pius the Second, Volaterranus, Paulus Jovius the valiant, Jemmy Cartier, Chaton the Armenian, Marco Polo the Venetian, Ludovico Romano, Pedro Aliares, and forty cart-loads of other modern historians, lurking behind a piece of tapestry, where they were at it, ding-dong, privately scribbling the Lord knows what, and making rare work of it, and all by hear-say.

Behind another piece of tapestry, (on which Naboth and Susanna's accusers were fairly represented,) I saw close by Hearsay, good store of men of the country of Perce and Maine, notable students, and young enough.

I asked what sort of study they applied themselves to? and was told, that from their youth they learned to be evidences, affidavit-men, and vouchers; and were instructed in the art of swearing; in which they soon became such proficients, that, when they left that country, and went back into their own, they set up for themselves, and very honestly lived by their trade of evidencing; positively giving their testimony of all things whatsoever, to those who feed them most roundly to do a job of journey-work for them: and all this by hearsay.

You may think what you will of it, but I can assure you, they gave some of us corners of their cakes, and we merrily helped to empty their hogsheads. Then, in a friendly manner, they advised us to be as sparing of truth as possibly we could, if ever we had a mind to get court preferment.

CHAPTER XXXII

How we came in sight of Lantern-land

HAVING been scurvily entertained in the land of Satin, we went on board, and having set sail, in four days came near the coast of Lantern-land. We then saw certain little hovering fires on the sea.

For my part I did not take them to be lanterns, but rather thought they were fishes, which lolled their flaming tongues on

the surface of the sea; or lampyrides, which some call cicindelas
or glow-worms, shining there as ripe barley does o'nights in
my country.

But the skipper satisfied us that they were the lanterns of
the watch, or more properly, light-houses, set up in many places
round the precinct of the place, to discover the land, and for
the safe piloting in of some outlandish lanterns, which, like good
Franciscan and Jacobin friars, were coming to make their
personal appearance at the provincial chapter.

However, some of us were somewhat suspicious that these
fires were the forerunners of some storm, but the skipper assured
us again they were not.

CHAPTER XXXIII

How we landed at the Port of the Lychnobii, and came to Lantern-land

Soon after we arrived at the port of Lantern-land, where
Pantagruel discovered, on a high tower, the lantern of Rochelle,
that stood us in good stead, for it cast a great light. We also
saw the lantern of Pharos, that of Nauplion, and that of Acropolis, at Athens, sacred to Pallas.

Near the port, there is a little hamlet inhabited by the Lych-
nobii, that live by lanterns, as the gulligutted friars in our
country live by nuns; they are studious people, and as honest
men as ever shit in a trumpet. Demosthenes had formerly
lanternised there.

We were conducted from that place to the palace by three
obeliscolichnys, military guards of the port, with high-crowned
hats, whom we acquainted with the cause of our voyage, and
our design; which was to desire the queen of the country to
grant us a lantern to light and conduct us, during our voyage to
the Oracle of the Bottle.

They promised to assist us in this, and added, that we could
never have come in a better time; for then the lanterns held
their provincial chapter.

When we came to the royal palace we had audience of her
highness the Queen of Lantern-land, being introduced by two
lanterns of honour, that of Aristophanes, and that of Cleanthes.
Panurge, in a few words, acquainted her with the causes of our
voyage, and she received us with great demonstrations of

friendship; desiring us to come to her at supper-time, that we might more easily make choice of one to be our guide; which pleased us extremely. We did not fail to observe intensely every thing we could see,—as the garbs, motions, and deportments of the queen's subjects,—principally the manner after which she was served.

The bright queen was dressed in virgin crystal of Tutia, wrought damaskwise, and beset with large diamonds.

The lanterns of the royal blood were clad partly with bastard-diamonds, partly with diaphanous stones; the rest with horn, paper, and oiled cloth.

The cresset-lights took place according to the antiquity and lustre of their families.

An earthen dark-lantern, shaped like a pot, notwithstanding this, took place of some of the first quality; at which I wondered much, till I was told it was that of Epictetus, for which three thousand drachmas had been formerly refused.

Martial's polymix lantern made a very good figure there; I took particular notice of its dress, and more yet of the icosimyx, formerly consecrated by Canopa, the daughter of Tisias.

I saw the pensile lantern, formerly taken out of the temple of Apollo Palatinus at Thebes, and afterwards by Alexander the Great carried to the town of Cymos.

I saw another that distinguished itself from the rest by a bushy tuft of crimson silk on its head. I was told it was that of Bartolus, the lantern of the civilians.

Two others were very remarkable for glisterpouches that dangled at their waist. We were told, that one was the greater light, and the other the lesser light of the apothecaries.

When it was supper-time, the queen's highness first sat down, and then the rest, according to their rank and dignity. For the first course, they were all served with large Christmas candles, except the queen, who was served with a hugeous, thick, stiff, flaming taper of white wax, somewhat red towards the tip; and the royal family, as also the provincial lantern of Mirebalais, who were served with nut-lights; and the provincial of Lower Poitou, with an armed candle.

After that, God wot, what a glorious light they gave with their wicks: I do not say all, for you must except a parcel of junior lanterns, under the government of a high and mighty one. These did not cast a light like the rest, but seemed to me dimmer than any long-snuff farthing candle, whose tallow has been half melted away in a hot-house.

After supper we withdrew to take some rest, and the next day the queen made us choose one of the most illustrious lanterns to guide us; after which we took our leave.

CHAPTER XXXIV

How we arrived at the Oracle of the Bottle

OUR glorious lantern lighting and directing us to our heart's content, we at last arrived at the desired island, where was the Oracle of the Bottle. As soon as friend Panurge landed, he nimbly cut a caper with one leg for joy, and cried to Pantagruel, Now we are where we have wished ourselves long ago. This is the place we have been seeking with such toil and labour. He then made a compliment to our lantern, who desired us to be of good cheer, and not be daunted or dismayed, whatever we might chance to see.

To come to the Temple of the Holy Bottle, we were to go through a large vineyard, in which were all sorts of vines, as the Falernian, Malvoysian, the Muscadine, those of Taige, Beaune, Mirevaux, Orleans, Picardent, Arbois, Coussi, Anjou, Grave, Corsica, Vierron, Nerac, and others. This vineyard was formerly planted by the good Bacchus, with so great a blessing, that it yields leaves, flowers, and fruit, all the year round, like the orange trees at Serene.

Our magnificent lantern ordered every one of us to eat three grapes, to put some vine-leaves in his shoes, and take a vine-branch in his left hand.

At the end of the close we went under an arch built after the manner of those of the ancients. The trophies of a toper were curiously carved on it.

First, on one side was to be seen a long train of flagons, leathern bottles, flasks, cans, glass bottles, barrels, nipperkins, pint-pots, quart-pots, pottles, gallons, and old-fashioned semaises, (swinging wooden pots, such as those out of which the Germans fill their glasses:) these hung on a shady arbour.

On another side was store of garlic, onions, shallots, hams, botargos, caviar, biscuits, neat's tongues, old cheese, and such like comfits, very artificially interwoven, and packed together with vine-stocks.

On another were a hundred sorts of drinking glasses, cups, cisterns, ewers, false cups, tumblers, bowls, mazers, mugs, jugs, goblets, talboys, and such other bacchic artillery.

On the frontispiece of the triumphal arch, under the zoophore, was the following couplet:

> You who presume to move this way,
> Get a good lantern, lest you stray.

We took special care of that, cried Pantagruel, when he read them; for there is not a better or a more divine lantern than ours in all Lantern-land.

This arch ended at a fine large round alley, covered over with the interlaid branches of vines, loaded and adorned with clusters of five hundred different colours, and of as many various shapes, not natural, but due to the skill of agriculture; some were golden, others blueish, tawny, azure, white, black, green, purple, streaked with many colours, long, round, triangular, cod-like, hairy, great-headed, and grassy. That pleasant alley ended at three old ivy-trees, verdant, and all loaden with rings. Our most illustrious lantern directed us to make ourselves high-crowned hats with some of their leaves, and cover our heads wholly with them, which was immediately done.

Jupiter's priestess, said Pantagruel, in former days, would not, like us, have walked under this arbour. There was a mystical reason, answered our most perspicuous lantern, that would have hindered her. For had she gone under it, the wine, or the grapes of which it is made, that is the same thing, had been over her head, and then she would have seemed over-topped and mastered by wine. Which implies, that priests, and all persons who devote themselves to the contemplation of divine things, ought to keep their minds sedate and calm, and avoid whatever may disturb and discompose their tranquillity; which nothing is more apt to do than drunkenness.

You also, continued our lantern, could not come into the Holy Bottle's presence, after you have gone through this arch, did not that noble priestess Bacbuc first see your shoes full of vine-leaves; which action is diametrically opposite to the other, and signifies that you despise wine, and having mastered it, as it were, tread it under foot.

I am no scholar, quoth Friar John, for which I am heartily sorry, yet I find, by my breviary, that in the Revelation, a woman was seen with the moon under her feet, which was a most wonderful sight. Now, as Bigot explained it to me, this was to signify, that she was not of the nature of other women; for they have all the moon at their heads, and, consequently, their brains are always troubled with a lunacy: this makes me willing to believe what you said, dear Madam Lantern.

CHAPTER XXXV

*How we went under-ground to come to the Temple of the Holy
Bottle, and how Chinon is the oldest city in the world*

WE went under ground through a plastered vault, on which
was coarsely painted a dance of women and satyrs, waiting on
old Silenus, who was grinning on horseback on his ass. This
made me say to Pantagruel, that this entry put me in mind of
the painted cellar, in the oldest city in the world, where such
paintings are to be seen, and in as cool a place.

Which is the oldest city in the world? asked Pantagruel. It
is Chinon, sir, or Cainon in Touraine, said I. I know, returned
Pantagruel, where Chinon lies, and the painted cellar also,
having myself drunk there many a glass of cool wine; neither
do I doubt but that Chinon is an ancient town—witness its
blazon. I own it is said twice or thrice,

> Chinon,
> Little town,
> Great renown,
> On old stone
> Long has stood;
> There's the Vienne, if you look down;
> If you look up, there's the wood.

But how, continued he, can you make it out that 'tis the oldest
city in the world? Where did you find this written? I have
found it in the sacred writ, said I, that Cain was the first that
built a town; we may then, reasonably conjecture, that from
his name he gave it that of Cainon. Thus, after his example,
most other founders of towns have given them their names:
Athena, that is Minerva in Greek, to Athens; Alexander to
Alexandria; Constantine to Constantinople; Pompey to Pom-
peiopolis in Cilicia; Adrian to Adrianople; Canaan, to the
Canaanites; Saba, to the Sabæans; Assur, to the Assyrians;
and so Ptolemais, Cæsarea, Tiberias, and Herodium in Judæa
got their names.

While we were thus talking, there came to us the great flask
whom our lantern called the philosopher, her holiness the
Bottle's governor. He was attended with a troop of the temple-
guards, all French bottles in wicker armour; and seeing us with
our javelins wrapped with ivy, with our illustrious lantern,
whom he knew, he desired us to come in with all manner of

safety, and ordered we should be immediately conducted to
the Princess Bacchus, the Bottle's Lady of Honour, and priestess
of all the mysteries; which was done.

CHAPTER XXXVI

How we went down the Tetradic steps, and of Panurge's fear

WE went down one marble step under ground, where there was
a resting, or, as our workmen call it, a landing-place, then,
turning to the left, we went down two other steps, where there
was another resting-place; after that we came to three other
steps, turning about, and met a third; and the like at four
steps which we met afterwards. There, quoth Panurge, is it
here? How many steps have you told? asked our magnificent
lantern. One, two, three, four, answered Pantagruel. How
much is that? asked she. Ten, returned he. Multiply that,
said she, according to the same Pythagorical tetrad. That is,
ten, twenty, thirty, forty, cried Pantagruel. How much is the
whole? said she. One hundred, answered Pantagruel. Add,
continued she, the first cube—that is eight: at the end of that
fatal number you will find the temple gate; and pray, observe,
this is the true psychogony of Plato, so celebrated by the
Academics, yet so little understood; one moiety of which consists
of the unity of the two first numbers full of two square and
two cubic numbers. We then went down those numerical
stairs, all under ground; and I can assure you, in the first place,
that our legs stood us in good stead; for had it not been for
them, we had rolled just like so many hogsheads into a vault.
Secondly, our radiant lantern gave us just so much light as is
in St. Patrick's hole in Ireland, or Trophonius's cavern in Bœotia;
which caused Panurge to say to her, after we had got down
some seventy-eight steps:

Dear madam, with a sorrowful, aching heart, I most humbly
beseech your lanternship to lead us back. May I be led to
hell, if I be not half dead with fear; my heart is sunk down
into my hose; I am afraid I shall make buttered eggs in my
breeches. I freely consent never to marry. You have given
yourself too much trouble on my account; the Lord shall
reward you in his great rewarding-place; neither will I be
ungrateful when I come out of this cave of Troglodytes. Let
us go back, I pray you. I am very much afraid this is Tænarus,

the low way to hell, and methinks I already hear Cerberus bark.
Hark! I hear the cur, or my ears tingle; I have no manner of
kindness for the dog, for there never is a greater tooth-ache than
when dogs bite us by the shins: and if this be only Trophonius's
pit, the lemures, hob-thrushes, and goblins will certainly swallow
us alive: just as they devoured formerly one of Demetrius's
halbardiers, for want of luncheons of bread.   Art thou here,
Friar John?   Pr'ythee, dear, dear cod, stay by me; I am almost
dead with fear.   Hast thou got thy bilbo?   Alas! poor pilgarlic
is defenceless: I am a naked man thou knowest: let us go back.
Zoons, fear nothing, cried Friar John, I am by thee, and have
thee fast by the collar; eighteen devils shall not get thee out of
my clutches, though I were unarmed.   Never did a man yet
want weapons who had a good arm with as stout a heart;
heaven would sooner send down a shower of them; even as in
Provence, in the fields of la Crau, near Mariannes, there rained
stones (they are there to this day) to help Hercules, who otherwise wanted wherewithal to fight Neptune's two bastards.
But whither are we bound?   Are we a-going to the little
children's limbo?   By Pluto, they will bepaw and conskite us
all.   Or are we going to hell for orders?   By cob's body, I will
hamper, bethwack, and belabour all the devils, now I have some
vine-leaves in my shoes.   Thou shalt see me lay about me like
mad, old boy.   Which way? where the devil are they?   I fear
nothing but their damned horns: but cuckoldy Panurge's bull-
feather will altogether secure me from them.

Lo! in a prophetic spirit I already see him, like another
Actæon, horned, horny, hornified.   Pr'ythee, quoth Panurge,
take heed thyself, dear frater, lest, till monks have leave to
marry, thou weddest something thou dost not like, as some
quartan ague; if thou dost, may I never come safe and sound
out of this hypogeum, this subterranean cave, if I do not tup
and ram that disease merely for the sake of making thee a
cornuted, corniferous property; otherwise I fancy the quartan
ague is but an indifferent bed-fellow.   I remember Gripe-men-
all threatened to wed thee to some such thing; for which thou
calledst him heretic.

Here our splendid lantern interrupted them, letting us know
this was the place where we were to have a taste of the creature,
and be silent; bidding us not despair of having the word of the
Bottle before we went back, since we had lined our shoes with
vine-leaves.

Come on, then, cried Panurge, let us charge through and

through all the devils of hell: we can but perish, and that is soon done: however, I thought to have reserved my life for some mighty battle. Move, move, move forwards; I am as stout as Hercules, my breeches are full of courage: my heart trembles a little, I own, but that is only an effect of the coldness and dampness of this vault; it is neither fear nor ague. Come on, move on, piss, pish, push on. My name is William Dreadnought.

CHAPTER XXXVII

How the temple gates in a wonderful manner opened of themselves

AFTER we were got down the steps, we came to a portal of fine jasper, of Doric order, on whose front we read this sentence in the finest gold, EN 'OINΩ 'AΛHΘEIA: that is, In wine, truth. The two folding doors of the gate were of Corinthian-like brass, massy, wrought with little vine-branches, finely embossed and engraven, and were equally joined and closed together in their mortise without any padlock, key-chain, or tie whatsoever. Where they joined, there hanged an Indian loadstone as big as an Egyptian bean, set in gold, having two points, hexagonal, in a right line; and on each side, towards the wall, hung a handful of scordium.

There our noble lantern desired us not to take it amiss that she went no farther with us, leaving us wholly to the conduct of the priestess Bacbuc: for she herself was not allowed to go in, for certain causes rather to be concealed than revealed to mortals. However, she advised us to be resolute and secure, and to trust to her for the return. She then pulled the load-stone that hung at the folding of the gates, and threw it into a silver box fixed for that purpose: which done, from the threshold of each gate she drew a twine of crimson silk, about nine feet long, by which the scordium hung, and having fastened it to two gold buckles that hung at the sides, she withdrew.

Immediately the gates flew open without being touched; not with a creaking, or loud harsh noise, like that made by heavy brazen gates; but with a soft pleasing murmur that resounded through the arches of the temple.

Pantagruel soon knew the cause of it, having discovered a small cylinder or roller that joined the gates over the threshold;

and, turning like them towards the wall on a hard well-polished ophites stone, with rubbing and rolling, caused that harmonious murmur.

I wondered how the gates thus opened of themselves to the right and left, and after we were all got in, I cast my eye between the gates and the wall, to endeavour to know how this happened; for one would have thought our kind lantern had put between the gates the herb æthiopis, which they say opens some things that are shut; but I perceived that the parts of the gates that joined on the inside were covered with steel; and just where the said gates touched when they were opened, I saw two square Indian loadstones, of a blueish hue, well polished, and half a span broad, mortised in the temple wall. Now, by the hidden and admirable power of the loadstones, the steel plates were put into motion, and consequently the gates were slowly drawn; however, not always, but when the said loadstone on the outside was removed, after which the steel was freed from its power, the two bunches of scordium being at the same time put at some distance, because it deadens the magnet, and robs it of its attractive virtue.

On the loadstone that was placed on the right side, the following iambic verse was curiously engraven in ancient Roman characters:

> Ducunt volentem fata, nolentem trahunt.
> Fate leads the willing, and the unwilling draws.

The following sentence was neatly cut in the loadstone that was on the left:

ALL THINGS TEND TO THEIR END

CHAPTER XXXVIII

Of the Temple's admirable Pavement

WHEN I had read those inscriptions, I admired the beauty of the temple, and particularly the disposition of its pavement, with which no work that is now, or has been under the cope of heaven, can justly be compared; not that of the Temple of Fortune at Præneste in Sylla's time; or the pavement of the Greeks, called asarotum, laid by Sosistratus in Pergamus. For this here was wholly in compartments of precious stones, all in their natural colours. One of red jasper, most charmingly

spotted. Another of ophites. A third of porphyry. A fourth
of lycophthalmy, a stone of four different colours, powdered
with sparks of gold, as small as atoms. A fifth of agate, streaked
here and there with small milk-coloured waves. A sixth of
costly chalcedony. And another of green jasper, with certain
red and yellowish veins. And all these were disposed in a
diagonal line.

At the portico, some small stones were inlaid, and evenly
joined on the floor, all in their native colours, to embellish the
design of the figures; and they were ordered in such a manner,
that you would have thought some vine leaves and branches
had been carelessly strewed on the pavement; for in some places
they were thick, and thin in others. That inlaying was very
wonderful everywhere: here were seen, as it were in the shade,
some snails crawling on the grapes; there, little lizards running
on the branches: on this side, were grapes that seemed yet
greenish; on another, some clusters that seemed full ripe, so
like the true, that they could as easily have deceived starlings,
and other birds, as those which Zeuxis drew.

Nay, we ourselves were deceived; for where the artist seemed
to have strewed the vine-branches thickest, we could not forbear walking with great strides, lest we should entangle our
feet, just as people go over an unequal stony place.

I then cast my eyes on the roof and walls of the temple,
that were all pargetted with porphyry and mosaic work; which
from the left side at the coming in, most admirably represented
the battle, in which the good Bacchus overthrew the Indians;
as followeth.

CHAPTER XXXIX

How we saw Bacchus's army drawn up in Battalia in Mosaic work

At the beginning, divers towns, hamlets, castles, fortresses,
and forests were seen in flames; and several mad and loose
women, who furiously ripped up, and tore live calves, sheep,
and lambs, limb from limb, and devoured their flesh. There
we learned how Bacchus, at his coming into India, destroyed
all things with fire and sword.

Notwithstanding this, he was so despised by the Indians,
that they did not think it worth their while to stop his progress,

having been certainly informed by their spies, that his camp was destitute of warriors, and that he had only with him a crew of drunken females, a low-built, old, effeminate, sottish fellow, continually addled, and as drunk as a wheelbarrow, with a pack of young clownish doddipoles, stark naked, always skipping and frisking up and down, with tails and horns like those of young kids.

For this reason the Indians had resolved to let them go through their country without the least opposition, esteeming a victory over such enemies more dishonourable than glorious.

In the mean time, Bacchus marched on, burning every thing; for, as you know, fire and thunder are his paternal arms; Jupiter having saluted his mother Semele with his thunder; so that his maternal house was ruined by fire. Bacchus also caused a great deal of blood to be spilt; which, when he is roused and angered, principally in war, is as natural to him, as to make some in time of peace.

Thus the plains of the island of Samos, are called Panema, which signifies all bloody, because Bacchus there overtook the Amazons, who fled from the country of Ephesus, and there let them blood, so that they all died of phlebotomy. This may give you a better insight into the meaning of an ancient proverb, than Aristotle has done in his problems; viz., Why, it was formerly said, Neither eat, nor sow any mint in time of war. The reason is, that blows are given in time of war without any distinction of parts or persons; and if a man that is wounded has that day handled or eaten any mint, it is impossible, or at least very hard, to stanch his blood.

After this, Bacchus was seen marching in battalia, riding in a stately chariot, drawn by six young leopards. He looked as young as a child, to show that all good topers never grow old: he was as red as a cherry, or a cherub, which you please; and had no more hair on his chin, than there is in the inside of my hand: his forehead was graced with pointed horns, above which, he wore a fine crown or garland of vine-leaves and grapes, and a mitre of crimson velvet, having also gilt buskins on.

He had not one man with him, that looked like a man; his guards, and all his forces, consisted wholly of Bassarides, Evantes, Euhyades, Edonides, Trietherides, Ogygiæ, Mimallonides, Mænades, Thyades, and Bacchides, frantic, raving, raging, furious, mad women, begirt with live snakes and serpents, instead of girdles, their dishevelled hair flowing about their shoulders, with garlands of vine-branches instead of forehead-cloths, clad with stags' or goats' skins, and armed with torches, javelins, spears, and halberts, whose ends were like pine-apples: besides, they had certain small light bucklers, that gave a loud sound if you touched them never so little, and these served them instead of drums; they were just seventy-nine thousand two hundred and twenty-seven.

Silenus, who led the van, was one on whom Bacchus relied very much, having formerly had many proofs of his valour and conduct. He was a diminutive, stooping, palsied, plump, gorbellied, old fellow, with a swinging pair of stiff-standing lugs of his own, a sharp Roman nose, large rough eyebrows, mounted on a well-hung ass; in his fist he held a staff to lean upon, and also bravely to fight, whenever he had occasion to alight; and he was dressed in a woman's yellow gown. His followers were all young, wild, clownish people, as hornified as so many kids, and as fell as so many tigers, naked, and perpetually singing and dancing country dances: they were called tityri and satyrs; and were in all eighty-five thousand, one hundred and thirty-three.

Pan, who brought up the rear, was a monstrous sort of a thing: for his lower parts were like a goat's, his thighs hairy, and his horns bolt upright; a crimson fiery phiz, and a beard that was none of the shortest. He was a bold, stout, daring, desperate fellow, very apt to take pepper in the nose for yea and nay.

In his left hand he held a pipe, and a crooked stick in his right. His forces consisted also wholly of satyrs, ægipanes, agripanes, sylvans, fauns, lemures, lares, elves, and hobgoblins; and their number was seventy-eight thousand, one hundred and fourteen. The signal or word common to all the army, was Evohé.

CHAPTER XL

How the battle, in which the good Bacchus overthrew the Indians, was represented in Mosaic work

IN the next place we saw the representation of the good Bacchus's engagement with the Indians. Silenus, who led the van, was sweating, puffing, and blowing, belabouring his ass most grievously; the ass dreadfully opened its wide jaws, drove away the flies that plagued it, winced, flounced, went back, and bestirred itself in a most terrible manner, as if some damned gad-bee had stung it at the breech.

The satyrs, captains, sergeants, and corporals of companies, sounding the orgies with cornets, in a furious manner went round the army, skipping, capering, bounding, jerking, farting, flying out at heels, kicking, and prancing like mad, encouraging their company to fight bravely; and all the delineated army cried out Evohé.

First, the Mænades charged the Indians with dreadful shouts, and a horrid din of their brazen drums and bucklers: the air rung again all round, as the mosaic work well expressed it. And pray, for the future do not so much admire Apelles, Aristides the Theban, and others who drew claps of thunder, lightnings, winds, words, manners, and spirits.

We then saw the Indian army, who had at last taken the field, to prevent the devastation of the rest of their country. In the front were the elephants, with castles well garrisoned on their backs. But the army and themselves were put into disorder; the dreadful cries of the Bacchides having filled them with consternation, and those huge animals turned tail, and trampled on the men of their party.

There you might have seen gaffer Silenus on his ass, putting on as hard as he could, striking athwart and alongst, and laying about him lustily with his staff, after the old fashion of fencing. His ass was prancing and making after the elephants, gaping and martially braying, as it were to sound a charge, as he did when formerly in the bacchanalian feasts, he waked the nymph Lottis, when Priapus, full of priapism, had a mind to priapise, while the pretty creature was taking a nap.

There you might have seen Pan frisk it with his goatish shanks about the Mænades, and with his rustic pipe excite them to behave themselves like Mænades.

A little further you might have blessed your eyes with the sight of a young satyr who led seventeen kings his prisoners; and a Bacchis, who with her snakes, hauled along no less than two and forty captains; a little faun, who carried a whole dozen of standards taken from the enemy; and goodman Bacchus on his chariot, riding to and fro fearless of danger, making much of his dear carcase, and cheerfully toping to all his merry friends.

Finally, we saw the representation of his triumph, which was thus. First, his chariot was wholly covered with ivy, gathered on the mountain Meros: this for its scarcity, which

you know raises the price of every thing, and principally of
those leaves in India. In this, Alexander the Great followed
his example at his Indian triumph. The chariot was drawn
by elephants joined together, wherein he was imitated by
Pompey the Great, at Rome, in his African triumph. In it
the good Bacchus was seen drinking out of a mighty urn, which
action Marius aped after his victory over the Cimbri, near
Aix in Provence. All his army were crowned with ivy; their
javelins, bucklers, and drums, were also wholly covered with
it; there was not so much as Silenus's ass, but was betrapped
with it.

The Indian Kings were fastened with chains of gold close by
the wheels of the chariot; all the company marched in pomp
with unspeakable joy, loaded with an infinite number of trophies,
pageants, and spoils, playing and singing merry epiniciums,
songs of triumph, and also rural lays and dithyrambs.

At the farthest end was a prospect of the land of Egypt;
the Nile with its crocodiles, marmosets, ibides, monkeys,
trochilos's, or wrens, ichneumons, or Pharaoh's mice, hippo-
potami, or sea-horses, and other creatures, its guests and neighbours. Bacchus was moving towards that country under the
conduct of a couple of horned beasts, on one of which was
written in gold, Apis, and Osiris on the other; because no ox or
cow had been seen in Egypt till Bacchus came thither.

CHAPTER XLI

How the temple was illuminated with a wonderful Lamp

BEFORE I proceed to the description of the Bottle, I will give
you that of an admirable lamp, that dispensed so large a light
over all the temple, that, though it lay under ground, we could
distinguish every object as clearly as above it at noon day.

In the middle of the roof was fixed a ring of massy gold, as
thick as my clenched fist. Three chains somewhat less, most
curiously wrought, hung about two feet and a half below it,
and in a triangle supported a round plate of fine gold, whose
diameter or breadth did not exceed two cubits and half a span.
There were four holes in it, in each of which an empty ball
was fastened, hollow within, and open at the top, like a little
lamp; its circumference about two hands' breadth: each ball
was of precious stone; one an amethyst, another an African

carbuncle, the third an opal, and a fourth an anthracites; they
were full of burning water, five times distilled in a serpentine
lymbeck, and inconsumptible, like the oil formerly put into
Pallas' golden lamp at Acropolis of Athens by Callimachus.
In each of them was a flaming wick, partly of asbestine flax, as
of old in the temple of Jupiter Ammon, such as those which
Cleombrotus, a most studious philosopher, saw; partly of
Carpasian flax, which were rather renewed than consumed by
the fire.

About two feet and a half below that gold plate, the three
chains were fastened to three handles, that were fixed to a
large round lamp of most pure crystal, whose diameter was
a cubit and a half, and opened about two hands' breadth on
the top; by which open place a vessel of the same crystal,
shaped somewhat like the lower part of a gourd-like lymbeck,
or an urinal, was put at the bottom of the great lamp, with such
a quantity of the afore-mentioned burning water, the flame of
asbestine wick reached the centre of the great lamp. This
made all its spherical body seem to burn and be in a flame,
because the fire was just at the centre and middle point, so that
it was not more easy to fix the eye on it than on the disc of the
sun, the matter being wonderfully bright and shining, and the
work most transparent and dazzling, by the reflection of the
various colours of the precious stones, whereof the four small
lamps above the main lamp were made, and their lustre was
still variously glittering all over the temple. Then this wandering light being darted on the polished marble and agate,
with which all the inside of the temple was pargetted, our eyes
were entertained with a sight of all the admirable colours which
the rainbow can boast, when the sun darts his fiery rays on some
dropping clouds.

The design of the lamp was admirable in itself, but, in my
opinion, what added much to the beauty of the whole, was,
that round the body of the crystal lamp, there was carved in
cataglyphic work, a lively and pleasant battle of naked boys,
mounted on little hobby-horses, with little whirligig lances and
shields, that seemed made of vine-branches with grapes on them;
their postures generally were very different, and their childish
strife and motions were so ingeniously expressed, that art
equalled nature in every proportion and action. Neither did
this seem engraved, but rather hewed out and embossed in
relief, or, at least, like grotesque, which, by the artist's skill,
has the appearance of the roundness of the object it represents;

this was partly the effect of the various and most charming light, which, flowing out of the lamp, filled the carved places with its glorious rays.

CHAPTER XLII

How the Priestess Bacbuc showed us a fantastic fountain in the temple, and how the fountain-water had the taste of wine, according to the imagination of those who drank of it

WHILE we were admiring this incomparable lamp, and the stupendous structure of the temple, the venerable priestess Bacbuc, and her attendants, came to us with jolly smiling looks, and seeing us duly accoutred, without the least difficulty, took us into the middle of the temple, where, just under the aforesaid lamp, was the fine fantastic fountain. She then ordered some cups, goblets, and talboys of gold, silver, and crystal to be brought, and kindly invited us to drink of the liquor that sprung there, which we readily did: for, to say the truth, this fantastic fountain was very inviting, and its materials and workmanship more precious, rare, and admirable than any thing Plato ever dreamt of in limbo.

Its basis or ground-work was of most pure and limpid alabaster, and its height somewhat more than three spans, being a regular heptagon on the outside, with its stylobates or footsteps, arulets, cymasults or blunt tops, and doric undulations about it. It was exactly round within. On the middle point of each angle brink stood a pillar orbiculated, in form of a circle of ivory or alabaster. These were seven in number, according to the number of the angles.

Each pillar's length, from the basis to the architraves, was near seven hands, taking an exact dimension of its diameter through the centre of its circumference and inward roundness; and it was so disposed, that, casting our eyes behind one of them, whatever its cube might be, to view its opposite, we found that the pyramidal cone of our visual light ended at the said centre, and there, by the two opposites, formed an equilateral triangle, whose two lines divided the pillar into two equal parts.

That which we had a mind to measure, going from one side to another, two pillars over, at the first third part of the distance between them, was met by their lowermost and fundamental

... in a consult line drawn as far as the universal
... ally divided, gave, in a just partition, the distance
line, which ... in opposite pillars in a right line, beginning at the
centre, ... le on the brink, as you know that an angle is always
of th ... ed between two others in all angular figures odd in
oh ...

... itly gives us to understand, that seven semidiameters
... metrical proportion, compass, and distance, somewhat
... the circumference of a circle, from the figure of which
... extracted; that is to say, three whole parts, with an
... nd a half, a little more, or a seventh and a half, a little
..., according to the instructions given us of old by Euclid,
Aristotle, Archimedes, and others.

The first pillar, I mean that which faced the temple gate,
was of azure, sky-coloured sapphire.

The second, of hyacinth, a precious stone, exactly of the
colour of the flower into which Ajax's choleric blood was transformed; the Greek letters A I being seen on it in many places.

The third, an anachite diamond, as bright and glittering as
lightning.

The fourth, a masculine ruby ballais (peach-coloured)
amethystizing, its flame and lustre ending in violet or purple,
like an amethyst.

The fifth, an emerald, above five hundred and fifty times
more precious than that of Serapis in the labyrinth of the
Egyptians, and more verdant and shining than those that
were fixed instead of eyes, in the marble lion's head, near
King Hermias's tomb.

The sixth, of agate, more admirable and various in the
distinctions of its veins, clouds, and colours, than that which
Pyrrhus, King of Epirus, so mightily esteemed.

The seventh, of syenites, transparent, of the colour of a
beryl, and the clear hue of Hymettian honey; and within it
the moon was seen, such as we see her in the sky, silent, new,
and in the wane.

These stones were assigned to the seven heavenly planets
by the ancient Chaldeans; and that the meanest capacities
might be informed of this, just at the central perpendicular
line, on the chapiter of the first pillar, which was of sapphire,
stood the image of Saturn in elutian lead, with his scythe in
his hand, and at his feet a crane of gold, very artfully enamelled,
according to the native hue of the saturnine bird.

On the second, which was of hyacinth, towards the left,

Jupiter was seen in jovetian brass, and on his brea...
of gold enamelled to the life.

On the third, was Phœbus in the purest gold, a whit... his right hand.

On the fourth, was Mars in Corinthian brass, and a l... his feet.

On the fifth, was Venus in copper, the metal of which A... tonidas made Athamas's statue, that expressed in a blushi... whiteness his confusion at the sight of his son Learchus, who died at his feet of a fall.

On the sixth, was Mercury in hydrargyre; I would have said quicksilver, had it not been fixed, malleable, and unmoveable; that nimble deity had a stork at his feet.

On the seventh, was Luna in silver, with a greyhound at her feet.

The size of these statues was somewhat more than a third part of the pillars on which they stood, and they were so admirably wrought, according to mathematical proportion, that Polycletus's canon (or rule) could hardly have stood in competition with them.

The basis of the pillars, the chapiters, the architraves, zoophores, and cornices, were Phrygian work of massy gold, purer and finer than any that is found in the rivers Leede near Montpellier, Ganges in India, Po in Italy, Hebrus in Thrace, Tagus in Spain, and Pactolus in Lydia.

The small arches between the pillars were of the same precious stone of which the pillars next to them were. Thus, that arch was of sapphire which ended at the hyacinth pillar, and that was of hyacinth which went towards the diamond, and so on.

Above the arches and chapiters of the pillars, on the inward front, a cupola was raised to cover the fountain; it was surrounded by the planetary statues, heptagonal at the bottom, and spherical on the top, and crystal so pure, transparent, well-polished, whole and uniform in all its parts, without veins, clouds, flaws, or streaks, that Zenocrates never saw such a one in his life.

Within it were seen the twelve signs of the Zodiac, the twelve months of the year, with their properties, the two equinoxes, the ecliptic line, with some of the most remarkable fixed stars about the antartic pole, and elsewhere, so curiously engraven, that I fancied them to be the workmanship of King Necepsus, or Petosiris, the ancient mathematician.

On the top of the cupola, just over the centre of the fountain, were three noble long pearls, all of one size, pear fashion, perfectly imitating a tear, and so joined together as to represent a flower-de-lis or lily, each of the flowers seeming above a hand's breadth. A carbuncle jetted out of its calix or cup, as big as an ostrich's egg, cut seven square, (that number so beloved of nature,) and so prodigiously glorious, that the sight of it had like to have made us blind, for the fiery sun, or the pointed lightning, are not more dazzling and insufferably bright.

Now were some judicious appraisers to judge of the value of this incomparable fountain, and the lamp of which we have spoke, they would undoubtedly affirm, it exceeds that of all the treasures and curiosities in Europe, Asia, and Africa put together. For that carbuncle alone would have darkened the pantarbe of Iarchus the Indian magician, with as much ease as the sun outshines and dims the stars with his meridian rays.

Now let Cleopatra, that Egyptian queen, boast of her pair of pendants, those two pearls, one of which she caused to be dissolved in vinegar, in the presence of Anthony the Triumvir, her gallant!

Or let Pompeia Plautina be proud of her dress covered all over with emeralds and pearls curiously intermixed, she who attracted the eyes of all Rome, and was said to be the grave-pit and magazine of the conquering robbers of the universe.

The fountain had three tubes or channels of right pearl, seated in three equilateral angles already mentioned, extended on the margin, and those channels proceeded in a snail-like line, winding equally on both sides.

We looked on them awhile, and had cast our eyes on another side, when Bacbuc directed us to watch the water; we then heard a most harmonious sound, yet somewhat stopped by starts, far distant, and subterranean, by which means it was still more pleasing than if it had been free, uninterrupted, and near us, so that our minds were as agreeably entertained through our ears with that charming melody, as they were through the windows of our eyes, with those delightful objects.

Bacbuc then said, Your philosophers will not allow that motion is begot by the power of figures; look here and see the contrary. By that single snail-like motion, equally divided as you see, and a five-fold infoliature, moveable at every inward meeting, such as is the vena cava, where it enters into the right ventricle of the heart; just so is the flowing of this fountain, and by it a harmony ascends as high as your world's ocean

She then ordered her attendants to make us a drink; and, to tell you the truth of the matter as near as possible, we are not, heaven be praised! of the nature of a drove of calf-lollies, who (as your sparrows cannot feed unless you bob them on the tail) must be rib-roasted with tough crab-tree, and firked into a stomach, or, at least, into an humour to eat or drink: no, we know better things, and scorn to scorn any man's civility, who civilly invites us to a drinking bout. Bacbuc asked us then, how we liked our tiff. We answered, that it seemed to us good harmless sober Adam's liquor, fit to keep a man in the right way, and, in a word, mere element; more cool and clear than Argyrontes in Ætolia, Peneus in Thessaly, Axius in Mygdonia, or Cydnus in Cilicia, a tempting sight of whose cool silver stream caused Alexander to prefer the short-lived pleasure of bathing himself in it, to the inconveniences which he could not but foresee would attend so ill-timed an action.

This, said Bacbuc, comes of not considering with ourselves, or understanding the motions of the musculous tongue, when the drink glides on it in its way to the stomach. Tell me, noble strangers, are your throats lined, paved, or enamelled, as formerly was that of Pithyllus, nicknamed Theutes, that you can have missed the taste, relish, and flavour of this divine liquor? Here, said she, turning towards her gentlewoman, bring my scrubbing-brushes, you know which, to scrape, rake, and clear their palates.

They brought immediately some stately, swingeing, jolly hams, fine substantial neats'-tongues, good hung-beef, pure and delicate botargos, venison, sausages, and such other gullet-sweepers. And, to comply with her invitation, we crammed and twisted till we owned ourselves thoroughly cured of thirst, which before did damnably plague us.

We are told, continued she, that formerly a learned and valiant Hebrew chief, leading his people through the deserts, where they were in danger of being famished, obtained of God some manna, whose taste was to them, by imagination, such as that of meat was to them before in reality: thus, drinking of this miraculous liquor, you will find its taste like any wine that you shall fancy to drink. Come, then, fancy and drink. We did so, and Panurge had no sooner whipped off his brimmer, but he cried, By Noah's open shop, it is vin de Baulne, better than ever was yet tipped over tongue, or may ninety and sixteen devils swallow me. Oh! that to keep its taste the longer, we gentlemen topers had but necks some three cubits long or so, as Philoxenus desired to have, or, at least, like a crane's as Melanthus wished his.

On the faith of true lanterners, quoth Friar John, it is gallant, sparkling Greek wine; now, for God's sake, sweetheart, do but teach me how the devil you make it. It seems to me Mirevaux wine, said Pantagruel; for, before I drank, I supposed it to be such. Nothing can be disliked in it, but that it is cold, colder, I say, than the very ice; colder than the water of Nonacris and Dircé, or the Conthoporian spring at Corinth, that froze up the stomach and nutritive parts of those that drank of it.

Drink once, twice, or thrice more, said Bacbuc, still changing your imagination, and you shall find its taste and flavour to be exactly that on which you shall have pitched. Then never presume to say that anything is impossible to God. We never offered to say such a thing, said I; far from it, we maintain he is omnipotent.

CHAPTER XLIII

How the priestess Bacbuc equipt Panurge, in order to have the word of the Bottle

WHEN we had thus chatted and tippled, Bacbuc asked, Who of you here would have the word of the Holy Bottle? I, your most humble little funnel, if it please you, quoth Panurge. Friend, said she, I have but one thing to tell you, which is, that when you come to the Oracle, you take care to hearken and hear the word only with one ear. This, cried Friar John, is wine of one ear, as Frenchmen call it.

She then wrapped him up in gaberdine, bound his noddle with a goodly clean biggin, clapped over it a felt, such as those through which hypocras is distilled, at the bottom of which, instead of a cowl, she put three obelisks, made him draw on a pair of old fashioned codpieces instead of mittens, girded him about with three bagpipes bound together, bathed his jobbernol thrice in the fountain; then threw a handful of meal on his phiz, fixed three cock's feathers on the right side of the hypocratical felt, made him take a jaunt nine times round the fountain, caused him to take three little leaps, and to bump his a— seven times against the ground, repeating I do not know what kind of conjurations all the while in the Tuscan tongue, and ever and anon reading in a ritual or book of ceremonies, carried after her by one of her mystagogues.

For my part, may I never stir if I do not really believe, that neither Numa Pompilius, the second King of the Romans, nor the Cerites of Tuscia, nor the old Hebrew captain, ever instituted so many ceremonies as I then saw performed; nor were ever half so many religious forms used by the sooth-sayers of Memphis in Egypt to Apis; or by the Euboians, at Rhamnus, to Rhamnusia; or to Jupiter Ammon, or to Faronia.

When she had thus accoutred my gentleman, she took him out of our company, and led him out of the temple, through a golden gate on the right, into a round chapel made of transparent speculary stones, by whose solid clearness the sun's light shined there through the precipice of the rock without any windows or other entrance, and so easily and fully dispersed itself through the greater temple, that the light seemed rather to spring out of it than to flow into it.

The workmanship was not less rare than that of the sacred temple at Ravenna, or that in the island of Chemnis in Egypt. Nor must I forget to tell you, that the work of that round chapel was contrived with such a symmetry, that its diameter was just the height of the vault.

In the middle of it was an heptagonal fountain of fine alabaster most artfully wrought, full of water, which was so clear that it might have passed for element in its purity and simplicity. The sacred Bottle was in it to the middle, clad in pure fine crystal, of an oval shape, except its muzzle, which was somewhat wider than was consistent with that figure.

CHAPTER XLIV

How Bacbuc, the high-priestess, brought Panurge before the Holy Bottle

THERE the noble priestess Bacbuc made Panurge stoop and kiss the brink of the fountain; then bade him rise and dance three ithymbi. Which done, she ordered him to sit down, between two stools placed there for that purpose, his arse upon the ground. Then she opened her ritual book, and, whispering in his left ear, made him sing an epileny, as follows:

BOTTLE ! whose mysterious deep
Does ten thousand secrets keep,
With attentive ear I wait ;
Ease my mind, and speak my fate.
Soul of joy, like Bacchus, we
More than India gain by thee.
Truths unborn thy juice reveals,
Which futurity conceals.
Antidote to frauds and lies,
Wine, that mounts us to the skies,
May thy father Noah's brood
Like him drown, but in thy flood.
Speak, so may the liquid mine
Of rubies or of diamonds, shine.
Bottle ! whose mysterious deep,
Does ten thousand secrets keep,
With attentive ear I wait ;
Ease my mind, and speak my fate.

When Panurge had sung, Bacbuc threw I do not know what into the fountain, and straight its water began to boil in good earnest, just for the world as doth the great monastical pot at Bourgueil, when it is high holiday there. Friend Panurge was listening with one ear, and Bacbuc kneeled by him, when such a kind of humming was heard out of the Bottle, as is made by a swarm of bees bred in the flesh of a young bull, killed and dressed according to Aristæus's art, or such as is made when a bolt flies out of a cross bow, or when a shower falls on a sudden in summer. Immediately after this was heard the word TRINC. By cob's body, cried Panurge, it is broken, or cracked at least, not to tell a lie for the matter; for, even so do crystal bottles speak in our country, when they burst near the fire.

Bacbuc arose, and gently taking Panurge under the arms, said, Friend, offer your thanks to indulgent heaven, as reason requires; you have soon had the word of the Goddess-Bottle: and the kindest, most favourable, and certain word of answer that I ever yet heard her give, since I officiated here at her most sacred oracle; rise, let us go to the chapter, in whose gloss that fine word is explained. With all my heart, quoth Panurge; by jingo, I am just as wise as I was last year; light, where is the book? Turn it over, where is the chapter? Let us see this merry gloss.

CHAPTER XLV

How Bacbuc explained the word of the Goddess Bottle

BACBUC having thrown I do not know what into the fountain, straight the water ceased to boil: and then she took Panurge into the greater temple, in the central place, where there was the enlivening fountain.

There she took out a hugeous silver book, in the shape of a half-tierce, or hogshead, of sentences; and having filled it at the fountain, said to him: The philosophers, preachers, and doctors of your world, feed you up with fine words and cant at the ears; now, here we really incorporate our precepts at the mouth. Therefore I will not say to you, read this chapter, see this gloss; no, I say to you, taste me this fine chapter, swallow me this rare gloss. Formerly an ancient prophet of the Jewish nation eat a book, and became a clerk even to the very teeth; now will I have you drink one, that you may be a clerk to your very liver. Here, open your mandibules.

Panurge gaping as wide as his jaws would stretch, Bacbuc took the silver book, at least we took it for a real book, for it looked just for the world like a breviary; but, in truth, it was a bruviary, a flask of right Falernian wine, as it came from the grape, which she made him swallow every drop.

By Bacchus, quoth Panurge, this was a notable chapter, a most authentic gloss, on my word. Is this all that the trismegistian Bottle's word means? In troth I like it extremely, it went down like mother's milk. Nothing more, returned Bacbuc; for *Trinc* is a panomphean word, that is, a word understood, used, and celebrated by all nations, and signifies drink.

Some say in your world, that sack is a word used in all tongues, and justly admitted in the same sense among all nations; for, as Æsop's fable hath it, all men are born with a sack at the neck, naturally needy, and begging of each other; neither can the most powerful king be without the help of other men, or can any one that is poor subsist without the rich, though he be never so proud and insolent; nay, even were it Hippias the philosopher, who boasted he could do every thing. Much less can any one make shift without drink than without a sack. Therefore here we hold not that laughing, but that drinking is the distinguishing character of man. I do not say drinking, taking that word singly and absolutely in the strictest sense: no, beasts then might put in for a share; I mean drinking cool delicious wine. For you must know, my beloved, that by wine we become divine; neither can there be a surer argument, or a less deceitful divination. Your academics assert the same, when they make the etymology of wine, which the Greeks call $OINO\Sigma$, to be from *vis*, strength, virtue, and power; for it is in its power to fill the soul with all truth, learning, and philosophy.

If you observe what is written in Ionic letters on the temple gate, you may have understood that truth is in wine. The goddess Bottle therefore directs you to the divine liquor; be yourself the expounder of your undertaking.

It is impossible, said Pantagruel to Panurge, to speak more to the purpose than does this true priestess; you may remember I told you as much when you first spoke to me about it.

Trinc then: what says your heart, elevated by Bacchic enthusiasm? With this, quoth Panurge,

Tring, trinc; by Bacchus let us tope,
And tope again; for, now I hope
To see some brawny, juicy rump,

Well tickled with my carnal stump.
E'er long, my friends, I shall be wedded,
Sure as my trap-stick has a red head;
And my sweet wife shall hold the combat,
Long as my baws can on her bum beat.
O what a battle of a—fighting
Will there be! which I much delight in?
What pleasing pains then shall I take
To keep myself and spouse awake!
All heart and juice, I'll up and ride,
And make a duchess of my bride.
Sing Iö pæan! loudly sing
To Hymen, who all joys will bring.
Well, Friar John, I'll take my oath,
This oracle is full of troth:
Intelligible truth it bears,
More certain than the sieve and shears.

CHAPTER XLVI

How Panurge and the rest rhymed with poetic fury

WHAT a pox ails the fellow? quoth Friar John. Stark staring mad, or bewitched on my word! Do but hear the chiming dotterel gabble in rhyme. What the devil has he swallowed? His eyes roll in his loggerhead, just for the world like a dying goat's. Will the addle-pated wight have the grace to sheer off? Will he rid us of his damned company, to go shite out his nasty rhyming balderdash in some bog-house? Will nobody be so kind as to cram some dog's-bur down the poor cur's gullet? or will he, monk-like, run his fist up to the elbow into his throat to his very maw, to scour and clear his flanks? Will he take a hair of the same dog?

Pantagruel chid Friar John, and said:

Bold monk, forbear; this, I'll assure ye,
Proceeds all from poetic fury;
Warmed by the God, inspired with wine,
His human soul is made divine.
　　For without jest,
　　His hallowed breast,
　　With wine possessed.
　　Could have no rest,
　　Till he had expressed
　　Some thoughts at least
　　Of his great guest.
　　Then strait he flies
　　Above the skies,
　　And mollifies,
　　With prophecies,
　　Our miseries.
And since divinely he's inspired,
Adore the soul by wine acquired,
And let the tosspot be admired.

How! quoth the friar, is the fit of rhyming upon you too? Is it come to that? Then we are all peppered, or the devil pepper me. What would I not give to have Gargantua see us while we are in this maggoty crambo-vein! Now may I be cursed with living on that damned empty food, if I can tell, whether I shall escape the catching distemper. The devil a bit do I understand which way to go about it: however, the spirit of fustian possesses us all, I find. Well, by St. John, I will poetise, since everybody does; I find it coming. Stay, and pray pardon me, if I do not rhyme in crimson; it is my first essay.

> Thou, who canst water turn to wine,
> Transform my bum, by power divine,
> Into a lantern, that may light
> My neighbour in the darkest night.

Panurge then proceeds in his rapture, and says:

> From Pythian Tripos n'er were heard
> More truths, nor more to be revered.
> I think from Delphos to this spring,
> Some wizard brought that conjuring thing.
> Had honest Plutarch here been toping,
> He then so long had ne'er been groping
> To find according to his wishes,
> Why oracles are mute as fishes
> At Delphos: now the reason's clear,
> No more at Delphos they're, but here.
> Here is the tripos, out of which
> Is spoke the doom of poor and rich.
> For Athenæus does relate
> This Bottle is the womb of Fate;
> Prolific of mysterious wine,
> And big with prescience divine;
> It brings the truth with pleasure forth,
> Besides you haven't a pennyworth.
> So, Friar John, I must exhort you
> To wait a word that may import you,
> And to inquire, while here we tarry,
> If it shall be your luck to marry.

Friar John answers him in a rage, and says:

> How, marry! by St. Bennet's boot,
> And his gambadoes, I'll ne'er do't.
> No man that knows me ne'er shall judge
> I mean to make myself a drudge;
> Or that pilgarlic e'er will doat
> Upon a paltry petticoat.
> I'll ne'er my liberty betray
> All for a little leap-frog play;
> And ever after wear a clog
> Like monkey or like mastiff-dog:
> No, I'd not have, upon my life,
> Great Alexander for my wife,

> Nor Pompey, not his dad-in-law,
> Who did each other clapper-claw.
> Not the best he that wears a head,
> Shall win me to his truckle-bed.

Panurge, pulling off his gaberdine and mystical accoutrements, replied:

> Wherefore thou shalt, thou filthy beast,
> Be damned twelve fathoms deep at least;
> While I shall reign in Paradise,
> Whence on thy loggerhead I'll piss,
> Now when that dreadful hour is come,
> That thou in hell receiv'st thy doom,
> E'en there, I know, thou'lt play some trick,
> And Proserpine shan't scape a prick
> Of the long pin within thy breeches.
> But when thou'rt using these capriches,
> And catterwauling in her cavern,
> Send Pluto to the farthest tavern,
> For the best wine that's to be had,
> Lest he should see and run horn mad:
> She's kind, and ever did admire
> A well-fed monk, or well-hung friar.

Go to, quoth Friar John, thou old noddy, thou doddipoled ninny, go to the devil thou art prating of; I have done with rhyming; the rheum gripes me at the gullet. Let us talk of paying and going; come.

CHAPTER XLVII

How we took our leave of Bacbuc, and left the Oracle of the Holy Bottle

Do not trouble yourself about anything here, said the priestess to the friar; if you be but satisfied, we are. Here below, in these circumcentral regions, we place the sovereign good not in taking and receiving, but in bestowing and giving; so that we esteem ourselves happy, not if we take and receive much of others, as perhaps the sects of teachers do in your world, but rather if we impart and give much. All I have to beg of you, is that you leave us here your names in writing, in this ritual. She then opened a fine large book, and as we gave our names, one of her (she) mystagogues, with a gold pin, drew some lines on it, as if she had been writing; but we could not see any characters.

This done, she filled three small leather vessels with fantastic water, and giving them into our hands, said, Now, my friends,

EVERYMAN'S LIBRARY

A LIST OF THE 983 VOLUMES
ARRANGED UNDER AUTHORS

Anonymous works are given under titles.

Anthologies, Dictionaries, etc., are arranged at the end of the list.

LONDON: J. M. DENT & SONS LTD.
NEW YORK: E. P. DUTTON & CO. INC.

*The Publishers regret that, owing to wartime
difficulties and shortages, some of the volumes
may be found to be temporarily out of print.*